SECOND EDITION

The WORLD *of* WHOLE Numbers

Number Theory for the Novice

AGNES M. RASH, Ph.D.

Saint Joseph's University

Kendall Hunt
publishing company

Cover image © Shutterstock, Inc.

www.kendallhunt.com
Send all inquiries to:
4050 Westmark Drive
Dubuque, IA 52004-1840

Previously published © 2015 by Springer International Publishing AG, Cham

Copyright © 2020 by Kendall Hunt Publishing Company

ISBN 978-1-5249-9305-4

Published in the United States of America

Dedication

To Bob (Robert L. Grimm)
Agnes M. Rash

Table of Contents

Testimonial

Inspired teaching of General Education courses is a challenging task due to a student audience that often is not interested in the subject matter. Similarly, high school mathematics teachers lack enrichment courses other than calculus. *The World of Whole Numbers - Number Theory for the Novice* is the book that evolved from the extensive practice and research of Dr. Agnes M. Rash. Its latest edition is a wonderful treatment of the Number Theory, with a broad range of innovative problems and mathematical proofs for non-mathematics majors or advanced high schoolers.

The book begins with a presentation of mathematical problem-solving strategies and methods of communicating mathematical ideas. It is a distinguishing feature for a typical mathematics textbook that allows students to learn how to study mathematics.

As an introductory Number Theory text, the book contains various types of learning tasks including puzzles, projects, real-life applications, and mathematical proofs. Each chapter contains numerous solved examples, proven statements, and practice exercises of varying degrees of difficulty. Also, each chapter concludes with a list of new terms and symbols, followed by review exercises and activities.

Humanizing mathematics is one of the methods for motivating students' learning of the subject. Dr. Rash has included numerous historical facts and engaging stories, with pictures to illustrate the evolution of human thought and power of its knowledge.

The World of Whole Numbers - Number Theory for the Novice is an opportunity to foster important development of mathematical and analytical thinking intended for a novice audience. The book will introduce the student to some of the genesis of mathematical algorithms including Euclidean, the Sieve of Eratosthenes, generation of primes and many others.

The instructor teaching from this book will find it an invaluable course book for capstone problem-solving or first-year seminar courses, enrichment courses, and a springboard for a number of interesting number theory projects, term papers, or honors studies.

Dr. Tetyana Berezovski
Saint Joseph's University
Mathematics Department
2019

Preface to the Instructor

This textbook introduces the field of number theory at a level accessible to non-math and non-science majors. The target audience is students in either a liberal arts mathematics course or a course focused on elementary education majors at any college or university. The content of this book consists of a subset of the material covered in a standard introductory number theory course offered for mathematics majors, but the presentation is much different. The book includes an introduction to logic and proofs, at a level suitable for liberal arts majors, as well as major concepts in number theory accessible to students familiar with high-school algebra, up to the quadratic formula. This text is designed to be used in a one-semester (15-week) course.

Choosing topics of interest to humanities majors, business majors, and also suitable for elementary education majors was a challenge. However, giving the latter group a grasp of the depth and usefulness of the natural numbers is key to helping students acquire a better understanding of the mathematics they will present to their students. For example: Why are prime numbers important? Why do we need to find the greatest common divisor of two numbers? While the syllabus is important, so is the need to reduce math anxiety among minimally-prepared students, and to have students enjoy their mathematical experience.

There are many web sites that can enhance the experience for the student by reiterating what is presented in the text, explaining the material in a different way, or adding historic content. Some of these links have been noted in this text.

Throughout the book, concepts have been linked and ordered to show connections between them. For example, the greatest common divisor is first defined in Chapter 1 and used to identify primitive Pythagorean triples in Chapter 2. In Chapter 3 the greatest common divisor is discussed in connection with prime factors, and then in Chapter 4 the Euclidean Algorithm is used to calculate greatest common divisors. Proof techniques and methods are introduced in Chapter 1 using the familiar concepts of even and odd. Subsequently, students continue to write proofs about each new topic they encounter throughout the text.

In Chapter 0, the importance of precise communication in mathematics is stressed, and some common problem-solving techniques are introduced. Examples are given using facts about integers, considering cases, and looking for a pattern. Terms such as even, odd, prime, and divisible are discussed, but these are formally defined in Chapter 1 so that it is possible to omit Chapter 0.

Knowing how to verify whether a statement is true or false is basic to mathematics. Students learn how to precisely state and justify ideas. Chapter 1 includes a brief introduction to logic including the basic logical connectives and the types of compound sentences formed using them. Section 1.2 includes formal definitions of some basic terms (even, odd, prime, divides, greatest common divisor). Sections 1.4–1.7 and

1.9 illustrate some common proof techniques, such as a direct proof, a proof by contradiction, and an indirect proof (proof by contrapositive).

Proofs by contradiction are useful in Chapter 3, in the proof that there are infinitely many primes. The contrapositive of a statement is also used in Chapter 3 to formulate a primality test; indirect proofs are used infrequently but are important. Proving statements false using counterexamples is also discussed in Chapter 1. The last section of Chapter 1 provides a review of divisibility rules which are useful throughout the text. Chapter 1 should be covered before proceeding to later chapters. Chapter 2 is not essential for understanding the concepts presented later, but it gives students practice of elementary proofs by building on their knowledge of a familiar topic: right triangles. While discussing this material, the author shows NOVA's film *The Proof*, about Andrew Wiles' path to proving Fermat's Last Theorem. This provides the opportunity to remark that you never know when an idea will have a new application.

Chapter 3 on prime numbers is central to the study of number theory. Section 3.2 discusses unique factorization and Section 3.4 discusses some unsolved questions in number theory as well as the search for larger primes and is optional.

In Chapter 4, the division algorithm is discussed in detail in order to motivate the study of the Euclidean Algorithm as well as modular arithmetic described in Chapter 5. Chapter 5.3 discusses solutions to linear congruences. Section 5.4 is an application of congruences to check digits and is independent. The Chinese Remainder Theorem in Section 5.5 is also optional.

In Chapter 6, Euler's Phi function and Euler's theorem (Sections 6.4 and 6.5) are essential to the study of cryptography in Chapter 7. Section 6.5 on examples of other numerical functions may also be omitted to make time for covering cryptography.

Chapter 7 introduces a modern application of number theory to public key cryptography and also includes several examples of private key codes in Sections 7.2 and 7.3 for contrast. If needed, these sections could be omitted to allow time for an introduction to the application of number theory to the RSA public key code, contained in Section 7.4.

Preface to the Student

"Archimedes will be remembered when Aeschylus is forgotten, because languages die and mathematical ideas do not." G. H. Hardy

Early in recorded history, humans began to count using the natural numbers, 1, 2, 3 …. The earliest counting did not progress very far in this sequence, partially because numbers were associated with the items that could be counted on the fingers (also called digits) and toes. Number theory is the study of the integers. The integers include positive and negative numbers zero. The natural numbers have been studied extensively at least since the time of the Babylonians and the golden age of Greece. Many learned people were fascinated with these numbers and proved theorems about whole numbers just for the personal satisfaction of finding these results. Indeed, in the third century BC, Archimedes remarked "All was numbers."

There is a certain satisfaction that one gets by accomplishing a goal, performing a difficult task, or discovering a new fact. Throughout the ages, this fascination with integers has led to many great discoveries and personal satisfactions. Breakthroughs, discoveries, and new ideas often occur as an inspiration, or an "aha" moment. Archimedes had such an "aha" moment and he ran through the streets proclaiming "Eureka, I have found it!"

Amazingly, there are concepts that were discovered just for the enjoyment of it that eventually turned out to be very useful and have profound implications on modern times. One such is the Euclidean Algorithm, discovered by Euclid in the third century BC. We now find this result most useful in cryptography, internet security, the design of secret codes, and code breaking discussed in Chapter 7. Mathematics never gets old!

The author hopes that you have "aha" moments as we journey through a portion of the vast knowledge of whole numbers.

Develop a Plan for Learning Mathematics

In any human endeavor, to become proficient one must be dedicated. Think about a particular activity, playing a guitar or shooting a basketball. Whether it is a hobby or a profession, to be proficient at the activity, one must be dedicated and practice the skill. Mathematics is a human endeavor and curiosity has led to many great discoveries. Below are a few suggestions to help you succeed in understanding mathematical concepts and being able to use them in the future.

Prior to a class, read the material that will be covered in class to get an idea of what the topic is and to determine if there are new terms that you will have to learn. Be sure that you have done the homework and organize any questions that you want to ask the instructor about the assignment.

In class, ask questions about what is unclear. Professors are happy to help students understand concepts, clarify ideas, and to eliminate errors in problems, whether they are small errors or large misunderstandings. Take notes during the class. Ask the instructor to repeat something if you missed it. Your instructor is there to help you.

After class, when reading your notes and the class materials, sit up straight, have paper and a pencil in your hand to jot down notes or questions. Fill in your class notes where necessary. Rewriting something makes it easier to remember later. Make sure that you understand the concepts and terms.

When reading an example, be sure you understand the problem, perhaps reading it more than once. After you have read one example, try to solve the next example before reading the solution.

The more you practice, the better you will be. Pick out a couple of easy problems, moderately difficult problems and problems that require extra effort and see if you can solve them. Often, explaining concepts to a fellow student will help clarify the concept in your own mind. When you read a theorem and its proof, be sure you know what the hypothesis (given information) is. Try to figure out what direction the proof might take before reading the proof. When you read the proof, you can see how close your ideas were to the actual proof.

When studying for a test, start preparing several days before the test. Make up problems that you think might appear in the exam. Read over your notes and the text to determine what concepts are key. Go over the problems that you had trouble with earlier and be sure that you can solve them. If you have any difficulty, talk to your instructor and get help. A study group is also helpful in preparing for a test. Cramming might get you through one test, but by the time of the final exam, you will have forgotten the material.

Reading mathematics is an active process. You may have to go back and refresh your memory of a concept, definition, or theorem. Don't get discouraged, some concepts have taken centuries to develop so it is not surprising if you don't understand it during your first reading.

During a test, begin by reading all of the problems. Find the ones that you can solve quickly and easily and do them first, leaving enough time to work on the other problems that require more effort. If you get stuck on a problem, take a deep breath and relax. Work on a different problem and come back to the difficult one later.

Agnes M. Rash

Acknowledgements

The author thanks the colleagues who taught from earlier versions of the work in their courses, and who offered suggestions to improve this book, in particular Tanya Berezovski and Sarah Bell. Their suggestions and input have greatly improved this edition. Mrs. Blisard was a great asset with a keen eye for typographical and grammar issues, and also deserves my thanks. I thank Springer Publishing House for publishing an earlier version of this work. Finally, I am very thankful that Kendall Hunt provided me with the opportunity to improve the text and to create an interactive e-version.

About the Author

Dr. Agnes M. Rash received her Ph.D. from the University of Pennsylvania and taught mathematics and mathematics education for many years. She is interested in number theory, problem solving, mathematics education, and math anxiety, and enjoys seeing her students grow in knowledge and confidence. Several of her students have presented their research at MAA meetings, and many have been engaged in writing Calendar problems for *The Mathematics Teacher*. She and her husband enjoy fly fishing, golfing, and traveling.

George Pólya

1887–1985

George Pólya was a Hungarian mathematician. He was a professor of mathematics from 1914 to 1940 at Eidgenössische Technische Hochschule (ETH) Zurich and from 1940 to 1953 at Stanford University.

Pólya's lasting contributions to mathematics education are his problem-solving strategy and his ability to engage students in conjecturing and creative thinking. He had an easy-going style that made students comfortable in his classes. He was a phenomenal teacher who believed that teaching is an art.

Pólya had many interests as a student: Greek, Latin, German, and Hungarian. Pólya's favorite subjects were biology and literature and he also liked geography but did not enjoy mathematics until later. His grades in mathematics were "satisfactory" but not outstanding. Pólya enrolled at the University of Budapest in 1905 and began studying law but found it boring. Next, he studied his favorite subjects of languages and obtained a certificate to teach Latin and Hungarian in a gymnasium, which he never did.

Pólya became interested in philosophy, and a professor advised him to take physics and mathematics. So, he studied mathematics at the University of Vienna from 1910 to 1911. In the following year he returned to Budapest and was awarded a doctorate in mathematics for his work in geometric probability. He spent much of 1912 and 1913 at Göttingen where he became involved with the leading mathematician of his time. He moved to Paris where he met the famous mathematician Hurwitz, who arranged an appointment as Privatdozent for Pólya at (ETH) Zürich, where Hurwitz himself held the chair of mathematics, Pólya decided to accept the appointment. In Zürich, in addition to Hurwitz, Pólya had other great mathematicians with whom he associated. He and his physicist wife coauthored a book with a novel approach to the subject. His idea was to classify problems not by their subject, but rather by their method of solution. The book was the first of its type and earned Pólya a reputation for being a master at problem solving. His book, *How to Solve It* is still recognized today as a classic.

From that time, Pólya's career skyrocketed. He was promoted to "extraordinary professor" at ETH in Zürich in 1920. He received a Rockefeller Fellowship in 1924 to study with Hardy in England. Pólya was very prolific, publishing 31 papers on various branches of mathematics during the three years 1926–1928. Due to political problems in Europe, Pólya was forced to move to the United States, where he was awarded a second Rockefeller Fellowship at Princeton. While he was in the United States, he held faculty appointments at Brown University and Smith College before joining the faculty at Stanford University.

Introduction

The single biggest problem in communication is the illusion that it has taken place.

--George Bernard Shaw, 1856–1950

Section 0.1   Communication in Mathematics

In order to share information with one another, we must be able to clearly and accurately communicate our thoughts and ideas. In the era of text messaging and cryptic notes, the art of understanding a communication has changed. Many parents and grandparents may be unable to understand a text message sent by you or one of your friends. In mathematics, precise language is important so that everyone can understand each other. This section highlights the components of precise mathematical language, and how that precision is used in logical arguments.

Definitions are used to ensure that everyone is discussing the same concept. Ambiguous or ill-defined words lead to confusion. For instance, the meaning of the word *terrific* can be different in different contexts. In some sentences it means something terrible (a terrific storm), and at other times it means something wonderful (a terrific vacation). Words that have opposing meanings and depend on context can create problems in interpretation. Mathematicians try to be consistent and precise with the language that is used to describe objects and concepts.

Think about a familiar term, such as an *odd number*. Given some numbers, you could probably identify which ones are even, and you can probably come up with a test to determine whether or not a given number is even. There are different ways to describe an odd number, but the one chosen as the definition must make it clear what is an odd number. All odd numbers must satisfy the definition and any number that is not odd cannot satisfy the definition. Part of this course will be learning precise definitions for mathematical concepts, some of which will be familiar, and some of which may be new.

The following list summarizes what makes a good explanation in mathematics.

Characteristics of Good Explanations in Mathematics:

1. The explanation addresses the specific question or problem that was posed.
2. Each step is factually correct, and clearly follows from the previous step(s) or prepares for the subsequent steps.
3. The explanation could be used to teach a concept to another person, possibly even one who is not in the class.
4. Key points are emphasized.

5. If applicable, supporting pictures, diagrams, examples, or equations are used appropriately and as needed to clarify a concept.

Section 0.2   Problem-Solving Strategies

Problem solving is central to all areas of endeavor. When learning something new for fun, whether it is a winning strategy for a game of cards or a new sport, you need a plan of action. You may need to solve a monetary problem, such as financing a college education or getting a mortgage to purchase a house. Each of these requires a strategy. Even determining how much sleep you need to feel your best or determining if you can stop your vehicle (as the traffic light is turning red) before you get to a crosswalk, require thought.

In mathematics, problem solving is essential, and conjecturing about a solution to a problem is helpful. Looking at alternative strategies and selecting what seems to be the best one is a useful approach. One of the most famous problem-solving strategies was proposed by mathematician George Pólya in his classic book, *How to Solve It*. The four-step strategy works for many types of problems. Here are his suggestions:

1. Understand the problem.
2. Devise a plan.
3. Carry out the plan.
4. Look back.

We will elaborate on Pólya strategy and add some helpful information.

1. Understand the problem.
    Do you understand all of the words and their definitions?
    Can you restate the problem in your own words?
    Do you know what the goal is? What are you asked to find out or show?
    Can you work out some numerical examples (special cases) that would help make the problem clearer?
    Is this problem similar to another problem that you have solved?

2. Devise a plan. (There are many strategies that can be useful. Below is a partial list.)
    Make a table of information.
    Guess and check, and then generalize from the examples.
    Modify the problem or solve a simpler problem.
    Search for a pattern.
    Work backwards.
    Divide into cases.
    Consider extreme cases.

3. Carry out the plan.
    Carrying out the plan is usually easier than devising the plan, because you are actually using the method you have already thought of to solve the problem. Do not let yourself get discouraged if the first strategy you tried is not working; be persistent and try a different one. Take a break when you need to! A fresh start or new strategy can lead to success if you are still having difficulty.

4. Check your results.

   Is your solution reasonable?

   Can you check to see if your solution is correct?

   Did you answer the question?

   Is there an easier solution? Could you have solved this problem another way?

Let us look at several examples.

Example 0.1. What are the possibilities for the missing digit so that the natural number 341725__ is divisible by 3?

Solution:

We will use Pólya's strategy for solving this problem.

Step 1: Understand the problem. We are asked to fill in the blank with a digit, which could be any of the values 0, 1, 2, 3, 4, 5, 6, 7, 8, or 9. Then, determine which of these digits produces a number divisible by 3.

Step 2: Devise a plan.

   There are 10 possible numbers to test in this problem, since there are ten different single digits: 0, 1, 2, 3, 4, 5, 6, 7, 8, 9 that could be filled in for the missing digit. We can make a list of the numbers, and then divide each one by 3 to see which is a multiple of 3.

Step 3: Carry out the plan.

   The numbers we must check are listed in Table 0.1

3417250	3417255
3417251	3417256
3417252	3417257
3417253	3417258
3417254	3417259

Table 0.1

For instance, 341720/3 = 113906.666… is not an integer. Table 0.2 shows the results of dividing each number by 3.

	Divisible by 3?		Divisible by 3?
3417250	N	3417255	Y
3417251	N	3417256	N
3417252	Y	3417257	N
3417253	N	3417258	Y
3417254	N	3417259	N

Table 0.2

Looking at the table, you can see that the last digit could be 2, 5, or 8.

Step 4: Check your results.

Make sure that your arithmetic is correct. While the problem is finished, and the answer has been given, look at the table to see if you can find any additional information. For example, it appears that when one number works, every third number after this also worked.

The symbol ◆ represents the end of an example.

Example 0.2. Sophie has pennies, nickels, and dimes in her purse, at least four of each, and she pulls out four coins. What would be the different totals that Sophie could get?

Solution:

This is another example of a problem where listing all the possible values could be helpful in finding a solution. Table 0.3 shows the possibilities.

Pennies	Nickels	Dimes	Total
4	0	0	4¢
3	1	0	8¢
3	0	1	13¢
2	2	0	12¢
2	0	2	22¢
2	1	1	17¢
1	3	0	16¢
1	0	3	31¢
1	1	2	26¢
1	2	1	21¢
0	4	0	20¢
0	0	4	40¢
0	3	1	25¢
0	1	3	35¢
0	2	2	30¢

Table 0.3

From the last column, the possibilities for the total amount of money Sophie pulled out are 4¢, 8¢, 13¢, 12¢, 22¢, 17¢, 16¢, 31¢, 26¢, 21¢, 20¢, 40¢, 25¢, 35¢, 30¢.

Example 0.3. Without using a calculator, show that the square root of 4356 is an integer.

Solution:

First square a few numbers to see if you can discover a pattern.

For example, $70^2 = 4900$, which is larger than 4356, but $60^2 = 3600$, which is smaller. Therefore, $\sqrt{4356}$ is between 60 and 70. At this point, we could just check each number between 60 and 70, but we can save some time by noticing that since the last digit of 4356 is a 6, the square of the unit's digit of $\sqrt{4356}$ must be 6.

The unit's digit can be 0, 1, 2, … 8, or 9. So, construct a table of the units' digits and their squares, shown in Table 0.4.

a	a^2
0	0
1	1
2	4
3	9
4	6
5	5
6	6
7	9
8	4
9	1

Table 0.4

Only the numbers ending in a 4 or a 6 have a square that ends in a 6. Therefore, testing 64 and 66, we find that $64^2 = 4096$ is too small, but $66^2 = 4356$. Thus, $\sqrt{4356} = 66$.

Exercise Set 0.2

1. List the 3-digit numbers that can be written using each of 1, 3, and 5 once and only once. Which strategy did you use?

2. List the 4-digit numbers than can be written using each of the digits 2, 3, 4, and 6 once and only once. Which strategy did you use?

3. Four friends ran a race:
   - Gavin finished seven seconds ahead of Wesley.
   - Ethan finished three seconds behind Rob.
   - Wesley finished five seconds behind Ethan.
   - In what order did the friends finish the race?

Exercises 4–9. Without a calculator, determine what integer is the square root of each of the numbers listed below.

4. 484   7. 676

5. 8464   8. 3249

6. 2116   9. 5041

10. Ethan, Gavin, and Everett go out to eat. The total bill is $45, including the tip. They decide to split the bill evenly, so each person owes $15. Gavin wants to put the total on a credit card and get cash or checks from the others. Everett has only one check, three $1 bills and a $5 bill. Ethan has only a $10 bill and a $20 bill. Explain how the three can settle among themselves so that the waiter has to take only Gavin's credit card for the total amount (and so that no one owes anything). Explain your reasoning.

11. Ryann had 32 coins in a jar. Some of the coins were nickels, the others were dimes. The total value of the coins was $2.80. Find out how many of each coin there were in the jar. What problem-solving strategy did you use?

12. The houses on Main Street are numbered consecutively from 1 to 150. How many house numbers contain at least one digit "7"?

13. The houses on Market Street are numbered consecutively from 1 to 150. How many house numbers contain at least one digit "4"?

14. Continue these numerical sequences by filling in the next three numbers in the pattern.
    a) 1, 4, 7, 10, 13, _____, _____, _____
    b) 19, 20, 22, 25, 29, _____, _____, _____
    c) 2, 6, 18, 54, _____, _____, _____

15. In order to save the world, MacGyver must time exactly three minutes. All he was able to find in the kitchen of the evil genius planning to destroy the earth were two egg timers: one timer can time an interval of exactly 4 minutes, and the other can time an interval of exactly 7 minutes. How can he use these two egg timers to time an interval of exactly 3 minutes?

16. A professor buys a new car every 3 years; he bought his first one in 1981. He gets a sabbatical leave every 7 years, starting in 1992. When will he first get both?

17. There are two species of cicadas; one emerges every 13 years, and the other every 17 years. Suppose both emerged in 2010.
    a) When is the next time that both species emerge?
    b) If the cicadas have a common predator that emerges every two years, and also emerged in 2010, when is the next time that all three emerge in the same year?

18. Sarah and Drew are playing drums together, making a steady beat. Sarah beats her drum hard on beats that are multiples of 8. Drew beats his drum hard on beats that are multiples of 12. Find the first 4 beats on which both Sarah and Drew will beat their drums hard together. Explain.

19. In the midst of the game show called "Child Support" on 11/16/2018, the contestant was asked the questions worth $50,000! If the contestant answered correctly, she would win and move to the next level. If not, the panel of children could provide support, i.e. answer the question correctly. See if you can answer this question: If a person has twice as many dimes as nickels and the total is 50 cents, how many nickels does the person have?

Section 0.3 Number Systems

Before proceeding to the next chapter, let us review the number systems that you have seen in your previous mathematics courses. You learned about different collections of numbers, and how to combine these numbers using arithmetic operations, such as addition, subtraction, multiplication, and division. You also learned arithmetic operations on a single element, such as taking the square root or cube root of a number. The number system that you worked with first, in elementary school, is the set of natural numbers. Later, you learned about fractions, also called rational numbers (from the word "ratio"), and finally the real numbers which include roots of numbers, such as $\sqrt{2}, \sqrt[3]{10}, \pi$, etc. Figure 0.1 shows the relationship among these sets of numbers.

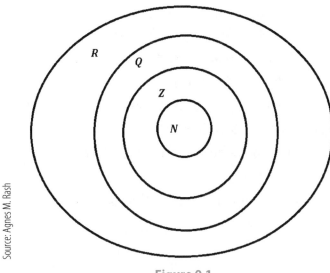

Source: Agnes M. Rash

Figure 0.1

Each set contains numbers that allow more arithmetic operations than the smaller set. For example, in the smallest set, the natural numbers, $\mathbb{N}$, addition, and multiplication of two numbers keeps you in the set. The set of whole numbers, $\mathbb{W}$, includes the set of natural numbers and zero. In the integers, $\mathbb{Z}$, subtraction of two numbers also keeps you in the set. In the rational numbers, $\mathbb{Q}$, division of two numbers (except by zero) keeps you in the set. Finally, in the real numbers, $\mathbb{R}$ taking roots of positive rational numbers keeps you in the set. The real numbers also include numbers, called *transcendental numbers*, such as e, π, and others.

Exercise Set 0.3

1. Solve the equation $3x + 1 = 7$. Which set of numbers is the smallest set to which the solution belongs?

2. Solve the equation $3x + 1 = 10$. Which set of numbers is the smallest set to which the solution belongs?

3. Solve the equation $3x + 1 = 9$. Which set of numbers is the smallest set to which the solution belongs?

4. Solve the equation $(2x + 1)^2 = 24$. Which is the smallest set that contains the solutions of this equation?

Section 0.4   Review Exercises

1. Everett and May both have computers, but May's is older and runs more slowly. In fact, it takes May twice as long to download a song as it takes Everett. Whenever they are working side-by-side to download music, Everett can get two songs in the same amount of time that May downloads one song. When they are working together, it takes them 2 hours to download the songs that they want. How long would it take May to download the music alone? How long would it take Everett to do the same task? Explain your answer.

2. Gavin and Ryann run a lawn-mowing service. Ryann's mower is twice as wide as Gavin's; so, whenever they both mow, Ryann mows twice as much as Gavin in a given time period. When Gavin and Ryann work together, it takes them four hours to cut the lawn of an estate. How long would it take Ryann to mow the lawn alone? How long would it take Gavin to mow the lawn alone?

3. Explain what is wrong with the following statement: $7^2 + 8^2 = 15^2$?

4. Explain what is wrong with the following statement: $6^2 + 5^2 = 11^4$?

5. Which digit cannot appear in the unit's column of a number that is a perfect square?

6. Which digit cannot appear in the unit's column of a number that is a perfect cube?

7. Let d represent the unit's digit in $n = 1050d$. Test different values of d to see which one makes the number a perfect square.

8. What is the smallest positive integer n such that $\sqrt{1050n}$ is a natural number?

Section 0.5   Activities

1. There are several videos on YouTube about Pólya's problem-solving strategy. The length of these vary widely. View and summarize the video: https://www.youtube.com/watch?v=zhL3EMFSm6o

2. In the following clip from HBO series *Silicon Valley*, billionaire investor Peter Gregory does a similar problem involving the occurrence of two unique cicada populations hatching in the same year. He uses this knowledge to make an investment projected to result in a 68-million-dollar return! Watch the video and determine the next time this will occur (given that they last hatched in 2015) https://www.youtube.com/watch?v=KUxMY77i0q4.

3. Solving Sudoku puzzles is an exercise in logical, deductive reasoning. In Sudoku, a 9 × 9 grid is filled in with the numbers 1, 2, …, 8, 9 such that no number appears more than once in any row, column or 3 by 3 sub-matrix. These puzzles appear in newspapers, on the internet, and in puzzle books. Find an easy Sudoku puzzle and solve the puzzle. Then,

    a) Write an explanation of the strategy that you used to solve the puzzle.
    b) Describe your strategy to a fellow student. If the person can solve the puzzle using your strategy, then your explanation was clear. If not, modify your explanation and try again.

4. Copy the Figure 0.2 and place the digits 1, 2, 3, 4, and 5 in these circles so that the sums across (horizontally) and down (vertically) are the same. Is there more than one solution?

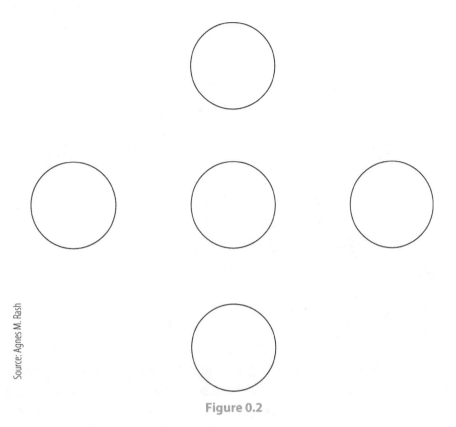

Source: Agnes M. Rash

Figure 0.2

5. From the quote at the beginning of this section, you may surmise that we will be very careful about the use of words. Find other examples where the meaning of a word depends on the context. Some words that come to mind are *chilly* and *fiery*.

6. In the next chapter, we will learn several techniques for finding new facts about numbers. In preparation for that, write what you think are the meanings of the words below. (Some may have the same meaning.) Your understanding of the word may differ from your friend's understanding of the word. Compare your understanding of each word with a friend's understanding of the same word.

Natural number	Counting number	Whole number	Integer
Rational number	Irrational number	Real number	Complex number

7. Research the definitions of each of the first four number definitions and summarize what you find.

8. The Mathematics Association of America (MAA) publishes journals, books, and magazines. Some of these are designed for students, others for professional mathematicians, others concentrate on ideas for teaching mathematics to college students. One of these is the MAA *Focus*. There is always a section that contains puzzles, called "The Puzzle Page." If you like to solve puzzles, and develop your own problem-solving strategies, your library is sure to have a subscription to the MAA publications.

9. The local newspaper in Philadelphia, *The Philadelphia Inquirer*, occasionally published a puzzle section entitled "Brain Busters." This contains a wide variety of puzzles that might interest you, and allow you to use your problem-solving skills. While the puzzles in the section are not original, many are very interesting. Find puzzles, such as Sudoku and More or Less, that involve logical thinking.

Hypatia of Alexandria

AD 350–370 to AD 415

Hypatia of Alexandria (born 350–370; died AD 415) was the daughter of a mathematician.

Hypatia was the first well known woman mathematician and is best known for her work on conic sections.

Hypatia was a Neoplatonist philosopher, astronomer, and mathematician, who traveled widely. She lived primarily in Alexandria, Egypt but also spent time in other areas of Egypt, then part of the Eastern Roman Empire. She was a prominent thinker who became a professor of mathematics and astronomy at the University of Alexandria. She was a very gifted and popular teacher who drew students from Europe, Asia, and Africa. As you can see from her image above, she appears to be a striking woman. Her father Theon was also a mathematician and astronomer, but his intellect was surpassed by that of his daughter. Hypatia collaborated with her father to edit Euclid's *Elements*.

She believed that each person has the right to think independently. Her legacy has been passed down through quotations attributed to her. However, her writings have been lost. Apparently, she died a gruesome death; she was beaten and dismembered by Christians for her pagan beliefs (Krantz, 44.)

Pythagoras lived c. 569–495 BC, Plato lived c. 427–347 BC, Aristotle c. 384–322 BC. All of these great thinkers were from *the Golden Age of Greece*. Euclid, 347–289 BC, was from Alexandria, Egypt and lived about six centuries before Hypatia. So, Euclid's work was enhanced over many centuries. You can see that great mathematicians and philosophers preceded Hypatia by several centuries and were also interested in the same areas of knowledge. While best known for her work on conic sections, her broad interest included philosophy and sound reasoning.

Conjectures, Proofs and Counterexamples

"Before we take to sea we walk on land.
Before we create we must understand."

—*Joseph-Louis Lagrange, 1736–1813*

Section 1.1   What Is Number Theory?

In early civilizations, natural numbers were used to count the number of objects. The concept "number of" is an abstract concept that applies to many collections of objects. For example, ranchers could determine how many sheep they had, and how many were in their pens. Since the time of the early Greek civilization, over 2000 years ago, people have been interested in the properties of counting numbers, and more generally, the properties of the integers, and the relationships between them.

In the middle ages, the study of integers, called Number Theory, was thought of as an interesting field because it contains many problems that are very simple to state but incredibly difficult to solve. For example, the Fibonacci sequence[1] of natural numbers has fascinated people for many centuries (https://www.youtube.com/watch?v=wTlw7fNcO-0). At that time, Number Theory was not believed to have much practical use. This view has changed as calculating devices have become more sophisticated. In 1974, the computer scientist Donald Knuth (1938–) said, "Virtually every theorem in elementary Number Theory arises in a natural, motivated way in connection with the problem of making computers do high-speed numerical calculations." In addition to being important to computer design, scientists have found many modern applications for Number Theory, one of the most studied being cryptology.

If you did activity 5 in Chapter 0, you noticed that some terms are not used consistently. We begin by clarifying some terminology **commonly** used and introducing new terms used by mathematicians.

> **Definition 1.1** The *integers* are defined as a set of numbers
> $$\{\ldots -267, \ldots, -3, -2, -1, 0, 1, 2, 3, \ldots, 259, \ldots\} = \mathbb{Z}$$
> where the dots indicate that the pattern continues indefinitely in each direction.

Occasionally, integers are also called ***whole numbers***[2] but we will differentiate between the terms so that when we use a term, we all know what set we are discussing. In this book, *natural numbers* are those that we use for counting and are sometimes referred to as *counting numbers*.

Definition 1.2 A set of *natural numbers* is the set $\mathbb{N} = \{1,2,3,4,...,259,...\}$. Whole numbers include natural numbers and zero, $\mathbb{W} = \{0,1,2,3,4...\}$.

Using set notation, we can write these three sets as

$$N = \{1,2,3,4,...,259,...\}$$
$$\mathbb{W} = N \cup \{0\}$$
$$\mathbb{Z} = \mathbb{W} \cup \{...-267,...,-3,-2,-1\}$$

Mathematicians often use symbols to represent ideas and concepts. For example, the letters a, b, m, and n usually represent integers. In algebra, x, y, and z are commonly used to represent unknown values.

Question: Do you know what the symbols $\cup, \cap, \subset, \in, \notin$ represent?

From the definitions above, each of the sets $\mathbb{N}$, $\mathbb{W}$, and $\mathbb{Z}$ is an infinite collection of numbers. In the integers, to get the next integer to the right in the list above, add 1 to the current number. To find the next integer on the left, subtract 1 from the current number. The symbol $\in$ represents "is an element of." We write $8 \in N$. To represent that a number is not in a set, we put a slash (/) through the symbol, for example $-9 \notin N$.

Having defined the set of integers, we can consider what is in the set and what is not. The symbol $\in$ represents "is an element of," while the symbol with a slash indicates "not an element of." Another example of this notation is $73 \in \mathbb{Z}$, read "73 is in the set of integers" or "73 is an integer." $0 \notin N$ represents that 0 is not in the set of natural numbers. More generally, a slash through a symbol means "not."

Exercise Set 1.1

Exercises 1–6: Give an example of an integer that fits the description and one that does not. Explain your answer.

1. Even
2. Prime
3. Divisible by 8

4. Odd
5. Not positive
6. Not negative

Exercises 7–10: Translate the symbolic statement into words and determine if the statement is true.

7. $10 \in N$

8. $-12 \in \mathbb{W}$

9. $N \subset \mathbb{Z}$

10. for some integer k.

Exercises 11–15: Translate the words into symbols.

   11. 9 is a natural number.

   12. 3.11 is not an integer.

   13. $\sqrt{3}$ is not an integer.

   14. 3 + 4 is a natural number.

   15. 3 − 4 is an integer but not a natural number.

Exercises 16–19: Rewrite the statement in symbols.

   16. 65 is an integer.

   17. 3.1 is not an integer.

   18. $\dfrac{32}{5}$ is not an integer.

   19. −22 is an integer.

Exercises 19–23: Translate the statement given in symbols into words.

   20. $15 \in \mathbb{Z}$

   21. $-7 \in \mathbb{Z}$

   22. $\dfrac{4}{9} \notin \mathbb{Z}$

   23. $0 \in \mathbb{Z}$

Section 1.2   Formal Definitions

As was discussed in Section 0.1, clear definitions are extremely important in mathematics. Section 1.1 presented some formal mathematical definitions, and more are introduced in Section 1.4. Many of the terms used in Number Theory are familiar to you. Let's begin by reviewing the concepts of *even*, *odd*, *divisible*, and *prime*. For now, the goal is to make sure you have a strong and complete understanding of these concepts.

One of the most basic classifications of the integers is even or odd. What exactly do we mean by an even integer? Is there another choice besides even or odd? You can probably list many even numbers without referring to a definition and the same is true of odd numbers. However, having precise definitions allows us to answer questions about what numbers are included in the set and what numbers are not included in the set. For now, we will make a tentative definition of the terms above.

   Definition 1.3 An integer is *even* if it is a multiple of 2. In symbols a is even if $a = 2k$ for some $k \in \mathbb{Z}$.

Example 1.1. (a)   10 is even since $10 = 2 \cdot 5$ and $5 \in \mathbb{Z}$.

           (b)   −26 is even because $-26 = 2(-13)$ and $-13 \in \mathbb{Z}$.

           (c)   27 is not even because $27 = 2 \cdot 13 + 1$ which is not a multiple of 2.

There are different ways to describe an even number. Other possibilities are: An even number leaves a zero remainder when divided by 2; or, an even number is divisible by 2 evenly. Can you think of others?

Example 1.2. Is the integer 0 even?

Solution:

Using the characterizations of even stated before this example, we can confirm that zero is even, since $0 = 2 \times 0$.

Definition 1.4 An integer b is **odd** if it can be written as $b = 2k + 1$, $k \in \mathbb{Z}$.

There are different ways to describe odd integers. For example, an odd integer is not a multiple of 2, or has a remainder of 1 when divided by 2. In Example 1.1, 27 is an odd integer because $27 = 2(13) + 1$.

Definition 1.5 A **conjecture** is a statement that generalizes observations and is not known to be true or false.

Frequently when trying to ascertain the truth of a statement, we look at examples and test cases and formulate an educated guess. Then, using definitions and logic we attempt to determine if the statement is true or false. We will use conjectures extensively in this chapter.

Example 1.3. Conjecture: Odd integers can be negative.

Solution:

First, $-11 \in \mathbb{Z}$, and using the description above, $-11 = 2(-6) + 1$, so it is odd. This means that the conjecture is true.

The idea of *divisible* is important for establishing relationships among integers, and while you may not be able to state a precise definition yet, it is probably familiar. If you were asked whether 50 is divisible by 5, you probably are able to answer correctly (yes). If you were asked if 76 is divisible by 7, you may be able to answer correctly again (no). Let us write a working definition of *divisible:*

Definition 1.6 An integer $a \in \mathbb{Z}$ is **divisible by** $m \in \mathbb{Z}$ if $a = mk$ where $k \in \mathbb{Z}$.

Example 1.4. (a) $50 = 5(10)$ so 50 is divisible by 5. 50 is also divisible by 10.
(b) $76 = 7(10) + 6$, so 76 is not divisible by 7.

There are other ways to phrase this concept. For instance, we could say that "5 divides 50" and "7 does not divide 76."

A property of integers that is very interesting and useful is the idea of a *prime* number.

Definition 1.7 A *prime number* is a natural number whose only positive divisors are 1 and itself.

Some examples of prime numbers are 5, 11, 17, and 47.

Example 1.5. Is the number 1 a prime number?

Solution:

A prime number has exactly two divisors. The number 1 is only divisible by itself; so, the integer 1 is not prime. The formal definition of prime in Section 1.4 makes it clear that negative integers and the number 1 are not included as primes.

One final definition is needed to understand some of the mysteries of Number Theory.

Definition 1.8 A *perfect number* is an integer whose sum of the divisors including itself is twice the number.

Example 1.6. For example, the divisors of 6 are 1, 2, 3, and 6. The sum is 12. Similarly, the divisors of 28 are 1, 2, 4, 7, 14, and 28. The sum is 56.

Remark: Pythagoras was the first person to discover perfect numbers. They were also discussed by Euclid (325–265 BC).

Exercise Set 1.2

Exercises 1–4: Give an example of a number that fits the description of the term given in this section, and one that does not fit the description. Explain your answer.

1. even
2. odd
3. divisible by 8
4. prime

Exercises 5–10: Determine which of the following integers are prime.

5. 28
6. 321
7. 31
8. 241
9. 3215
10. −541

Exercises 11–15: Determine if the following integers are perfect

11. 128

12. 24

13. 25

14. 322

15. 1458

16. Write the even numbers as the sum of two primes: 88, 102.

17. Write the following even numbers as the sum of two primes: 28, 42.

18. Write these even numbers as the sum of two primes: 246, 1224.

19. Show that 1 is an odd integer.

Exercises 20–23: Use the definition of even to verify that the expression is an even integer.

20. $6k$

21. $2m + 4n$

22. $4k + 2$

23. $6 - 4m$

Exercises 24–27: Use the definition of odd to verify that the expression is an odd integer.

24. $2m + 2n + 1$

25. $4k + 1$

26. $2k + 5$

27. $2m + 2k + 3$

Section 1.3   Unsolved Problems and Unanswered Questions in Number Theory

While many questions in Number Theory are easily understood, the answers may not be known. In modern times, fields of mathematics require a significant amount of background and terminology to understand the unsolved questions in the field. A long-standing question in Number Theory, called Fermat's Last Theorem is: Are there integer solutions to the equation $a^n + b^n = c^n$ when $n \geq 3$? In the seventeenth century Pierre de Fermat claimed to have found proof that the answer is no. However, he did not provide proof. In the twentieth century, Andrew Wiles finally proved the theorem.

Source: Associated Press

Since Number Theory is the study of the integers, you are familiar with these numbers and probably understand many of the statements of the unsolved problems of Number Theory. Finding solutions to these questions is another matter. We will discuss some of these questions throughout this book. This section will discuss some of the unproven statements and unsolved questions in Number Theory.

Remark: Mathematicians frequently use the phrase "*infinitely many A*" to express the fact that there an infinite number of "*A*". For example: "There are infinitely many integers."

Definition 1.9 Pairs of primes that differ by 2 are called ***twin primes***.

Examples include 3, 5; 5, 7; 11, 13; 17, 19.

Definition 1.10 *Mersenne Primes* are primes that can be expressed as $2^n - 1$.

For example, $3 = 2^2 - 1$, $7 = 2^3 - 1$ are Mersenne Primes.

Unsolved Conjectures

1. The "**Twin Prime Conjecture**" states that there are an infinitely many such pairs, but so far no one has been able to prove it.

2. **Goldbach's Conjecture**: Every even integer greater than 2 can be written as the sum of two primes.

   For example: $4 = 2 + 2$, $6 = 3 + 3$, $8 = 3 + 5$, $10 = 5 + 5$, $28 = 11 + 17$. This famous conjecture has been tested for very large numbers, and has been true for all of them, but no one has been able to prove it is always true, despite a $1,000,000 prize and a novel about the topic.[3]

Unanswered Questions

3. Are there infinitely many primes that can be expressed as $2^n + 1$? For example, $5 = 2^2 + 1$ and $17 = 2^4 + 1$.

4. Are there infinitely many Mersenne primes?

5. Are there an infinite number of *perfect* numbers?

6. Are there any odd perfect numbers?

Exercise Set 1.3

1. Give an example of a number that fits the description of each term given in this section, and one that does not fit the description. Explain your answer.

Exercises 2–7: There have been many attempts to find a formula that will generate prime numbers, and only prime numbers. Evaluate each expression and determine whether or not it is prime. Explain the method you use.

2. $2^6 - 1$

3. $2^6 + 1$

4. $2^7 - 1$

5. $2^7 + 1$

6. $2^9 - 1$

7. $2^9 + 1$

8. Find three examples of twin primes not already given in this Section.

9. Write these even numbers as the sum of two primes: 246, 1224.

10. *Cousin primes* are primes that differ by 4. Find two pairs of cousin primes.

11. Show that Goldbach's Conjecture is true for 20.

12. Find a number that makes Goldbach's Conjecture false.

13. Show that Goldbach's Conjecture is true for 32.

14. Find two more examples of primes that fit conjecture 2 in the list above.

Section 1.4   Inductive and Deductive Reasoning

Once we have agreed on terminology, the language of mathematics, relationships, and concepts are developed. Many of these are based on observations, which lead to a conjecture or an educated guess about the properties observed. To be more convinced that a concept is correct, more evidence is sought, and an inductive reasoning process leads to a more general conjecture. A generalization of this type is known to be true in all observed cases, not in all possible cases. In order to prove that the general statement is true in all possible cases, we must move to a deductive reasoning process which we will describe below.

Inductive and deductive reasoning are important mathematical tools that can be used to make everyday decisions. We frequently reason inductively, which means to draw a general conclusion from observing specific instances. For example, every day when you go to the cafeteria at noon, you see the same person at the check-out counter. On your way to the cafeteria tomorrow, you expect to see the same person at the check-out counter.

More importantly, inductive reasoning is used in scientific investigations and also in the social sciences. Observations are made and conjectures formulated. Additional observations that provide mounting evidence for a phenomenon leads to a "law" about that phenomenon. For example, the law of gravity explains the phenomenon observed every day. Social scientists perform experiments to observe the results and to develop theories about the behaviors that they study. For example, studies were performed to determine the relationship between sleep deprivation and efficiency in performing tasks.

We would be surprised if we dropped a ball from the top of a set of stairs and it did not bounce down the steps. We have generalized on our past experiences and the law of gravity. In the second example, social scientists kept people awake for extended periods of time and observed their efficiency in performing a task the next day. From many observations a general statement is proposed. If an exception was found in either of these cases, the generalization would be false.

Question: Can you name some other "laws" that you know?

This type of reasoning, where conclusions are made by generalizing observations, is called **inductive reasoning**. Inductive reasoning is used whenever you make observations and use them to formulate a hypothesis or conjecture, a statement that you believe to be true. However, since inductive reasoning is based on specific examples, it will never result in a proof.

> **Definition 1.11** *Inductive reasoning* is a process of building an argument on the basis of reasoning from observations and examples to a generalization.

The process is used when one observes specific examples, identifies patterns in the observations, and then creates a conjecture based on these observations.

Example 1.7. Characterize the sum of two odd integers.

Solution:

Observe the sum of several pairs of odd integers:
$5 + 9 = 14, 15 + 321 = 336, 1 + 11 = 12, -111 + 23 = -88$
Form a conjecture based on your observations: The sum of two odd integers is even.

The goal of inductive reasoning is to develop a new conjecture or test an existing conjecture. Inductive reasoning can provide support for a conjecture, but it does not prove that the conjecture is *always* true. The difference between mathematics and other sciences is that you can study examples and make a strong argument using inductive reasoning, but it is not proof.

In mathematics and logic, we have another tool, *deductive reasoning* with which one can prove that a statement is true when a rational argument begins with a true statement. The goal of deductive reasoning is to prove that a conjecture is a true statement.

Deductive reasoning starts with some basic assumptions and uses rules of logic to deduce conclusions. This type of reasoning is used to draw conclusions in mathematics. Beginning with definitions of terms and axioms (called assumptions or hypotheses), we arrive at a conclusion. Below are several examples of deductive reasoning that you have seen in geometry and algebra, and some basic assumptions (definitions and axioms) that you have used.

1.   If equals are added to equals, the sums are equal. (If $x = y$ then $x + 5 = y + 5$.)
2.   A line extends indefinitely in two directions.
3.   Parallel lines never meet.
4.   If a and b are numbers, then $a + b = b + a$ (the commutative property)
5. $a(b+c) = ab + ac$ (the distributive property)

Definition 1.12 *Deductive reasoning* is a sequential process of steps that is based on known facts and (axioms, definitions, and theorems) and uses rules of logic to reach a true conclusion (a new fact).

Deductive reasoning begins with known facts. The goal of deductive reasoning is to prove that a new statement is true. The conclusion of a deductive argument is guaranteed to be true as long as the initial information is also true.

Example 1.8. The conjecture in Example 1.7 is true. We can prove it by using a logical argument and known information. Let a and b be odd integers.

Then $a = 2k+1$, $b = 2j+1$ where $k, j \in \mathbb{Z}$ by definition of *odd* integer

$a + b = (2k+1) + (2j+1)$ by substitution

$= 2k + 2j + 2$ by combining similar terms

$= 2(k + j + 1)$ by the distributive property

$(k + j + 1) \in \mathbb{Z}$ by the closure axiom of $\mathbb{Z}$

$\therefore a + b$ is even, by definition of even.

Note: The closure axiom is defined later. Basically, it says that when you add integers, the sum in also an integer.

Both types of reasoning, inductive and deductive reasoning, are very useful. It is important to know the difference between these two types of reasoning, since each has a different purpose and leads to a different type of conclusion. Inductive reasoning is used to test statements to decide what may be true and what statements you may want to prove. Even if every example supports the truth of the statement, though, it still may be false in some cases not yet tested. If the statement is indeed true, deductive reasoning is the tool that is used to prove it.

Mathematicians use inductive reasoning to discover a pattern and state a conjecture. Then they use deductive reasoning starting with some known facts, such as definitions and axioms, to prove that a conjecture is always true, that is, the conjecture is actually a *theorem*; or find an example in which the conjecture fails to be true, in which case the general statement is false.

Example 1.9. Determine whether each example illustrates inductive reasoning or deductive reasoning.

   a) Sarah concludes her grade for the semester will be a B, because her grades on the first two quizzes were B's.
   b) At the end of the semester, Julia averages her quiz grades and finds that her quiz average is an A.
   c) Scientists have learned a lot by studying Mars, so they will also learn a lot by studying Neptune.
   d) Birds are dinosaurs and dinosaurs are reptiles, so birds must be reptiles.

Solution:

   a) This is an example of inductive reasoning because Sarah generalized the examples of her grades on two quizzes to her grade for the semester.
   b) This is deductive reasoning since Julia used the formula for computing an average and the grading scale for the class to find her quiz average.
   c) Since this argument generalizes from the example of Mars to another planet, this is inductive reasoning.
   d) This is a deductive argument, starting with the premises that birds are dinosaurs and dinosaurs are reptiles. As for whether or not the premises and conclusion are true, you may need to consult your local paleontologist.

Inductive reasoning is used to create new conjectures, as well as to test existing statements. Examples 1.10–1.12 illustrate this.

Example 1.10. Test the following conjecture: All primes are odd.

Solution:

A common application of inductive reasoning is to test conjectures by looking at examples to see if the conjecture is supported. For example, 3, 5, 7, and 11 are all prime and they are all odd. There are many other examples that support this statement. However, no number of examples that support this statement can prove that it is true. In fact, the conjecture is false because 2 is an even number and 2 is a prime.

Notice that while testing examples cannot prove a general statement is true, Example 1.10 shows that an example can be used to prove it is false. This idea is more carefully discussed in Section 1.7.

Example 1.11. Create a conjecture about the result of adding two even numbers.

Solution:

One way to formulate a conjecture is to try some examples and look for patterns. Choose some pairs of even integers:

$$6 + 4 = 10$$
$$0 + 8 = 8$$

$$-6+4=-2$$
$$2+12=14$$

Notice that in every case, the sum of the two even integers is an even integer. These examples do not prove that this will always be the case, but they allow us to make a conjecture that we can then try to prove.

Example 1.12. Test the conjecture: The sum of the squares of two integers is a perfect square.

Solution:

Choose a few pairs of integers (a) 3 and 4, (b) –3 and 6 (c) 7 and 11 (d) 12 and 14.
(Note: We have chosen both odd and even integers, and positive and negative integers, and primes and composites to see a variety of different situations.)

    a. $3^2 + 4^2 = 9 + 14 = 25 = 5^2$. So, the statement is true
    b. $(-3)^2 + 6^2 = 9 + 36 = 45$. The statement is false.

Since we have an example that is true in one instance and false in another. The statement is not always true. Try the other two examples yourself.

Since the purpose in using deductive reasoning is to write proofs, we now establish exactly what is meant by a proof.

> **Definition 1.13** A *proof* uses deductive reasoning and logic to connect a sequence of statements, definitions, and theorems to verify that a particular conclusion is true.

The goal of a proof is to provide a clear and convincing argument that the conclusion is true. In the next three sections, we will look carefully at these components of a proof. In Section 1.4, we will examine statements and explain when different types of statements are true or false. In Section 1.5, some basic definitions related to the integers are introduced. Finally, in Section 1.6, these components are combined with rules of logic to write mathematical proofs.

Exercise Set 1.4

Exercises 1–7: Determine which of the following situations involve inductive reasoning and which involve deductive reasoning.

1. It has rained for four of the last five days. Today is sunny, so I expect it to rain for the next few days.

2. Your low fuel light came on in your car. The last time this happened, you were able to drive for two more days without running out of gas, so this time you will be able to drive for two days as well.

3. Your low fuel light came on in your car, so you get out the manual to see how many gallons of gas are left in the tank. You find that you have two gallon in reserve. In traffic, your car gets 20 mpg. Can you make it to the grocery store and back if the grocery store is 7 miles away?

4. Clark has calculated the amount of money he earned over the summer and is now calculating whether any additional income tax will have to be paid over what was taken as a payroll deduction.

5. When budgeting for next month, Ryann assumes the deductions from her paycheck will be the same as they were in the previous month.

6. The stock market has been going down for most of the past month. However, you have observed that the market rarely goes down two months in a row. So, you plan to invest some money in the market at the beginning of next month.

7. George liked the first three books by his favorite author, so he is ordering an advance copy of her latest book since he is sure to like it.

8. In order to determine if a statement is true or false, we can test examples. We want to determine the truth value of the statement: The sum of the squares of two odd integers is not a perfect square.
   a) Test the conjecture on at least four examples and use these examples to draw a conclusion about whether the statement is true or false.
   b) What type of reasoning did you use to make the conclusion in part a)?
   c) Is your conclusion in part a) still a conjecture? Is it false, or is it a theorem (e.g. a statement that can be proved by deductive reasoning)?

9. Add the pairs of numbers: $2+4$, $6+8$, $14+(-10)$, $2+(-2)$.
   a) Do you see a pattern in the numbers that were given? (Hint: Think about whether they are odd or even).
   b) Do you notice a pattern in the sums?
   c) Create a conjecture about what you observed when these pairs of numbers are added.

10. Add the pairs of numbers: $7+(-9)$; $3+(-11)$; $9+(-3)$; $-27+27$.
    a) Do you see a pattern in the numbers that were given? (Hint: Think about whether they are odd or even).
    b) Do you notice a pattern in the sums?
    c) Create a conjecture about what you observed when these pairs of numbers are added.

11. Add the pairs of numbers: $6+3$, $9+4$, $-5+16$, $-5+10$, $58+21$.
    a) Do you see a pattern in the numbers that were given?
    b) Do you notice a pattern in the sums?
    c) Make a conjecture about what you observed when these pairs of numbers are added.

12. Use Exercises 9–11 to create a conjecture that covers all three cases. Create several new examples to test your conjecture and see if it is true in these new examples.

13. Multiply the pairs: 2×3, 5×8, 11×10, 124×9.
    a) Do you see a pattern in the numbers that were given?
    b) Do you notice a pattern in the products?
    c) Make a conjecture about what you observed when these pairs of numbers are multiplied.

14. Multiply at least three pairs of odd integers and make a conjecture about the product of two odd integers.

15. Multiply at least three pairs of even integers together and make a conjecture about the product of two even integers.

16. Use Exercises 13–15 to create a conjecture that covers all three cases. Create several new examples to test your conjecture and see if it is true in these new examples.

17. Multiply at least three sets of three odd numbers and make a conjecture about the product of three odd integers.

18. Using inductive reasoning to fill in the blank with a conclusion.
    a. The sum of two odd numbers is _____.
    b. The product of two even numbers is _____.
    c. The product of two odd numbers is _____.
    d. The sum of two natural numbers is _____
    e. The difference between two natural numbers is _____.

Exercises 19–21: Find a pattern in the sequences of integers and make a conjecture about the next three integers in the sequence.

19. 1, 2, 3, 4, 5, ___, ___, ___, …
20. 2, 5, 9, ___, ___, ___, …
21. 1, 1, 2, 3, 5, 8, ___, ___, ___, …
22. Find all examples of inductive or deductive reasoning in the passage below from Induction and *Analogy in Mathematics* Volume 1 of Plausible Reasoning by George Polya (page 11 – Chapter 1: Induction). In each case, determine whether the conclusion made matches the type of reasoning used.

> **The logician, the mathematician, the physicist, and the engineer.**
>
> "Look at this mathematician," said the logician. "He observes that the first ninety-nine numbers are less than [a] hundred and infers hence, by what he calls induction, that all numbers are less than a hundred."
>
> "A physicist believes," said the mathematician, "that 60 is divisible by all numbers. He observes that 60 is divisible by 1, 2, 3, 4, 5, and 6. He examines a few more cases, as 10, 20, and 30, taken at random as he says. Since 60 is divisible also by these, he considers the experimental evidence sufficient."
>
> "Yes, but look at the engineers," said the physicist. "An engineer suspected that all odd numbers are prime numbers. At any rate, 1 can be considered as a prime number, he argued. Then there comes 3, 5, and 7, all indubitably primes. Then there comes 9; an awkward case, it does not seem to be a prime number. Yet 11 and 13 are certainly primes. 'Coming back to 9,' he said, 'I conclude that 9 must be an experimental error.'"

Section 1.5   Statements and Connectives

An important part of mathematics is determining when something is true. Languages have many ways of expressing an idea or asking a question. Some of these are called *statements*. However, sentences or exclamations like "Really?", "Okay", or "Are you going to study math today?" do not qualify as statements.

> **Definition 1.14** A *statement* is a declarative sentence that has a truth value, either true or false.

When discussing the properties of statements, statements are usually represented by letters, such as p, q, or r. The goal is to understand when a statement is true and when it is false, called the **truth value** of the statement. Since both the initial information in a proof as well as the conclusion to be shown are made up of statements, it is important to understand exactly what the statements mean. There are both simple statements as well as compound statements.

A simple statement is the simplest declarative sentence. Some examples are:

> Triangles have three sides. (True)
> Nine is a prime number. (False)
> How are you doing? (Not a statement)

The last example shows that there are many pronouncements that are not declarative sentences. Questions fall into this category. "Are you going to study math today?" is one example. There are other examples of utterances that are not true or false, such as "maybe" or "I don't know." In addition to questions, other remarks that are not statements include exclamations: "Wow!" or "Gosh!" and phrases such as "o.k." Number Theory studies conjectures and statements about integers.

The truth value of simple statements is easy to determine provided you have the necessary information, such as the definition of a triangle of a prime number. Compound statements are formed by joining simple statements with a *connective* word such as "and" or "or." There are many possible connectives in the English language (and, but, and furthermore to name a few); however, each of them can be expressed in terms of the five given in the next definition.

> **Definition 1.15** A *logical connective* joins statements to form a new statement. There are five logical connectives used to represent logical operations. These are:
>
> > not
> > and
> > or
> > if...then...
> > ...if and only if...

All of the other connectives can be rewritten in terms of these five, used in logic.

Mathematics frequently involves proving that a general statement is true or false. A statement such as "The sum of any two even integers is even," or "Multiplying both sides of a true equation by the same number produces a true equation." Our goal is to be able to prove that a statement is either true or false.

When proving a statement given information is provided, usually preceded by the words: "let" or "suppose" since they are being defined by the statement that follows. This allows us to identify different statements. If, for example, p represents the statement "Ten is a prime number." (which is false) and q represents the statement "All triangles have three sides." (which is true), we show this assignment by:

> Let p represent the statement: Ten is a prime number.
> Let q represent the statement: All triangles have three sides.

When defining symbols to represent statements, the expressions are abbreviated with a colon.

p: Ten is a prime number.

q: All triangles have three sides.

We can apply connectives such as and (*p and q*), and *if ... then....* (*if p then q*) to indicate different ways of combining these statements into compound statements.

Negations

The first word that is used to make a new statement is the only one that does not connect two statements. "Not" changes the meaning of the statement from true to false, or from false to true. The word "not" forms the **negation** of a statement. The negation of a statement *p* is another statement that has the opposite truth value as *p*. For example, the negation of the statement, "The integer *a* is even" is "The integer *a* is not even," or "The integer *a* is odd."

> **Definition 1.16** The **negation** of a statement *p* is a statement with the opposite truth value of *p*. If *p* is true, then the negation is false, and if *p* is false, then the negation is true. The negation of *p* is written as not *p,* or in symbols ~*p*.

The negation of any statement can be formed by adding "It is not true that..." to the beginning of the sentence. So, for a statement *p*, the negation can be expressed as "It is not true that *p*." This sounds awkward and difficult to use, but expressing the sentence this way first can be helpful in figuring out the correct negation for the statement.

Example 1.13. Write the negation of each simple statement in symbols and words and determine whether the negation is true or false.

   a)   *t:* Triangles have three sides.
   b)   *n:* Nine is a prime number.
   c)   *w:* There are not eight days in a week.
   d)   *s:* The sum of two even numbers is even.

Solution:

   a)   ~*t* Triangles **do not** have three sides. False, notice that the original statement was true.
   b)   ~*n* Nine is **not** a prime number. True, notice that the original statement was false.
   c)   ~*w* There are eight days in a week. False, the original was true.
   d)   ~*s* The sum of two even numbers is not even. False, the sum of two even numbers is even and we will prove this fact in Section 1.5.

Unfortunately, not all statements are so straightforward. We now consider some examples of more complicated statements. When statements have modifiers (or quantifiers) like *many, some,* or *all,* forming the negation is slightly more complicated.

Example 1.14. Determine which choice is the correct negation of statement *p* and explain why.

p: Some people like math.

Possible negations: a) All people like math.

b) Some people do not like math.

c) No people like math.

Solution:

We can get a sense of the statement and its negation by looking at the Venn diagram in Figure 1.1.

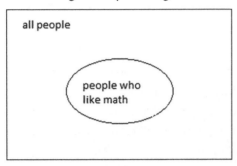

Figure 1.1

If the statement *p* is false, then the set of people who like math must be empty. So, assuming that this original statement is true, the correct negation makes the original statement false. Similarly, if the negation is a true statement, then the original "Some people like math" must be false. Keeping this in mind, we will examine the choices.

Choice a) If it is true that all people like math, then there are definitely some who like math. These statements do not have opposite truth values—they can both be true at the same time.

Choice b) is interesting, but examining it closely shows that it does not form the negation of the given statement. To see this, notice that if it is true that some people do not like math, it may still be true that there are some other people who do. Thus, these two statements do not have opposite truth values.

This leaves Choice c), the correct negation. To make the original statement "Some people do like math" false, there must be **no** people who like math. You can see this in the Venn diagram. If it is false that some people like math, the set in the circle must be empty. Therefore, the correct negation is "No people like math" or "All people do not like math," a sad state of affairs if it were true.

From this discussion, we see that the negation of a statement of the form SOME *a* **are** *b* is **NO** *a* **are** *b*.

Note: The term "therefore" is symbolized by ∴.

Example 1.15. Find the negation of the statement: "All grapefruit are yellow."

Solution:

One way to think about the negation is to think about what makes the statement false. If it is not true that all grapefruit are yellow, then there is a grapefruit of another color. Therefore, the negation of "All grapefruit are yellow" is "Some grapefruit are not yellow."

Notice that to show that the statement "All grapefruit are yellow" is not true, only one example of a non-yellow grapefruit is needed (such as a pink grapefruit). This idea will be important in Section 1.7, which discusses how to prove that a statement is false.

Example 1.16. Find the negation of the following statement and determine the truth values of the statement and its negation: All polygons are regular polygons.

Solution:

To form the negation of this statement, first form the sentence, "It is not true that all polygons are regular polygons." This can be expressed more clearly by saying "Some polygons are not regular polygons."

To determine the truth values, remember that a polygon is just a closed shape with straight sides, and a regular polygon has sides of equal length and angles of all the same measure. The original statement is then false because there are examples of polygons such as rectangles or isosceles triangles which are not regular polygons. This also shows the statement "Some polygons are not regular polygons" is true.

Question: Which of the following words are synonyms: Each, every, all?
To help you answer this question, fill in the blank with each of the choices ___ triangle(s) has (have) three sides. Are these words interchangeable?

Conjunction of statements
Other than simple sentences, discussed above, there are also compound sentences, formed by putting two simple sentences together with a connective. Two examples were given above. First, we examine statements connected using the word "and" called a conjunction.

Definition 1.17 The *conjunction* of two statements p and q is the statement p and q, or in symbols $p \wedge q$.

A conjunction, "*and*" statement, is true when both parts of the statement are true, that is, $p \wedge q$ is true when p is true and q is true. The statement $p \wedge q$. is false when either one of p or q is false.

Example 1.17. For each statement below, use the simple statements to convert symbols into words or words into symbols. Then determine whether each statement is true or false.

Simple statements:

p: Four is an even number   *r*: There are 12 months in a year
q: Six is an odd number.   *s*: A triangle has four sides.

a) Four is an even number and there are 12 months in a year.
b) Four is an even number and six is an odd number.
c) A triangle has four sides and six is not an odd number.
d) $\sim s \wedge q$

Solution:

a) In symbols, this statement is $p \wedge r$. Since both p and r are true, the conjunction $p \wedge r$ is also true.

b) In symbols, this statement is $p \wedge q$. Since q is a false statement, the conjunction $p \wedge q$ is false, even though p is true.

c) In symbols, this statement is $s \wedge \sim q$. Since s is a false statement, the conjunction is also false, even though $\sim q$ (six is not an odd number) is true.

d) In words, the statement $\sim s \wedge q$ is "A triangle does not have four sides and six is an odd number." This conjunction is false since q is false.

Caution Rewriting statements in a mathematical form can be tricky because there are sentences that seem to be simple statements, but when we try to write them in a mathematical form, they are actually compound sentences.

For example: The sum of two even numbers is even. To write the "two even numbers" mathematically, we write the compound sentence:

> *a* is an even number and *b* is an even number.

When we applied the definition of *even* to the integers *a* and *b*, different letters are used. If we used the same letter, both numbers are the same. Just as in English, if we say "I saw two people that I know …." Most likely they will not have the same name. Changing the letter to represent each of them individually indicated that they are different people, such as Joe and Jane. The same for two integers, using different letters indicates that the integers can be different even numbers.

Disjunction of Statements

A compound statement formed by joining two (or more) statements with the connective "or" is called a *disjunction*. The symbol $\vee$ is used to represent the connective "or." If p and q are statements then the statement *p or q* is a disjunction, called an "or statement."

> **Definition 1.18** The *disjunction of two statements* p and p is the statement *p or q*, or $p \vee q$. The statement $p \vee q$ is true when either p is true, q is true, or both p and q are true. The only time the statement $p \vee q$ is false is if both p and q are false.[4]

Question: Two integers are given that are not both even. Can you rewrite the statement: (a) as a compound statement? (b) Can you rewrite the statement in symbols?

Using the idea given in the **Caution** above:

(a) For the first part of the statement, we can say: One of the integers is even and the other is odd. For the second part of the statement we can say: Both of the integers are odd. So the entire statement is: One of the integers is even and the other is odd, or both integers are odd.

(b) In symbols, let's call the even integer *c* and one odd integer *d* and the other one *e*. Then we can write "*c* is even and *d* is odd, or *d* and *e* are odd." Next, give the statements names:

(c) Now let p represent the statement: *c* is even. Let q represent: *d* is odd, and let r represent *e* is odd. Rewriting using the connective, we have: $(p \wedge q) \vee (q \wedge r)$.

We can also find negations of compound statements. The negation of a statement of the form $p \wedge q$ is a statement that is false when $p \wedge q$ is true. A conjunction is false when **either** of the statements it contains is false. $\therefore$, the negation of "p **and** q" is "not p **or** not q" symbolized, $\sim p \vee \sim q$.

Example 1.18. Use the simple statements given below to write the compound statements in symbols, and then determine whether each compound statement below is true or false.

Simple statements:

p: A square has five sides   r: Three is a prime number
q: A platypus is a mammal   s: Nine is an even number

Compound statements:
a)   Three is a prime number and a platypus is a mammal.
b)   A square has five sides or three is a prime number.
c)   Nine is an even number or a square has five sides.
d)   Nine is an even number or three is not a prime number.

Solution:

a)   In symbols, this statement is $r \wedge q$, and is true since three is prime and a platypus is an egg-laying mammal.
b)   In symbols, this statement is $p \vee r$ which is true since even though p is false, r is true.
c)   In symbols, this statement is $s \vee p$, which is a false statement since it is false that a square has five sides, and also false that nine is even.
d)   In symbols, this statement is $s \vee \sim r$ which is a false statement since both s and $\sim r$ are false.

Example 1.19. Find the negation of each of the compound statements in Example 1.18. Write the negations in words and symbols.

Solution:

a)   Three is not a prime number or a platypus is not a mammal. $\sim r \vee \sim q$
b)   A square does not have five sides and three is not a prime number. $\sim p \wedge \sim r$
c)   Nine is not an even number and a square does not have five sides. $\sim s \wedge \sim p$
d)   Nine is not an even number and three is a prime number. $\sim s \wedge r$

Example 1.20. Write the negation of the statement, "It is raining and I forgot my umbrella," using symbols.

Solution:

We will start by labeling the two simple statements included in the given compound statement:

r: It is raining.   u: I forgot my umbrella.

Then, the original statement can be written $r \wedge u$. To form the negation, either r or u must be false. In words, "It is not raining or I did not forget my umbrella," and in symbols, $\sim r \vee \sim u$.

Note that Example 1.20 shows that the negation of any statement of the form $p \wedge q$ is $\sim p \vee \sim q$.

Conditional statements

A *conditional statement* is formed when two statements are connected with the expression *if … then* …. For statements p and q, one possible conditional statement is *If p then q*.

> **Definition 1.19** The statement p that follows the "if" is called the **condition** or **hypothesis** and the statement q that follows the "then" is called the **consequence** or **conclusion**.

Statements of the form *If p then q* are called conditionals because they only tell you what will happen if the condition is true. For example, consider the following statement: If I win one million dollars then I will give you half. What happens if I do not win one million dollars? You will not have a chance to test this statement. It only specifies what will happen in the event that I do win that money.

Mathematicians are frequently concerned with proving that conditional statements are true or false. In this course, we will only be concerned with conditional statements with p being true. To prove that a conditional statement is true, it must be true in all cases, and a general proof using variables to represent the numbers is appropriate. To show that a conditional statement is false, you need to find one instance in which the statement fails to be true, called a counterexample.

Returning to the very familiar statement: "The sum of two even numbers is even" we rewrite the statement in symbols: p: a is even, q: b is even, and r: $a + b$ is even. So, we have the sentence: If a and b are even, then $a + b$ is even. Finally, the symbolic representation is $(p \land q) \Rightarrow r$. As we were warned by the **Caution statement**, rewriting a simple sentence in its symbolic form takes precision.

A second conditional statement using the same two simple statements is *If q then p*. Notice that this is a different statement with a different meaning, since q is the condition and p is the consequence.

> **Definition 1.20** A *conditional statement* is a statement of the form If p then q, written as $p \Rightarrow q$, and is read as "If p then q" or "p implies q". A conditional statement is true if the conclusion q is true whenever the condition p is true. For a conditional statement to be false, there must be an example when the condition p is true, and the conclusion q is false.

Sometimes a statement is not written in the conditional form but can be rewritten as a conditional statement. When possible, rewrite a statement in the conditional form since we will develop techniques to prove this type of statement in the next section. The following example shows some statements that can be rewritten as conditionals.

Using our recent example $r \Rightarrow (p \land q)$ says: If the sum of two integers is even, then each of the integers is even. This is false since the sum of two odd numbers is also even.

Example 1.21. Rewrite each of the following statements as a conditional statement with the same meaning.

   a)   A line extends indefinitely in two directions.
   b)   All integers are real numbers.
   c)   The sum of two even integers is an even integer.
   d)   Every rectangle is a quadrilateral.
   e)   Each line segments has two endpoints.

Solution:

   a)   If L is a line, then L extends indefinitely in two directions.
   b)   If a is an integer, then a is a real number.
   c)   If a and b are two even integers, then $a+b$ is an even integer.
   d)   If r is a rectangle, then r is a quadrilateral.
   e)   If L is a line segment, then L has two endpoints.

How will we write the negation of a conditional statement $p \Rightarrow q$? The negation must be false when the conditional statement is true. To make a conditional false, the condition must be true, and the conclusion to be false. $\therefore$ the negation of $p \Rightarrow q$, $\sim(p \Rightarrow q)$ is $p \wedge \sim q$.

Example 1.22. Write the negation of the statement: If you build it, they will come.

Solution:

You built it, and they did not come. (Note that the statement "You build it, but they did not come." has the same meaning, but it is an alternate connective for *and*.)

Biconditional

There is one additional logical connective to consider, the ***biconditional***. A biconditional statement, or "if and only if" statement, has the form *p if and only if q*. The symbol $\Leftrightarrow$ is used to represent "if and only if."

> **Definition 1.21** The ***biconditional statement***, *p* if and only if *q* or $p \Leftrightarrow q$, is true when both *p* and *q* are true or both are simultaneously false. If $p \Leftrightarrow q$ is true, then *p* and *q* are called ***logically equivalent***. For *p* $\Leftrightarrow q$ to be false, *p* or *q* must be true when the other is false.

"if and only if" statements are used to make mathematical definitions. Whenever a term such as *natural number* is used, it always has the exact meaning that is given in the definition. On the other hand, if a set is written as {1, 2, 3, 4, ...} then this represents natural numbers. In the next section, formal definitions of some familiar terms about the integers: even, odd, and prime, and others are introduced.

Notice that another way to think about an "if and only if" statement $p \Leftrightarrow q$ is as a combination of the two conditionals $p \Rightarrow q$ and $q \Rightarrow p$. For the biconditional $p \Leftrightarrow q$ to be true, both $p \Rightarrow q$ and $q \Rightarrow p$ must be true.

Example 1.23. Write the following biconditional statement in symbols, and determine its truth value.

A polygon is a triangle if and only if it has three sides.

Solution:

If p represents the statement "A polygon is a triangle" and t represents "It has three sides," then in symbols, the statement is $p \Leftrightarrow t$.

To determine whether the statement is true or false, look at the two conditionals combined in the biconditional.

$p \Rightarrow t$: If a polygon is a triangle, then it has three sides.
$t \Rightarrow p$: If a polygon (closed figure with straight line segments as its sides) has three sides, then the polygon is a triangle.

Every triangle has three sides, so the first conditional, $p \Rightarrow t$, is true since whenever the condition is met, the conclusion is true. Also, any polygon with three sides will be a triangle so the second conditional $t \Rightarrow p$ is also true. $\therefore$, the biconditional statement is true.

Example 1.24. Use the simple statements below to write out the "if and only if" statements $p \Leftrightarrow q$ and $r \Leftrightarrow t$ in words and determine their truth values.

p: S has five sides.	r: The number m is an even integer.
q: S is a regular pentagon.	t: m is divisible by 4.

Solution:

$p \Leftrightarrow q$: In words, S has five sides if and only if S is a regular pentagon.

To determine the truth value, look at the two conditionals combined in this statement.
$\quad$ $p \Rightarrow q$: If S has five sides, then S is a regular pentagon.
$\quad$ $q \Rightarrow p$: If S is a regular pentagon, then S has five sides.

The first conditional is false. For example, if S has sides of unequal length, then it is not a regular figure. But, the second conditional statement is true since every shape that is a regular pentagon will have five sides. Since both conditionals are not true, the biconditional statement $p \Leftrightarrow q$ is FALSE.

Now consider $r \Leftrightarrow t$. In words, the number m is an even integer if and only if m is divisible by 4.

Again, we can rewrite this biconditional as two conditional statements.
$\quad$ $r \Rightarrow t$: If the number m is an even integer, then m is divisible by 4.
$\quad$ $t \Rightarrow r$: If m is divisible by 4, then m is an even integer.

The first conditional is false since 2 is an even number that is not divisible by 4. Therefore, the biconditional $r \Leftrightarrow t$ is FALSE (even though the second conditional $t \Rightarrow r$ is true).

Exercise Set 1.5

Exercises 1–8: Determine if the following pronouncements are statements.

1. Ethan is a STEM major.

2. Exercise!

3. Thank you very much!

4. The clock is running slowly or the time is correct.

5. How many pedals does a daisy have?

6. Heart disease is the leading killer of women.

7. If you eat less and exercise more, you will lose weight.

8. To get good grades, you have to study.

Exercises 9–22: Form the negation of each of the following statements. Then determine the truth value of the original statement and the negation.

9. Seven is an odd number.

10. A quadrilateral has four sides.

11. All four-sided shapes are squares.

12. Eleven is a composite number.

13. Some triangles have zero area.

14. Some people do not swim.

15. The sum of two even numbers is even.

16. All students are diligent.

17. All prime numbers are odd.

18. Two and three are factors of six.

19. Zero is a whole number.

20. Zero is neither even nor odd.

21. Not all polygons are regular polygons.

22. The number 6 has factors of 1, 2, and 3.

23. We discussed several terms that can be replaced with the connective "and." Can you think of any other?

24. Can you think of alternative words for "or"?

25. Which logical connective replaces each of these words: moreover, because, while?

Exercises 26–31: Using the simple statements below, write each compound statement in words, and decide whether the statement is true or false.

p: Two is an odd number

q: Six is a multiple of 3.

r: Nine is a prime number.

s: n is an odd number.

26. $p \wedge q$

27. $p \wedge \sim r$

28. $r \wedge s$

29. $s \wedge p$

30. $\sim q \wedge r$

31. $q \wedge p$

Exercises 32–37: Using the simple statements below, write each compound statement in words, and decide whether the statement is true or false. Compare the truth value to the corresponding statement in the previous section.

p: Two is an odd number r: 15 is a prime number.
q: Nine is a multiple of 3. s: n is an odd number.

32. $p \vee q$

33. $p \vee \sim r$

34. $r \vee s$

35. $s \vee p$

36. $\sim q \vee r$

37. $p \vee p$

Exercises 38–42: For each pair of statements, do the following.

    a) Form the conditional statement $p \Rightarrow q$ and determine whether it is true or false. If the conditional statement is false, give an example that shows it is false.

    b) Form the conditional $q \Rightarrow p$ and determine whether it is true or false. If the conditional statement is false, give an example that shows it is false.

    c) Determine whether the biconditional statement $p \Leftrightarrow q$ is true or false

38. p: a is even q: a is divisible by 6

39. p: the last digit of n is 0 q: n is even

40. p: the last digit of n is 5 q: n is divisible by 5

41. p: a is divisible by 3 q: a is odd

42. p: the last digit of n is 0 q: n is divisible by 10

Exercises 43–47: Determine whether the biconditional statement is true or false. (It may be helpful to write out the two conditional statements combined in the biconditional).

    43. A car's windshield wipers are on if and only if it is raining.

    44. The sum of two integers is even if and only if the two integers are even.

    45. An integer is prime if and only if it is odd.

    46. R is a pentagon if and only if R has five sides.

    47. The integer m is a perfect square if and only if the square root of m is an integer.

Exercises 48–51: Represent each simple statement with a letter and then write each compound statement below in symbols.

    48. If R is a rectangle, then R has 4 right angles.

    49. If two even integers are added, then their sum is an even integer.

    50. If two odd integers are added, then their sum is an even integer.

    51. If two even numbers are multiplied, then the product is an even number.

Exercises 52–55: Form the negation of each of the following statements.

    52. The number three is prime and there are 12 months in a year.

    53. I like peas or carrots with dinner.

    54. The integer a is odd or b is odd.

    55. Two consecutive integers can both be even.

Section 1.6   Properties of the Integers

Two important components of a proof are axioms and definitions. Axioms are statements that are basic and are accepted as true without proof. An example of an axiom is: If equals are added to equals, then the sums are equal. Axioms provide a starting point for reasoning. Definitions make use of "if and only if" statements to provide a concrete characterization of mathematical terms so that everyone has the same understanding of the meaning. Since definitions are "if and only if" statements, the two sides are interchangeable and can be substituted for each other in a proof. This section introduces more formal definitions of even, odd, and prime, as well as an axiom about the integers.

> **Definition 1.22** An integer a is *even* $\Leftrightarrow$ if and only if $a = 2n$ where $n \in \mathbb{Z}$.

If an integer a is even, then a can be replaced with the expression $2n$. Also, if a can be written as $2n$ for an integer n, then you can conclude that a is even. This definition is frequently used in proofs.

Example 1.25. Use the definition of even to show that 22 is even but 23 is not.

Solution:

Since $22 = 2(11)$ and $11 \in \mathbb{Z}$, 22 satisfies the definition of even. Since $23 = 2(11.5)$, and $11.5 \notin \mathbb{Z}$, 23 is not even.

> **Definition 1.23** An integer b is *odd* if and only if $b = 2n+1$ for $n \in \mathbb{Z}$.

Restated, if an integer b is odd, it can be replaced with the formula $2n+1$, where n is an integer and in reverse: if an integer b can be written in the form of twice another integer plus 1, then you can conclude b is odd.

Example 1.26. Use the definition of odd to verify that 81 is odd but 80 is not odd.

Solution:

Since $81 = 2(40) + 1$ and $40 \in \mathbb{Z}$, 81 is odd. Since $80 = 2(39.5) + 1$, and $39.5 \notin \mathbb{Z}$, 80 is not odd. (In fact, since $80 = 2(40)$, 80 is even.)

> **Definition 1.24** An integer $p > 1$ is *prime* if and only if the only positive divisors of p are 1 and q.

Before beginning to write proofs about the integers, there is one more familiar fact that needs to be made explicit. A set of numbers usually has operations defined on the set that allow one to combine the elements of the set. The simplest operations are addition, subtraction, multiplication, and division. Let us agree on this informal definition of an operation.

> **Definition 1.25** An *operation* on a set is a method of combining two elements of a set so that the result is also in the set.

Think about what happens when two integers are added: whether they are positive, negative, or zero, the result will be another integer. Similarly, if two integers are multiplied, the result will be another integer. This property is called closure.

> **Definition 1.26** A set is called *closed* under an operation, if the result when that operation is performed on members of the set, is in the set.

This property is an axiom of integer arithmetic and is stated below.

> **Closure of $\mathbb{Z}$ Axiom** The integers are closed under addition, subtraction, and multiplication.

Notice that the operation division is missing from this list. That is because the integers are not closed under division. For example, while $4 \div 2 = 2$, is in the integers, $4 \div 3 = \dfrac{4}{3}$, is not an integer. Since the result of dividing an integer by an integer is not always an integer, we say that the integers are not closed under division.

Example 1.27. If k and m are integers, determine if $2(k + 2km + 1)$ is an integer.

Solution:

Since 2, k, m, and 1 are all integers, and they are combined using multiplication and addition, $2(k + 2km + 1)$ must be an integer because $\mathbb{Z}$ is closed under addition and multiplication.

Example 1.28. If a and b are integers, use the definition of even to verify that $4a + 2$ is even.

Solution:

Since $4a + 2 = 2(2a + 1)$, and $2a + 1 \in \mathbb{Z}$ because $\mathbb{Z}$ is closed under addition and multiplication, $4a + 2$ is even by the definition of even.

Example 1.29. If a and b are integers, determine if $a(4 + 3ab - 1)$ is an integer.

Solution:

Since the integers are closed under multiplication, $3ab$ is an integer. Also, the integers are closed under addition and subtraction, so $4 + 3ab - 1$ is an integer. Finally, again using the closure under multiplication fact, $a(4 + 3ab - 1)$ is an integer.

Exercise Set 1.6

Exercises 1–10: If a and b are integers, determine whether or not the given expression **always** represents (a) a natural number and (b) an integer. Explain your work.

1. $a + b$
2. $a - b$
3. a/b
4. $a - 2b + 1$
5. πab (where $\pi \approx 3.14159\ldots$)
6. $10ab$

7. $2a + b + 1$
8. $4b - 2$
9. $\dfrac{a + b}{2}$
10. $\sqrt{2} \cdot ab$

11. For each term below, give an example that satisfies its definition and an example that does not. Explain using the definition.
    a) even
    b) odd
    c) prime
    d) composite

Exercises 12–17: Determine whether each integer is even or odd. Justify your answer using the definitions.

12. 412
13. –25
14. 0
15. –34
16. 147
17. 2

Exercises 18–25: If a and b are integers, determine whether or not each expression is even or odd, if possible. Justify your answer using the definitions. If it is not possible to determine whether the expression is even or odd, explain why.

18. $2a + 2b$

19. $a + 2$

20. $4a + 2b$

21. $2a + 2b + 3$

22. $a + b + 2ab$

23. $4b + 1$

24. $a^2 + b^2$

25. $2a + 4ab + 4$

26. Explain why 2 is the only even prime number, using the definitions in this section.

27. If $k \in \mathbb{Z} \land m \in \mathbb{Z}$ show that $2km + 3k^2 - 3m \in \mathbb{Z}$.

Section 1.7   Rules of Logic and Direct Proofs

The rules of logic are used to determine when a statement is true. Definitions and the Closure of $\mathbb{Z}$ Axiom provide a basis for drawing conclusions. Additional axioms provide crucial information. As stated in the Rules of Logic, premises are facts that are given in the statement of the problem as well as definitions. Proofs are an example of valid arguments, and logical rules explain how to construct a valid argument, based on the statements in the premises and the conclusion you want to show.

For example, if you know that "Everett has $5.00 and a quarter in his pocket." is a true statement, then it is valid to conclude that Everett has at least $5.00 in his pocket. (In fact, he has $5.25.) On the other hand, if you are given that "Everett has no bills or coins in his pocket." is a true statement, it is not be valid to conclude that Everett has money in his pocket.

These rules of logic, based on what makes a statement true, allow us to connect the definitions, theorems, and given information into a ***mathematical proof***. The purpose of a proof is to provide a clear argument that you or another person can read and understand that the statement being proved is true. When writing a proof, the goal is always to connect the information known to be true to the conclusion you want to show is true. In order to make proofs as clear as possible, there are some general properties they all share.

Both mathematicians and logicians use rules of logic to draw conclusions. There is a branch of philosophy that studies symbolic logic and a branch of mathematics that studies mathematical logic in great detail. In this section, we discuss the rules of logic that are used to draw conclusions from given information.

Definition 1.27 An ***argument*** is a sequence of statements that lead to a conclusion.

Definition 1.28 An argument is ***valid*** if the conclusion is true whenever the given information, is true.

Definition 1.29 The ***premise(s)*** is (are) the information that is given to be true.

The form of an argument is very important. Below we list the rules of logic that allow us to draw valid conclusions. We will explain the use of each of these rules with examples.

Section 1.7.1   Symbolic Logic—Rules of Logic

Rule 1: The basic form of an argument   In English:

$p \Rightarrow q$ If p then q

p p (premise)

$\therefore q$ Therefore, q. (conclusion)

Rule 2: A syllogism   Transitivity law

$p \Rightarrow q$

$q \Rightarrow r$

$\therefore p \Rightarrow r$

Rule 3: Disjunction   Elimination of possibilities

$p \vee q$ $p \vee q$

$\sim p$ $\sim q$

$\therefore q$ $\therefore p$

Rule 4: Contrapositive   If the conclusion is false, the premise must also be false.

$p \Rightarrow q$

$\sim q$

$\therefore \sim p$

When proving a statement using these Rules 1 and 2, the proof is often referred to as a "direct" proof. When using Rule 3, one of the choices is eliminated. This rule can be expanded to cover several options:

$$p \vee q \vee r$$

$$\sim p$$

$$\sim q$$

$$\therefore r$$

If neither of the first two statements is true, then r must be true. We use this when we want to consider cases. Each of these rules is explained with examples in this section.

Section 1.7.2   General properties of a direct proof:

- The beginning and end of the proof are always labeled, so that readers know when the argument starts, and at what point the reader will be convinced the statement is true.
- The premises are clearly stated at the beginning of the proof.
- Each step in the proof is supported with a reason, a definition, an axiom, or a rule of logic.
- The last line of the proof matches the consequence or conclusion you were to show.

The most common proof is an application of Rule 1: a conditional statement, *if p then q*. For a conditional to be true, the consequence q is true whenever the premise (or given condition) p is true. This type of proof is called a ***direct proof***.

Proof Technique: Direct Proof

To prove a statement of the form If p then q:
  1. Take p as a premise.
  2. Using Rules 1 and 2, logically connect definitions, theorems, and axioms to show that q *is* true.

The structure of this type of proof is explained in the examples below. The first example illustrates how these ideas fit together to prove a statement about the integers.

Remarks: A *lemma* is a small theorem that frequently appears in preparation for a larger theorem. The symbol ▪ indicated the end of the proof. The last two lines of the proof verify that the SHOW statement is true.

Lemma 1.1 Prove that if two integers are even, then their sum is even.

Solution:

p represents the statement "two integers are even." and q represents the statement "Their sum is even." We want to prove the conditional statement *If p, then q*. Therefore,

SHOW: that $a + b$ is even.
Equivalently: Prove that $a + b = 2m$, where $m \in \mathbb{Z}$

  (1) Take p as the premise. Rewrite the statement p as: a is an even integer and b is an even integer.
  (2) Show that q is true. Rewrite the statement q as: $a + b$ is even is also true.

   Step 1: State the premises on the left and keep track of the desired conclusion on the right. If an explanation is needed, put the reasons to the right of the statement. Note that the statement headed "SHOW" is a tool to keep track of where we are headed, but is not actually considered part of the proof.

Proof: Let a be an even integer and let b be an even integer (premises)
   Rewrite in symbols:
   $a = 2n$ for $n \in \mathbb{Z}$.
   $b = 2k$ for $k \in \mathbb{Z}$ (definition of *even*)
   Add: $a + b = 2n + 2k$ (axiom: equals added to equals are equal)
     $= 2(n + k)$ (distributive property of the integers)
   Now, $n + k \in Z$ (closure of Z)
   Let $n + k = m$
   $\therefore a + b = 2m$ *is* even (definition of *even*).
   This is what we wanted to prove.

▪

The symbol above represents the end of the proof. ▪ There are several things to notice in this proof.

Note that if one cannot fill in the middle statements to show that q must be true, it may be for two reasons:

1. q may not always be true when p is true and "*If p then q*" is actually a false statement. (We will discuss what to do in this case in Section 1.7).
2.   There is a piece of information missing that is needed to complete the proof.

Whenever you are trying to better understand a statement, or determine whether it is actually true or false, inductive reasoning is helpful.

Theorem 1.1 The product of two odd integers is odd.

Proof: Rewrite the statement in a conditional form:
If a and b are odd integers, then the product ab is odd.

> SHOW: ab is an odd integer,
> i.e., $ab = 2n+1$, for $n \in \mathbb{Z}$

The proof has the same format as the lemma, beginning with the premise p: a is odd and b is odd. The conclusion, or consequence is q: the product ab is odd.

Let a be an odd integer and let b be an odd integer.
$a = 2k+1$ for $k \in Z$, and $b = 2j+1$ for $j \in \mathbb{Z}$,

	definition of odd integer
$ab = (2k+1)(2j+1)$	substitution
$ab = 4jk + 2j + 2k + 1$	distributive property
$\quad = 2(2jk + j + k) + 1$	distributive
$(2jk + j + k) \in \mathbb{Z}$	closure of $\mathbb{Z}$

$2jk + j + k = n$ for some $n \in \mathbb{Z}$
$ab = 2n + 1$
$\therefore ab$ is odd.

■

Proofs in textbooks (except for geometry textbooks) and mathematical articles are often written in paragraph form, rather than the column form shown in the two previous examples. The proofs still contain the same information (premises are clearly stated, and each step is justified with a reason), but it is presented in a different format. If you are writing a proof in this form, it is often useful to start with a column proof to organize the information, and then translate it into paragraph form. The proof for Theorem 1.1 is shown again in Theorem 1.2 that is written in a more traditional mathematical style.

Theorem 1.2 If a and b are odd integers, then their product ab is odd.

Proof: Let a and b be odd integers. Then, by the definition of odd, there are integers n and k such that $a = 2n+1$ and $b = 2k+1$. Multiplying a and b and substituting these formulas, we obtain:

$$ab = (2n+1)(2k+1)$$
$$= 4nk + 2n + 2k + 1$$
$$= 2(2nk + n + k) + 1.$$

Since $\mathbb{Z}$ is closed under multiplication and addition, $2nk+n+k \in \mathbb{Z}$.

$\therefore$ ab is odd by the definition of odd.

∎

One common technique to show that an "or" statement is true is to assume that one of the statements is false, using Rule 3. Then, if we are able to show that the other statement in the "or" statement must be true, that proves the original statement is true. We employ this strategy in the following examples.

Example 1.30. Suppose you have the following two premises.

Steve plays the piano or the guitar.
Steve plays the piano.
Can you make a valid conclusion about whether or not Steve plays the guitar?

Solution:

In this case, an "or" statement is true when one of the statements is true. Since the first statement is true, the "or" statement is true. We do not know anything about the second premise.

On the other hand, if we know that Steve does not play the piano, we can conclude that Steve plays the guitar, by Elimination, Rule 3.

Example 1.31. Prove that if $a+b$ is odd then one of a or b is odd.

Solution:

Let $a+b$ be odd. Also suppose that a is even.

Then $a+b = 2k+1$ for some integer $k \in Z$ and $a = 2n$.

For some integer $n \in Z$.

By substitution,

$a+b = 2n+b = 2k+1$. Solving for b:

$b = 2k-2n+1 = 2(k-n)+1$.

By closure of Z under addition, $k-n \in Z$ and by definition of odd,

$b = 2(k-n)+1$ is odd.

> SHOW: a is odd or b is odd.
> SHOW: b is odd.

Example 1.32. Suppose that you have the following two premises.

1) If R is a rectangle, then pairs of opposite sides are parallel.

2) R, pictured below, is a rectangle.

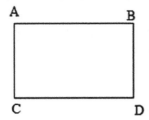

Can you make a valid conclusion about sides AB and CD? If so, what? If not, why not?

Solution:

In this case the premises support a valid conclusion. If a conditional statement is true, then the consequence is true every time the condition is true. Since the shape R is a rectangle, the condition is true for R.

∴ the opposite sides AB and CD must be parallel by a theorem in geometry.

Exercise Set 1.7

1. Complete each of the following to form a valid argument.
   a) If John is delivering the shipment, then the shipment will arrive on time.
      The shipment will not arrive on time.
   b) If you get a C or better, then you will pass the class.
      You did not pass the class.

In Problems 2–12, prove the given statement.

2. Zero is an even number.
3. If n is even, then $n+1$ is odd.
4. If n is odd, then $n+1$ is even.
5. If a is even and b is odd, then the sum of a and b is odd.
6. If two integers are odd, then their sum is even.
7. The product of an even number and an odd number is even.
8. The product of an even number and any integer is even.
9. The difference of two odd numbers is even.
10. The product of two even integers is divisible by 4.
11. The sum of two consecutive integers is odd.
12. The sum of three odd numbers is odd.

Section 1.8   Interlude (Optional)

Source: Time Life Pictures/The LIFE Picture Collection/Getty Images

Charles Lutwidge Dodgson (1832–1898), better known by his pen name **Lewis Carroll**, was an English writer of world-famous children's fiction, notably *Alice's Adventures in Wonderland* and its sequel *Through the Looking-Glass*. As a boy, **Carroll** excelled in mathematics and won many academic prizes. At age 20, he received a scholarship to Christ College.

Before continuing with the discussion of logic and proofs, we will take a little break, and look at the accomplishments of the famous author Lewis Carroll. Dodgson was a prolific writer, whose works included political pamphlets, mathematical works, and children's tales. In 1881 he gave up his mathematics lectureship to devote himself full time to his writing. "Lewis Carroll" had mixed feelings about his fame as an author of children's stories. He preferred to think of himself as a man of science and mathematics who also happened to write nonsense.

In fact, his field is mathematics. Many of his writings are infused with logic puzzles. You will see some of the witty remarks of his characters in the rest of this section, typed in **brown**. One of these is: *'But I don't want to go among mad people,' said Alice. 'Oh, you can't help that,' said the cat. 'We're all mad here.'*

Section 1.9   Indirect Proofs and Proofs by Contradiction

In Section 1.3, we saw that two statements p and q can be combined to form the conditional If p then q, and If q then p. In symbols, these are written as $p \Rightarrow q$ and $q \Rightarrow p$. The conditional $q \Rightarrow p$ is called the ***converse*** of $p \Rightarrow q$.

> **Definition 1.30** The ***converse*** of the conditional statement "If p then q" is "If q then p". In symbols, the converse of $p \Rightarrow q$ is $q \Rightarrow p$.

If both $p \Rightarrow q$ and its converse $q \Rightarrow p$ are true, then the biconditional statement $p \Leftrightarrow q$ is true, and p and q are logically equivalent. Sometimes a statement and its converse are both true. For example, "If a and b are even then $a + b$ is even." is true while the converse "If the sum $a + b$ is even the a is even and b is even." is false because the sum of two odd integers is also even.

The ***contrapositive*** is one more conditional statement, and it is based on Rule 4.

> **Definition 1.31** The ***contrapositive*** of the conditional statement "If ***p*** then ***q***" is "If not ***q*** then not ***p***" In symbols, the contrapositive of ***p*** $\Rightarrow$ ***q*** is ~***q*** $\Rightarrow$ ~***p***.

Notice that there are two steps to forming the contrapositive of $p \Rightarrow q$:
   1) interchange the order of p and q (this is the converse), and
   2) negate both q and p.

Example 1.33. Form the contrapositive of each of the following statements.

   a) If you play well, then your team will win.
   b) If S is a square then S has four sides.
   c) If you get enough sleep then you feel energetic and enthusiastic.

Solution:

   a) Label p: You play well, and q: Your team wins. Then the form for the contrapositive is $\sim q \Rightarrow \sim p$.
      In words:

      > If your team does not win, then you did not play well.

   b) The contrapositive is, "If S does not have four sides, then S is not a square." Notice that both the original conditional and the contrapositive are true statements.
   c) In this example, the conclusion is an "and" statement: You will feel energetic and enthusiastic. The negation is "You do not feel energetic or you do not feel enthusiastic." Thus, the contrapositive is, "If you do not feel energetic or you do not feel enthusiastic, then you did not get enough sleep."

The contrapositive of a conditional statement is useful because the contrapositive is logically equivalent to the original conditional statement. In other words, $p \Rightarrow q$ and $\sim q \Rightarrow \sim p$ are either both true or both false. This means that an alternative to proving the statement "If p then q" using a direct proof is to prove that the contrapositive is true instead. This method is called an ***indirect proof***. Although a direct proof is the first method to try, if it is not working sometimes proving the contrapositive is easier.

Section 1.9.1   Indirect Proofs

Definition 1.32 An ***indirect proof*** of the statement $\boldsymbol{p \Rightarrow q}$ is a proof of the statement $\boldsymbol{\sim q \Rightarrow \sim p}$.

To prove a statement "If p then q" using an indirect proof, you first assume that $\sim q$ is true and then show that $\sim p$ is true.

Proof Technique: Indirect Proof

To prove a statement of the form "If p then q", prove the contrapositive "If $\sim q$ then $\sim p$".

1. Take $\sim q$ as a premise.
2. Logically connect definitions, theorems, and axioms to show that $\sim p$ must be true.

Let us look at an example of an indirect proof. At the end of this section, we will examine why a conditional and its contrapositive are logically equivalent.

Example 1.34. Prove that if $3a + 5$ is odd, then a is even.

Solution:

Using the direct approach to a proof, the premise is that $3a + 5$ is odd. Applying the definition of odd, this can be written as $3a + 5 = 2k + 1$ for an integer k. Solving for a, the first step is $3a = 2k - 4 = 2(k - 2)$.

Since the conclusion is that a is even, we must show that $a = 2n$ for an integer n. It may be possible to continue by dividing the problem up between when k is even and k is odd, but instead let us see if proving the contrapositive is easier.

The contrapositive of the statement is: If a is odd, then $3a + 5$ is even. Notice that the premise is much simpler this time. We will now proceed with the proof.

Proof (of the contrapositive):
Let a be an odd integer.
Then $a = 2n + 1$ for $n \in \mathbb{Z}$ by the definition of odd.

SHOW: $3a + 5$ is even.
SHOW: b is odd.

Substituting for a in $3a + 5$, we have
$3a + 5 = 3(2n + 1) + 5 = 6n + 3 + 5$

$\quad\quad = 6n + 8 = 2(3n \mp 4)$ which is even by definition.

$\therefore$, if a is even then $3a + 5$ is odd.

It would be so nice if something made sense for a change."

"Why, sometimes I've believed as many as six impossible things before breakfast."

Source: ©Pushkin/Shutterstock.com

Remark: To this textbook author, indirect proofs seem like magic!

Section 1.9.2 Proof by Contradiction

Another proof technique very closely related to an indirect proof is called a *proof by contradiction*. Sometimes rewriting a statement as its contrapositive does not make a proof more approachable. In this case, a proof by contradiction can be helpful because it gives you an extra premise to work with. Proofs by contradiction are often useful when you are trying to prove that something is not true or does not exist.

In order to prove a statement using a proof by contradiction, start by stating the premise or premises, as in a direct proof. Where this method differs is that we also assume that the desired conclusion is false. Then use the original premises as well as this extra piece of information to reach an impossible statement (such as one of the premises being false). Since the premises are given as true, it follows that the assumption the conclusion was false is incorrect. Therefore, the conclusion must be true. As usual, first try some examples to see if the statement seems to be true.

Proof Technique: Proof by Contradiction

1. State any premises.
2. Assume that the desired conclusion is false.
3. Logically connect definitions, theorems, and axioms to find a contradiction of one of the premises or some other fact known to be true.
4. Conclude that the conclusion cannot be false as assumed, and must in fact be true.

Example 1.35. Determine if the statement is true: The difference of two primes is never 13.

a) Test this statement on some examples to convince yourself it is true.

b) Prove that the statement is true.

Solution:

a) Test the statement.

1. Looking at a few pairs of primes, we see that $13-7=6$, $23-3=20$, $47-39=8$. Notice that the difference is always even if both primes are odd, so it appears that to have a difference of 13, one of the primes must be even. The only even prime is 2.
    Arguing from this information, we have

2. In symbols, the statement says that if p and q are primes, then $p-q \neq 13$. Another way to say this is that if $p-q=13$, then p and q cannot both be prime. Assume that q is prime.

3. Then, $p=13+q$. Now if p is not a prime number, the statement that a difference of two primes cannot yield 13 is true. If p is prime, then this is a *counterexample* which proves the statement false. The only even prime number is 2, and that makes q in the equation a negative number.

b) Formalizing this discussion, we create a proof (by contradiction).
    Prove: If p and q are primes, then $p-q \neq 13$. Assume the statement is false: There are two primes p and q such that $p-q=13$. Since 13 is odd, either p is odd and q is even or p is even and q is odd. Otherwise, their difference is even. We will examine the two possibilities separately.

    Case 1: Suppose that p is odd and q is even. Then, since q is prime, q must equal 2. Substituting into $p-q=13$, we obtain $p-2=13$, which means that $p=15$. This contradicts the premise that p is prime.

    Case 2: Suppose that p is even and q is odd. Then, since p is prime, p must be equal to 2. Substituting again into $p-q=13$, we obtain $2-q=13$, which means that $q=-11$. This also contradicts the premise that q is prime since primes are defined to be greater than 1.

    In each case, we reached a contradiction of one of the premises of the proof. Therefore, the assumption that primes p and q exist such that $p-q=13$ must be false. Thus, there are no primes with a difference of 13.

    ∎

Section 1.9.3   A Conditional Statement and Its Contrapositive Are Logically Equivalent

Reminder: Two statements are logically equivalent if they always have the same truth values, so there are two parts to this proof. Part 1: Prove: If $p \Rightarrow q$ is true then $\sim q \Rightarrow \sim p$ is also true. Part 2: Prove: If $\sim q \Rightarrow \sim p$ is true, then $p \Rightarrow q$ is true. This result is stated in Theorem 1.3 below.

Theorem 1.3 A conditional statement "If p then q" is logically equivalent to its contrapositive "If $\sim q$ then $\sim p$." In symbols, the statements $p \Rightarrow q$ and $\sim q \Rightarrow \sim p$ are logically equivalent.

Proof:

Part I. Show that if $p \Rightarrow q$ is true, then $\sim q \Rightarrow \sim p$ is true.

Let $p \Rightarrow q$ be true and q is not true. By definition of the conditional statement, $p \Rightarrow q$, q cannot be false when p is true. $\therefore$ when q is false, so is p. Thus, $\sim q \Rightarrow \sim p$ is true.

Part II. Show that if $\sim q \Rightarrow \sim p$ is true, then $p \Rightarrow q$ is true.

Let $\sim q \Rightarrow \sim p$ be true. Since this statement is a conditional, we will apply the result proved in Part I, the negative inverse statement is true. $\therefore$, $\sim(\sim p) \Rightarrow \sim(\sim q)$ is a true statement. Since $\sim(\sim p)$ is equivalent to p and $\sim(\sim q)$ is equivalent to q the statement $\sim(\sim p) \Rightarrow \sim(\sim q)$ is the same as $p \Rightarrow q$.

$\therefore$, $p \Rightarrow q$ is true.

■

To put this result in context, suppose that the following is a true statement: If you worked a full week, then you are paid a full-week salary. The contrapositive of this statement is: If you did not get a full-week's salary, then you did not work the full week. If one of these statements is true, then the other has to be as well. The original conditional and its contrapositive are giving you the same information, but in two different forms.

"It's no use going back to yesterday, because I was a different person then."

Exercise Set 1.9

Exercises 1–7: Write the contrapositive of the statement and decide if the statement (and its contrapositive) is true or false.

1. If it is raining, then she is wearing her poncho.
2. If you are not there, then you cannot vote.
3. If at first you do not succeed, then try again.
4. If n is odd, then 2 does not divide n.
5. If n is even, then 2 does not divide n.
6. If p is prime, then p is odd.
7. If p is odd, then p is prime.

8. Prove that every prime number greater than 2 is odd.
9. Prove that if $5b - 1$ is even, then b is odd.
10. Prove that if $7a + 2$ is even, then a is even.
11. a) Rewrite the proof of **Theorem 1.5** in the column form introduced in Section 1.5.
    a) Explain why the proof of **Theorem 1.5** fails if $a = 0$.
12. Rewrite the proof of Example 1.35 in paragraph form.

Section 1.10 Counterexamples—Proving a Statement Is False

Reminder: For a general statement to be true, it must be true of **every** element of the set. That is "All A are B." is not true if there is even just one element of A that is not in B. To show that a general statement is false, find one example for which the statement fails to be true, called a **counterexample**. There are two parts to providing a complete counterexample: (1) find an example and (2) provide an explanation that shows the statement is false.

Example 1.36. "All prime numbers are odd."

Solution:

Find a prime that is not odd. The number 2 is even and also prime. Even though there are many prime numbers that are odd, the statement is false because it is not true for the prime 2.

$\therefore$, the number 2 is a counterexample to the statement that "All prime numbers are odd."

Example 1.37. Show that the statement "Every multiple of 3 is a multiple of 6" is false.

Solution:

If x is a multiple of 3, then x is a multiple of 6.

To show this statement is false, we need only one choice for x that makes the statement false. Any choice for x that makes the statement false is a counterexample. Let $x = 9$, then x is a multiple of 3 because $3 \cdot 3 = 9$, so the condition is true. But it is false that 9 is a multiple of 6 since there is no integer that can be multiplied by 6 to equal 9. Therefore $x = 9$ is a counterexample for the given statement.

Notice that even though the statement is true for some values of x, such as $x = 12$ or $x = 24$, it is still a false statement since it is not true for every value of x. Also, notice that 9 is not the only possible counterexample. The values $x = 15$ or $x = 3$ are also counterexamples to the statement. (Make sure that you can justify that they are actually counterexamples.)

Example 1.38. Provide a counterexample to the statement below and explain why it is a counterexample. "The product of two primes is odd."

Solution:

Again, one can find many examples that make the statement true, for instance, 3×5, 7×11, 3×73. However, this statement is false. Here is a counterexample: 2 is a prime number and 3 is a prime number, but $2 \times 3 = 6$, and 6 is an even, not odd.

Example 1.39. Disprove the statement: The sum of an even number and an odd number is even.

Solution:

Disproving a statement means to show that the statement is false, so we need a counterexample. One counterexample is the pair of integers 2 and 3; 2 is even and 3 is odd, but the sum $2 + 3 = 5$ which is odd, not even. Thus, the statement is false.

Exercise Set 1.10

Exercises 1–14: Prove that the statement is FALSE by providing a counterexample, and explaining why the example shows the statement is false.

1. If you are a teenager then you must be in high school.

2. If you are a millionaire then you have a college degree.

3. If you have a college degree then you have a lucrative career.

4. All water is safe to drink.

5. The sum of an odd number and an odd number is an odd number.

6. If n is a multiple of 4 then n is also a multiple of 8.

7. If the sum $a+b$ is even, then a and b must both be even.

8. The product of two prime numbers is odd.

9. The sum of two prime numbers is even.

10. The sum of an even number and an odd number is an even number.

11. The difference of two prime numbers is even.

12. The formula n^2+n+5 is a prime number for all integers $n>0$.

13. All multiples of 6 are multiples of 12.

14. The sides of a right triangle, a, b, c *(hypotenuse)* satisfy the equation $a^2+b^2=c^2$.

15. Two is not a prime number.

16. 28 is not a perfect number.

Section 1.11   Divisors and the Greatest Common Divisor

Two familiar ideas that you learned in school are the concepts of divisors and common divisors, which are central ideas in Number Theory and will be used in every subsequent chapter of this book. Divisors are very important in modern applications of mathematics in a variety of settings, including cryptography which is studied in Chapter 7. We review these concepts now to ensure that we all have the background for further study.

> **Definition 1.33** *d* **divides** *m* if and only if $m=dk$ for some integer k. The notation for "*d* divides *m*" is $d\,|\,m$.

This is an important and useful concept, and there are many ways to express the information "*d* divides *m*". Some common alternatives include:

d is a factor of *m*	*d* is a divisor of *m*
d divides *m* evenly	*m* is a multiple of *d*

Example 1.40. Determine whether each of the following statements are true or false.

a) $8\,|\,72$ b) $6\,|\,21$ c) $2\,|\,43326$ d) $6\,|\,3$ e) $5\,|\,0$

Solution:

a) Since $72=8(9)$, and 9 is an integer, $8\,|\,72$ is true.

b) Because $20=6(3)+2$, 6 does not divide 20, so $6\,|\,20$ is false. Another way to see this is that $20=6(3)+2$, and there is a remainder of 2.

c) Since $43326 = 2(21663)$, $2 \,|\, 43326$ is true.

d) Since $3 = 6(.5)$, $6 \,|\, 3$ is false. (Note that $3 \,|\, 6$ is true, but reversing the order makes a false statement since a number cannot be a divisor of a smaller number).

e) Because $0 = 5(0)$, $5 \,|\, 0$ is true!

Example 1.41. Determine whether each of the following statements are true or false and explain your answer.

   a) $-8 \,|\, 72$ b) $2 \,|\, (6n+4)$ c) $0 \,|\, 11$ d) $4 \,|\, (-128)$ e) $0 \,|\, 0$

Solution:

   a) True, because $72 = -8(9)$
   b) True, because $6n + 4 = 2(3n + 2)$.
   c) This statement is false. There is no integer k such that $11 = 0 \cdot k$ since $0 \cdot k$ is always 0.
   d) True, because $-128 = 4(-32)$.
   e) True, because $0 \cdot 0 = 0$.

Caution The symbols "/" and "|" look similar but have completely different meanings. $a \,|\, b$ means that "a divides b." This is a shorthand representation of a statement, not a number. Whereas, a/b means that "a divided by b", and represents a particular number.

Since we are studying the properties of integers, we will avoid division because the integers are not closed under division.

In Part a) of Examples 1.32 and of Example 1.33, we saw that $8 \,|\, 72$ and $-8 \,|\, 72$ are both true. In the next statement, we will prove that this relationship is true in general.

> **Lemma 1.2** If $a \,|\, b$ then $-a \,|\, b$.

Proof:

Let $a \,|\, b$. Then, using the definition of divides, we know that $b = ak$ for some $k \in \mathbb{Z}$. Notice that $ak = (-a)(-k)$, so $b = (-a)(-k)$. Since $-k$ is also an integer (because $-k = -1 \cdot k$ and $\mathbb{Z}$ is closed under multiplication), we can conclude that $-a \,|\, b$ by the definition of divides.

■

Example 1.42. Prove that if 6 divides n, then 2 divides n and 3 divides n.

Solution:

The conclusion is an "and" statement, so to prove the statement we have to verify that both $2 \,|\, n$ and $3 \,|\, n$ are true. The proof of this statement is shown below in column form. In Exercise 65, you are asked to rewrite it in paragraph form.

Suppose $6 \mid n$

Then $n = 6j$ for $j \in \mathbb{Z}$, by definition of "divides"

$n = (2 \times 3)j = 2(3j)$ by the associative law

$n = 3(2j)$ by the commutative law

Both $2j$ and $3j$ are integers by closure of $\mathbb{Z}$.[5]

Hence, $2 \mid n$ and $3 \mid n$ by definition of "divides."

> SHOW: $3a + 5$ is even
> $n = 2k$, $n = 3m$, integers k, m

■

Example 1.43. Prove or disprove the conjecture below. If true, prove the statement. If false, provide a counterexample. If $3 \mid a$ and $6 \mid a$, then $18 \mid a$.

Solution:

Begin by testing a few choices for a. Let's say $a = 18, 36, 42$. While both 18 and 36 are divisible by 18, $42 = 2(18) + 6$ and is not divisible by 18. Hence 42 is a counterexample and the statement is false.

Example 1.44. Prove or disprove: If $3 \mid a$ and $4 \mid a$, then $12 \mid a$.

Solution:

The condition is true in this case, because $3 \mid 12$ (since $12 = 3(4)$) and $4 \mid 12$ (since $12 = 4(3)$). We will try to prove the statement is true.

Let $a = 3k$ and $a = 4j$ for integers k and j. Since $4 \mid a$, we know that $4 \mid 3k$ but 4 and 3 share no common factors other than 1. So, $4 \mid k$. Similarly, $3 \mid j$. Substituting, we have

$k = 4q$, $j = 3r$ and

$a = 3(4q) = 12q$ $a = 4(3r) = 12r$

$\therefore 12 \mid a$ by definition of divides.

The next theorem shows that "divides" satisfies the transitive property: If $a \mid b$ and $b \mid c$ then $a \mid c$.

> **Theorem 1.4** If $a \mid b$ and $b \mid c$ then $a \mid c$.

Proof: Let $a \mid b$ and $b \mid c$. Then by the definition of divides, there are integers m and k such that $b = am$, and $c = bk$. Substituting for b in the second equation,

$$c = bk$$
$$= (am)k$$
$$= a(mk).$$

Because $\mathbb{Z}$ is closed under multiplication, $mk \in \mathbb{Z}$. $\therefore$, $a \mid c$ by the definition of divides.

■

Often, we are interested in what divisors are shared by two (or more) integers. Any pair of integers will have at least one shared positive divisor since 1 divides every integer. The concepts of common *divisors* and *greatest common divisor* may be familiar to you, but we define these terms formally.

> **Definition 1.34** An integer d is a ***common divisor*** of a and b if and only if $d \mid a$ and $d \mid b$. The greatest common divisor is the largest of the common divisors, denoted by $\gcd(a, b)$.

Remark: The greatest common divisor of two numbers is always positive. As we have shown, if $c \mid a$ then $-c \mid a$ and the positive one is the larger value. The following theorem is a useful property of common divisors. We will use this property in Chapter 2.

> **Theorem 1.5** If d is a common divisor of m and n, then for any integers a and b, $d \mid (am + bn)$.

Proof: Let d be a common divisor of m and n. Then by the definition of common divisor, $d \mid m$ and $d \mid n$. Therefore, by the definition of divides, $m = dk$ for $k \in \mathbb{Z}$ and $n = dl$ for $l \in \mathbb{Z}$. Substituting for m and n in the expression $am + bn$, we obtain:

$$am + bn = a(dk) + b(dl) = d(ak + bl) \text{ by the distributive property.}$$

Since $\mathbb{Z}$ is closed under addition and multiplication, $ak + bl \in \mathbb{Z}$. $\therefore d \mid (am + bn)$.

Notice that since 1 is a common divisor of every pair of integers (positive or negative), we only need to consider the positive divisors when looking for the greatest common divisor of two integers, since any common negative divisors will be less than 1.

■

Example 1.45. Find the greatest common divisors of the following pairs of numbers.

    a)   18, 4

    b)   21, 4

    c)   16, 40

Solution:

    a)   Since the positive divisors of 4 are 1, 2, and 4, the greatest common divisor will be one of these numbers. Since 4 is not a divisor of 18, but both 1 and 2 are divisors of 18, $\gcd(18, 4) = 2$.

    b)   The divisors of 4 are again 1, 2, and 4. The only value on this list that also divides 21 is 1, so $\gcd(4, 21) = 1$.

    c)   The divisors of 16 are 1, 2, 4, 8, and 16. From this list, 1, 2, 4, and 8 are also divisors of 40. So, the greatest common divisor of 16 and 40 is $\gcd(16, 40) = 8$.

Example 1.46. Find $\gcd(120, 45)$.

Solution:

When the numbers are large, you may want to list the divisors of one number under the other. The positive divisors of 120 are 1, 2, 3, 4, 5, 6, 10, 12, 15, 20, 30, 60, 120 and the positive divisors of 45 are 1, 3, 5, 15, 45. Comparing these lists, the largest divisor on both lists is 2, so $\gcd(120, 45) = 15$.

Factoring an integer and finding common factors and the greatest common factor of two numbers can be done using factor trees. If you have not seen this concept before, there are many examples on the Internet. Factor a number into two numbers, and write them as branches below the number. Continue this process until you reach a prime number, as in Figure 1.2 below.

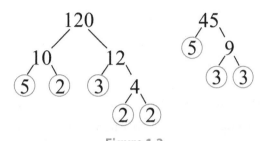

Figure 1.2

Every number in the tree is a factor of the original number; however, all the factors do not appear in the tree. The last number in a branch (circled) is a prime factor of the number. Using the factor tree, we can see the prime divisors that were listed above.

In the examples above, we looked only at the greatest common divisors of positive integers. Here is another example with negative numbers.

Example 1.47. Find gcd(12, –18).

Solution:

Notice that –18 has the same positive divisors as 18: 1, 2, 3, 6, 9, and 18. The common divisors of –18 and 12 are then 1, 2, 3, and 6. Since 6 is the largest of these that also divides 12, the gcd(12, –18) = 6.

These examples show that it is possible to find all of the positive factors of each number and then look at the lists of factors to find the greatest integer common to both lists. However, as numbers become large, it may be difficult to find **all** of the factors. Chapters 3 and 4 will introduce alternate methods for finding the greatest common divisor of two numbers.

Example 1.48. Create a conjecture about the value of gcd(a, 0).

Solution:

To create a conjecture, we will choose some values for a to look for a pattern. Try choosing a variety of values: a prime, a nonprime, and maybe a negative value.

$a = 7$ The positive divisors of $a = 7$ are 1 and 7, and both of these also divide 0 since $1 \cdot 0 = 0$ and $7 \cdot 0 = 0$. $\therefore$ gcd(7, 0) = 7.

$a = 15$. The positive divisors of a are 1, 3, 5, and 15, and again all of these also divide 0 so gcd(15, 0) = 15.

$a = -6$. The positive divisors of –6 are 1, 2, 3, and 6, and you have probably picked up on the pattern here. Since $0 \cdot m = 0$ for any integer m, the divisors of a will also always be divisors of 0. So again, $\gcd(-6, 0) = 6$. Notice that in this case, $\gcd(-6, 0) = |-6|$.

Based on the examples above, the following conjecture seems reasonable.

If a is an integer, then $\gcd(a,0) = |a|$.

Notice that if a is positive, then $|a| = a$, so this says that for a positive a, $\gcd(a, 0) = a$.

Example 1.49. Test the conjecture from Example 1.48 on the value $a = 0$.

Solution:

If $a = 0$, we are looking for the value of $\gcd(0, 0)$. Since $a \cdot 0 = 0$ for every integer a, every integer is a divisor of 0. Therefore, there is no largest common divisor, and $\gcd(0, 0)$ does not exist! Thus, we will revise the conjecture from Example 1.48.

If a is an integer not equal to 0, then $\gcd(a, 0) = |a|$.

The version of the conjecture in Example 1.49 is true, and is stated for positive integers in Theorem 1.4 below.

> **Theorem 1.6** If a is a positive integer not equal to 0, then $\gcd(a, 0) = a$.

Proof.
Let a be a positive integer. Then, $a \mid a$, so a is its own largest divisor. Since $a \cdot 0 = 0$, a is a common divisor of a and 0. $\therefore \gcd(a, 0) = a$.

■

One particularly interesting case is when two numbers have no common divisors besides 1. When two numbers share this property, they are called *relatively prime*. The definition is stated below.

> **Definition 1.35** Two integers a and b are **relatively prime** if and only if $\gcd(a, b) = 1$

Here are several examples: $\gcd(7, 8) = 1$, $\gcd(22, 25) = 1$, $\gcd(3, 7) = 1$. $\gcd(123, 331) = 1$

Questions:
1. What do you think is the gcd of two distinct primes?
2. What do you think is the gcd of two nonzero consecutive integers?
3. What do you think is the gcd of zero and a positive integer?

A related topic to the greatest common divisor is the *least common multiple* which is defined below.

> **Definition 1.36** A common multiple of a and b is an integer that both a and b divide. The integer m is the **least common multiple** of a and b if and only if m is the smallest positive multiple of both a and b. The least common multiple is denoted by lcm(a, b).

For example, $\text{lcm}\,(5, 12) = 60$ since 60 is the smallest number that both numbers divide. On the other hand, $\text{lcm}\,(12, 18) = 36$ since both numbers divide 36 but they do not both divide any number between 18 and 36. One way to find the least common multiple of two numbers is to find their factors and make sure that each factor in both lists divides the least common multiple.

Example 1.50.   Find the lcm (20, 35).

Solution:

The divisors of 20 are 1, 2, 4, 5, 10, 20, and the divisors of 35 are 1, 5, 7, 35. So the least common multiple must be divisible by each of these. 20×35 is divisible by each of the numbers and no smaller number will suffice. So, lcm (20, 35) = 700.

Exercise Set 1.11

Exercises 1–4: Rewrite each of the following statements using the notation $a \mid b$.

1. 24 is a multiple of 8
2. 16 divides 32
3. 5 is a factor of 0.
4. 7 is a divisor of 49.

Exercises 5–12: Determine whether the statement is true or false. Explain your answer.

5. 8 divides 56
6. 27 is a multiple of 6
7. 9 is a factor of 108
8. 2 is a divisor of 67
9. 21 is a multiple of 7
10. 7 is a multiple of 21
11. 6 is a factor of 76
12. 35 divides 7

Exercises 13–19: Determine whether the statement is true or false. Justify your answer using the definition of *divides*.

13. $7 \mid 63$
14. $9 \mid 0$
15. $2 \mid 3426$
16. $14 \mid 4988$
17. $0 \mid 18$
18. $6 \mid 2$
19. $2 \mid (4n + 2)$

Exercises 20–23: Test the statement to develop a conjecture about whether it is true or false. Explain your answer.

20. If 6 divides a and 12 divides a then 72 divides a.

21. If $2\,|\,a$ and $4\,|\,a$ then $8\,|\,a$.

22. If $2\,|\,a$ and $7\,|\,a$ then $14\,|\,a$.

23. If $6\,|\,n$ then $3\,|\,n$.

24. Find an integer d that divides 15 but does not divide 25.

25. Find an integer d that divides 20 but does not divide 26.

26. Write the contrapositive of the statement proved in Example 1.53: If 6 divides n, then 2 divides n and 3 divides n.

27. Consider the statement: "If m is not even then m is not divisible by 4."
    a) Write the contrapositive of the statement.
    b) Prove the statement using an indirect proof. (In other words, prove the original statement by proving its contrapositive).

Exercises 28–33: Find the greatest common divisor and least common multiple of the pairs of numbers.

28. (42, 130)

29. (15, 421)

30. (3289, 561)

31. (45, 75)

32. (183, 27)

33. (3443, 5775)

34. Find a value for a so that a and 12 are relatively prime.

35. Find a counterexample to the following statement, and explain your example:

$$\text{If } a\nmid b \text{ and } b\nmid a \text{ then } a \text{ and } b \text{ are relatively prime.}$$

36. For what integers a is $1\,|\,a$ true? Justify your answer.

37. For what integers is $0\,|\,a$ true?

38. Prove that if $d\,|\,m$ and $d\,|\,n$ then $d\,|\,(m+n)$.

39. Prove that if $d\,|\,m$ and $d\,|\,n$ then $d\,|\,(m-n)$.

40. Consider the following statement: If $a\,|\,b$ and $b\,|\,c$, then $ab\,|\,c$.
    a) Try some examples to determine whether the conjecture seems to be true or false.
    b) Either prove the conjecture true, or give a counterexample to show it is false.

41. Consider the following statement: If $a\,|\,m$ and $b\,|\,m$, then $ab\,|\,m$.
    a) Try some examples to determine whether the statement seems to be true or false.
    b) Either prove the conjecture true, or give a counterexample to show it is false.

42. When is it true that $a\,|\,b$ and $b\,|\,a$? Explain.

43. The following statement is FALSE. Find a counterexample and explain your example.

$$\text{If } a\,|\,c \text{ and } b\,|\,c \text{ then } ab\,|\,c.$$

Prove the statements in Exercises 46–51:

44. The sum of three consecutive even integers is divisible by six.

45. The product of three even numbers is divisible by eight.

46. If $a \in \mathbb{Z}$ then $a \mid 0$.

47. If $a \mid b$ then $-a \mid b$.

48. If $a \mid b$ and $c \mid d$, then $ac \mid bd$.

49. If a, b, c, and d are integers, prove that if $d \mid a$ and $d \mid b$, then $d^2 \mid ab$.

50. a) Fill in the table below and construct a conjecture about the relationship among the values in each row.
    b) Test the conjecture from part a) on two more pairs of integers.
    c) If the conjecture in (a) is true, explain how can it be used.

a	b	gcd(a, b)	lcm(a, b)	ab
3	7			
4	26			
24	48			
15	35			
36	142			
101	123			

51. Find the lcm(m, $m+1$) for any positive integer m.

52. What is the value of lcm(0, 5)? Explain your answer.

53. What is the value of lcm(0, 0)? Explain your answer.

Section 1.12   Divisibility Rules

Over many years, mathematicians have found rules that help us factor large numbers. These rules help to determine the divisors of a number and will be used throughout the text. The rules are particularly helpful in determining if two numbers are relatively prime and also to determine if a particular integer is a prime. In this section, a few of the rules are presented. More rules appear in Chapter 3 on Primes.

You may already know some of these rules presented here, stated using the term *divides* which was discussed in Section 1.8. Notice that each of these rules is an "if and only if" statement. These rules can be proven using the mathematics developed in Chapter 5.

Let a be any integer.

$2 \mid a$ if and only if   the last digit of a is even (0, 2, 4, 6, 8).

$3 \mid a$ if and only if   the sum of the digits of a is divisible by 3.

$4 \mid a$ if and only if   the number formed from the last two digits of a is divisible by 4.

$5 \mid a$ if and only if   the last digit of a is 0 or 5.

$6 \mid a$ if and only if $2 \mid a$ and $3 \mid a$.

$7 \mid a$ if and only if	when you double the last digit of a and subtract that from the number that remains after removing the last digit of a, that value is divisible by 7.
$8 \mid a$ if and only if	the number formed by the last three digits of a is divisible by 8.
$9 \mid a$ if and only if	the sum of the digits of a is divisible by 9.
$10 \mid a$ if and only if	the last digit of a is a 0.
$11 \mid a$ if and only if	the number formed by alternately subtracting and adding the digits of a is divisible by 11.
$12 \mid a$ if and only if	$3 \mid a$ and $4 \mid a$.

Example 1.51.   Does 3 divide 123456789?

Solution:

Add the digits to obtain 45. $3 \mid 45$, so $3 \mid 123456789$.

Example 1.52.   What other integers listed above divide 123456789?

Solution:

Two and four do not divide the number. Looking at the sum of the digits given in Example 1.51, we see that $9 \mid 45$, so $9 \mid 123456789$. Factoring, $123{,}456{,}789 = 9 \times 13{,}717{,}421$. 13717421 is still a large number, but we will find other ways to factor this number in Chapters 3 and 4.

Example 1.53.   Determine if the statement is true: If $2 \mid a$ and $3 \mid a$ then $12 \mid a$.

Solution:

To test this statement, choose some values for a that make the condition "$2 \mid a$ and $3 \mid a$" true. If the conclusion that $12 \mid a$ also holds true, this is evidence supporting the conjecture. If we find an example where the conclusion is false, then we have a counterexample. Let $a = 6$.

Then the condition is true since $2 \mid 6$ and $3 \mid 6$. However, $12 \mid 6$ is false since $6 = 12\left(\dfrac{1}{2}\right)$ and $\dfrac{1}{2} \notin \mathbb{Z}$.

$\therefore$ the conjecture is FALSE, and $a = 6$ is a counterexample.

The most complicated tests on this list are the ones for checking divisibility by 7 and by 11. They are less useful than the others because they are more complex and harder to remember, but it may be interesting to think about why all of these tests work. The tests for 7 and 11 are illustrated in the examples below.

Example 1.54.   Does $7 \mid 1876$?

Solution:

Using the divisibility test, we need to know if 7 divides the number $187 - 2(6) = 175$. Since 175 is still fairly large, we can apply the test again to get $17 - 2(5) = 7$. It is true that $7 \mid 7$, and therefore $7 \mid 1876$.

Example 1.55. Does $11 \mid 5212$?

Solution:

Applying the divisibility test for 11, form the number $5-2+1-2=2$. Since 11 does not divide 2, $11 \nmid 5212$ either.

Exercise Set 1.12

Exercises 1–6: Determine whether 516 is divisible by each of the following numbers using the divisibility tests in this section.

1. 2
2. 3
3. 4
4. 5
5. 6
6. 9

7. Let p and q be the statements below.

    p: n is divisible by 3
    q: n is divisible by 9

    a) Form the statement $p \Rightarrow q$ and determine whether it is true or false. If it is false, provide a counterexample.
    b) Form the statement $q \Rightarrow p$ and determine whether it is true or false. If it is false, provide a counterexample.
    c) What do parts a) and b) tell you about the truth value of $p \Leftrightarrow q$?

8. Let p and q be the statements below.

    p: n is divisible by 2
    q: n is divisible by 6

    a) Form the statement $p \Rightarrow q$ and determine whether it is true or false. If it is false, provide a counterexample.
    b) Form the statement $q \Rightarrow p$ and determine whether it is true or false. If it is false, provide a counterexample.
    c) What do parts a) and b) tell you about the truth value of $p \Leftrightarrow q$?

9. Which of the following numbers are divisible by 9?
    a) 784
    b) 7668
    c) 1327
    d) 8964

10. Which of the following numbers are divisible by 3?
    a) 657
    b) 791
    c) 3334
    d) 3336

Exercises 11–18: Determine whether the statement is true or false, and explain.

11. 137 is a prime number

12. 141 is a prime number

13. 149 is a prime number

14. 151 is a prime number

15. 153 is a prime number

16. 119 is a prime number

17. 861 is a prime number

18. 2401 is a prime number

Section 1.13   Summary and Review Exercises

Vocabulary and Symbols

integer, $\mathbb{Z}$

whole number

$\in$

divisible

twin primes

Mersenne primes

perfect number

Goldbach's Conjecture

conjecture

inductive reasoning

divides

deductive reasoning

premises

proof

truth value

prime

negation, $\sim$

conjunction, $p \wedge q$

disjunction, $p \vee q$

conclusion

conditional statement, $p \Rightarrow q$

biconditional statement, $p \Leftrightarrow q$

logically equivalent

even

odd

Closure of $\mathbb{Z}$ Axiom

direct proof

converse

natural number

contrapositive

indirect proof

lemma

counterexample

twin primes

common divisor

greatest common divisor

relatively prime

common multiple

least common multiple

hypothesis

syllogism

Suggested Readings

Dodge, Clayton W. "What Is a Proof?" *Pi Mu Epsilon Journal* 10 (Fall, 1998): 725–727.

Lamport, Leslie. "How to Write a Proof." *The American Mathematical Monthly* 102 (August–September, 1995): 600–608.

Chapter 1 Review Exercises

1. Which, if any, of the following terms has the same meaning: integer, natural number, nonnegative integer, positive integer, whole number.

2. What does each symbol represent?

$$\sim \qquad \Leftrightarrow \qquad \wedge \qquad \vee \qquad \Rightarrow \qquad \mathbb{Z} \qquad \mathbb{N}$$

3. Rewrite each of the following statements using the notation $a \mid b$.
   a) 5 is a factor of 70
   b) 7 is a divisor of 4

4. Find the gcd(1245, 3579).

5. Find the gcd(5368, 8793).

6. Write the following statement symbolically using $p : n$ *is an integer* and $q: n^2$ *is negative.*

   If n is an integer, then n^2 is not a negative number.

7. By choosing letters, such as p, q, r to represent simple statements, write the following statement using letters and logical connectives. If you press the MEMORY or RETURN button while the display appears in the screen, the display disappears.

8. By choosing letters, such as p, q, r etc. to represent simple statements, write the following statement using letters and logical connectives. If you press the F7 or press the display button while the display appears in the screen, the display disappears.

9. Explain the difference between $a \mid b$ and $a \, / \, b$. Give an example of each.

10. Give an example of two nonprime integers that are relatively prime.

Exercises 11–15: Write the contrapositive of the statement, eliminating any occurrences of "not not." Then state whether the pair of statements is true or false.

11. If n is odd, then 2 does not divide n.

12. If n is even, then 2 does not divide n.

13. If a and b are even then the product ab is divisible by 4.

14. If n is prime, then n is odd.

15. If n is odd, then n is prime.

16. Label each of the following statements as true or false. If false, give a counterexample.
    a) If 10 divides ab then 10 divides a or 10 divides b.
    b) If $a \mid b$ then $a^2 \mid b^2$.
    c) If 3 divides ab then $3 \mid a$ or $3 \mid b$.

17. Find the greatest common divisor and the least common multiple of each of the following pairs of integers.
    a) 216, 288
    b) 675, 1125
    c) 234, 233
    d) 356, 32

18. Find all $d > 0$ such that $18 \mid d$ and $d \mid 216$.

19. Find all $d > 0$ such that $20 \mid d$ and $d \mid 300$.

20. If p and q are distinct primes, find all positive divisors of pq.

21. Find the smallest integer $n > 0$ such that n has exactly 6 positive divisors.

22. Prove or disprove the following conjecture: If $b \mid c,$ then $\gcd(a, b) \leq \gcd(a, c)$.

In Problems 23–31 Prove the statement.

23. a and $-a$ have the same multiples.

24. Zero is an even number.

25. If $a \mid b$ and $a \mid c,$ then $a \mid (b + c)$.

26. The square of an even number is divisible by 4.

27. The sum of any 3 odd numbers is an odd number.

28. The product of any 2 even numbers is an even number.

29. The product of any 2 consecutive integers is even.

30. The square of an odd number is odd.

31. The sum of two consecutive primes is never twice a prime. (Hint: try some examples to convince yourself this is true. To prove it, try a proof by contradiction).

Section 1.14   Activities

1. Look up early calculating devices. (a) Determine at what time in history a particular device was invented. (2) Describe what arithmetic operations these devices were capable of doing. For example, the abacus was a very early calculating device; adding machines were invented much later. How many different devices did you find?

2. "Iff" is a mathematical shorthand for one of the connectives discussed in this chapter. Which one?

3. Search the web for factor trees and discuss the best explanation that you found.

4. There are many definitions and theorems in this section. To keep track of them, make a list so that you can refer to it when trying to construct proofs.

5. Watch the YouTube video on deductive reasoning and summarize what you learned that is not in this chapter. https://www.youtube.com/watch?v=ZTfVIMPV8KY

6. Read the article: O'Shea, Edwin. "Proofs Are Like Love Songs." *Math Horizons* 26, no. 2 (2018): 34. DOI: 10.1080/10724117.2018.1518811 Look up Fermat's Theorem to learn the history of the problem and why Fermat did not include his "proof" of the statement.

7. Look up Fermat's Last Theorem to learn why he did not prove the statement that bears his name.

8. Bertrand Russell's good friend, Alfred North Whitehead coauthored the famous work *Principia Mathematica*. Find out more about this person.

9. **Multi-Sudoku Puzzles** The game of *Multi-Sudoku* is an extension of the usual Sudoku game. In Multi-Sudoku, the numbers in the grid are $d, 2d, 3d, \ldots, 9d$, where $d > 1$ is a common factor for all of the nine numbers. Thus, the goal is to fill in each row, each column and each 3 by 3 subset with the values $d, 2d, 3d, \ldots, 9d$. Your first task is to find the greatest common divisor of all of the entries in the grid. Next, use any puzzle-solving strategy for ordinary Sudoku puzzles to solve the Multi-Sudoku puzzles that follow.

10		16			6			18
14	8	6	16			4		10
		18		10				
	10	14			4	2		
8					10		16	
16			14	2				4
	18		10					
		10	6	12	16	8		2
6		2	18		8	14		

Puzzle 1

		12				6		
		27	6		12	24		
15				24			9	27
	6	21	12		24		18	
		18				9		
	27		9		15		12	
24	18			12			6	21
		9	15		18	27		
		15				18		

Puzzle 2

Now, create your own Multi-Sudoku puzzle and challenge your friends to solve the puzzle.

Endnotes

1   The Fibonacci sequence is the set of numbers 1, 1, 2, 3, 5, 8, … where the number after the first number is the sum of the previous two integers.

2   The term **whole numbers** does not have a standard definition. It is sometimes used to represent the positive integers (1, 2, …), sometimes the non-negative integers (0, 1, 2, …), and sometimes the entire collection of integers.

3   The novel is called *Uncle Petros and Goldbach's: A Novel of Mathematical Obsession* by Apostolos Doxiadis.

4   Sometimes an *or* statement can specify that both options cannot be true at the same time. This is called the **exclusive or** in logic. For example, with the *exclusive or*, the statement "You can have a cookie or some ice cream." means that you can have one or the other, but not both. In this text, we will not use the exclusive or. Any statement of the form $p \vee p$ will be true when either or both p and q are true.

5. This statement will be proven later in the text.

Bertrand Russell

1872–1970

Bertrand Russell 1872–1970 was born in Trelleck, Britain, but was orphaned at a young age and raised by his grandmother. He was taught by governesses/tutors, from whom he learned French and German. In 1890 he went to Trinity College, Cambridge, and graduated "with distinction" in philosophy.

After he left the College at Cambridge in the summer of 1894, for some months he was attaché at the British embassy at Paris. In December 1894 he married Alys Smith. He was elected a fellow of Cambridge in 1895. He then went to Berlin to study social democracy, before moving near Haslemere, where he devoted his time to the study of philosophy. In 1900 he attended the Mathematical Congress at Paris, and was impressed by the work of the Italian mathematician Peano, who was interested in making mathematics more axiomatic. In 1903 he wrote his famous book, *The Principles of Mathematics*, with his teacher and friend Dr. Alfred North Whitehead. They developed and extended the mathematical logic of their predecessors Peano (one of the inventors of symbolic logic) and Frege. He spent a few years traveling abroad before returning to Trinity. In 1910 he was appointed lecturer at Trinity College. After World War I began, he was fined £100 as the author of a pamphlet criticizing a jail sentence for a conscientious objector. His college removed him of his lectureship in 1916. He was offered a post at Harvard University, but was refused a passport. In 1918 he was sentenced to six months' imprisonment for a pacifistic article he had written in the *Tribunal*. His *Introduction to Mathematical Philosophy* (1919) was written in prison. His *Analysis of Mind* (1921) was the outcome of some lectures he gave in London, which were organized by a few friends who got a subscription for the purpose.

In 1920 Russell went to Russia to study Bolshevism practiced there. He also went to China to lecture on philosophy at the Peking University. In 1927 he and his second wife started a school for young children, which they ran until 1932. In 1938 he and his third wife went to the United States and during the next several years Russel taught at many of the country's leading universities. When his appointment to a college faculty was cancelled because of his views on morality, he accepted a five-year contract as a lecturer for the Barnes foundation, Merion, PA, but this contract was also cancelled in 1943 by Albert C. Barnes, director of the foundation.

Russell was elected a fellow of the Royal Society in 1908, and re-elected a fellow of Trinity College in 1944. He was awarded the Sylvester Medal of the Royal Society, 1934, the de Morgan medal of the London Mathematical Society in the same year, the Nobel Prize for Literature, 1950. Russell's *Principles of Mathematics* led the way in formalizing and organizing symbolism in mathematics. The logic notation that we used today was created by Russell and Whitehead.

Pythagoras

~569–495 BC

Pythagoras was a Greek philosopher and mathematician who discovered the importance of abstraction and abstract idea, particularly the concepts of number, periodicity, rhythm, and music. He was very contemplative and observant. Pythagoras was a mystic and a monk. He believed that number is basic to all things and is a way to organize the universe. The Pythagorean Theorem holds the world record in the number of proofs that have been given.

In this era, the only numbers known were the integers (not including zero) and the rational numbers. Pythagoras had a secret society of disciples, the Pythagorean Brotherhood. When he discovered and proved the Theorem that bears his name, he had an inexplicable problem: An isosceles right triangle may have a hypotenuse whose side cannot be calculated. For example, $1 - 1 - \sqrt{2}$. If you joined his society, you had to promise not to let this conundrum be known.

Many great thinkers were from Greece, including Aristotle, Plato, and Pythagoras. In the time that these great philosophers, scientists, and mathematicians lived (400–200 BC), life was much simpler than it is today. Compare how you spend your "free time" today—searching the Web, watching television, playing games, or something else entertaining—with what these men did gazing at the sky, making, music, seeking explanations for what they observed. The mathematics that they discovered is timeless, for example, the Pythagorean Theorem, the concept of parallel, the idea of drawing to scale (similar figures) and rhythm or periodicity, to name a few.

In Chapter 0, we discussed number systems. Early civilizations, perhaps even earlier than 3000 BC, knew the natural numbers, and created numerals, to describe the number of objects. This helped them to trade with other tribes. Inscriptions from the Sumerians and Babylonians show the use of numerals to represent numbers. Which number systems did Pythagoras know about?

Since numerals were well-established to count and for trade, he has a number system to work with, so he knew the natural numbers. Zero was represented by a dash, -, or a dot · but was not used as a placeholder until much later. The Greeks were interested in geometry and astronomy and know ratios and proportions (fractions). The concept of negative integers came later, as did the idea of irrational numbers, even simple ones like $\sqrt{2}$, which was mystifying to the Greeks.

Pythagorean Triples

"I had this rare privilege of being able to pursue in my adult life, what had been my childhood dream."

Andrew Wiles, 1953–

Section 2.1   Right Triangles and the Pythagorean Theorem

This chapter begins with a summary of some familiar facts about right triangles. The side opposite the right angle is called the *hypotenuse*, and the other two sides are called the *legs* of the right triangle. Right triangles are sometimes called Pythagorean triangles because the Pythagorean Theorem tells us how to determine the length of one side of the triangle when two sides are known, as shown in Figure 2.1.

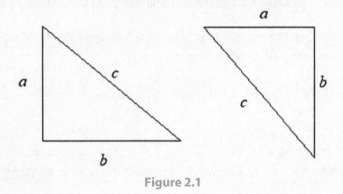

Figure 2.1

The well-known Theorem says:

Theorem 2.1 The Pythagorean Theorem

Let a and b be the lengths of the two legs of a right triangle, and c the length of the hypotenuse. $a^2 + b^2 = c^2$ if and only if the triangle is a right triangle.

You may remember some "special triangles" such as the isosceles right triangle 45° – 45° – 90° or the 30° – 60° – 90° triangles, where you can find the lengths of two missing sides if you know the length of one side. In both of these triangles, two sides have lengths that are integers, but the third side is not. In number theory, we are interested in Pythagorean triangles whose sides are all natural numbers.

Example 2.1. Find the missing side of the right triangle below.

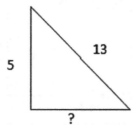

Solution:

Label the missing side b. Using the Pythagorean Theorem, we have

$5^2 + b^2 = 13^2$

$b^2 = 169 - 25 = 144$ and $b = 12$.

Therefore, the length of the missing side is 12.

Definition 2.1 The triple of positive integers $a - b - c$ is a ***Pythagorean triple*** if and only if $a^2 + b^2 = c^2$.

Question 1: Do you know of any other Pythagorean triangles whose sides are integers? If yes, list them.

In Example 2.1, we are given that the triangle is a right triangle, but we can also test a triple of integers to see if they can be the length of the sides of a right triangle.

Example 2.2. Can the numbers 5 – 7 – 10 be the length of the sides of a right triangle?

Solution:

Since the hypotenuse is the longest side, we are asking if $5^2 + 7^2 = 10^2$? Equivalently, does $25 + 49 = 100$? No. So, this triple of numbers does not represent the lengths of the sides of a Pythagorean triangle.

Example 2.3. Determine if 6 – 8 – 10 is a Pythagorean triple.

Solution:

Checking the Pythagorean Theorem, we see that $6^2 + 8^2 = 10^2$. Thus, 6 – 8 – 10 is a Pythagorean triple.

Remark: The triangle 3 – 4 – 5 was probably one of your answers to Question 1. Recall that the triangle 6 – 8 – 10 is similar to the 3 – 4 – 5 right triangle. (Similar triangles have the same angles and proportional sides.)

You now know there are at least three Pythagorean triples. More questions about Pythagorean triples that we may want to answer are listed below.

Question 2: How many Pythagorean triples are there?

Question 3: Are there an infinite number of Pythagorean triangles that are not similar to each other?

Question 4: Is there a formula to generate non-similar Pythagorean triangles?

Lemma 2.1 If $a - b - c$ is a Pythagorean triple, and k is a positive integer, then $ka - kb - kc$ is also a Pythagorean triple.

Proof: Let $a - b - c$ be a Pythagorean triple. Then $a^2 + b^2 = c^2$
Multiplying both sides of the equation by k^2 yields $k^2 a^2 + k^2 b^2 = k^2 c^2$
or $(k\,a)^2 + (k\,b)^2 = (k\,c)^2$. Hence, $ka - kb - kc$ is a Pythagorean triple.

∎

The converse of this Theorem is also true. Starting with a Pythagorean triple and factoring out a common factor will result in values that will also form a Pythagorean triple.

Theorem 2.2 If $ka - kb - kc$ is a Pythagorean triple, where k is a positive integer, then the triple $a - b - c$ is a Pythagorean triple.

Proof: Let $ka - kb - kc$ be a Pythagorean triple.
Then $(k\,a)^2 + (k\,b)^2 = (k\,c)^2$ or $k^2 a^2 + k^2 b^2 = k^2 c^2$
Factoring, we have $k^2(a^2 + b^2) = k^2 c^2$
Cancelling the common factor results in $a^2 + b^2 = c^2$.
∴ $a - b - c$ is a Pythagorean triple.

∎

The converse of this Theorem is also true.

Theorem 2.3 If $a - b - c$ is a Pythagorean triple, and if k is a common factor of a, b, and c, then the resulting triangle when the common factor is removed is also a Pythagorean triple.

Proof (by contradiction): Suppose there is an integer $f > 1$ that divides a and b but not c.

Then we can write $a = df$, $b = ef$ for integers d and e. Then $a^2 + b^2 = c^2$ can be written as

$$(df)^2 + (ef)^2 = f^2\left(d^2 + e^2\right) = c^2.$$

Since f^2 divides the left side of the equation, f^2 divides c^2. This implies that $f \mid c$, which is a contradiction of the hypotheses.

We can repeat this argument using the hypotenuse and one side to get the same result, which is: If two sides of a Pythagorean triangle share a common factor 1, then the third side also shares this factor. We are more interested in triangles whose sides do not have a common factor.

∎

This answers *Question* 2: There are infinitely many Pythagorean triples. However, our answer is not completely satisfying because the new Pythagorean triangles we have found are all *similar* to the ones already known. *Question* 3 is more interesting.

Question 3: Are there an infinite number of Pythagorean triangles that are not similar to each other? If no, then we probably can list them all. On the other hand, if the answer is yes, we will proceed to *Question 4*.

So far, we have found several *non-similar* Pythagorean triples: 3 – 4 – 5 and 5 – 12 – 13. In the next definition, the idea of the greatest common divisor of two numbers is extended to more than two numbers.

> **Definition 2.2** A collection of integers, {*a, b, c,* etc.}, has a ***common divisor*** *d* if *d* divides every integer in the collection. The largest of the common divisors is the greatest common divisor of *a, b, c,* ….

We will use the same notation for the greatest common divisors of more than two numbers, so the greatest common divisor of the numbers 6, 8, and 10 is written gcd (6, 8, 10) = 2. Being able to find the common divisors of three numbers is useful in the search for *non-similar* Pythagorean triples.

Example 2.4. Find the greatest common divisor of each collection of numbers below.
   a) 4, 8, 10
   b) 5, 6, 8
   c) 3, 6, 9

Solution:

One way to find the greatest common divisor is to list all divisors of each number.
   a) gcd (4, 8, 10) = 2, since 2 is the largest number that divides all three of the numbers in the list.
   b) Even though 2 is a divisor of both 6 and 8, it does not divide 5. gcd (5, 6, 8) = 1
   c) Only one and three are common divisors of these three numbers. gcd (3, 6, 9) = 3.

As the numbers get larger, it is more difficult to find the greatest common divisor. Listing all divisors of each number and then comparing the lists works to find the greatest common divisor, but is cumbersome for larger numbers. Factor trees are also cumbersome. In Chapters 3 and 4, other methods to find the greatest common divisors will allow us to work more easily with larger numbers.

Example 2.5. Show that 9 – 12 – 15 is a Pythagorean triple. Then find two similar triangles by factoring out common divisors or by multiplying by a natural number.

Solution:

First, since $9^2 + 12^2 = 15^2$, 9 – 12 – 15 is a Pythagorean triple.

Since 3 is a common divisor of these three values, factor out a 3 to get the triangle 3 – 4 – 5. Multiplying by a different natural number will produce a new Pythagorean triple.

   Multiplying 3, 4, 5 by 6 produces the triangle 18 –24 – 30 and multiplying 3, 4, 5 by 10 produces the triangle 30 – 40 – 50.

Note that Lemma 2.1 says that these new triples are also Pythagorean triples.

Exercise Set 2.1

Exercises 1–6: Find the missing side of the right triangle with legs a and b, and hypotenuse c. NOTE: In this problem, all sides of triangles are not necessarily integers.

1. $b = 7, c = 12$

2. $a = 16, c = 34$

3. $a = 5, b = 6$

4. $a = 15, b = 11$

5. $a = 4, c = 5$

6. $a = 8, b = 13$

7. Determine the greatest common divisor of each of the sets of numbers below.
   a.   12, 14, 18
   b.   11, 21, 31

8. Determine the greatest common divisor of each of the sets of numbers below.
   a.   15, 18, 24, 42
   b.   15, 20, 25

9. Which of the following are Pythagorean triples?
   a.   8 – 10 – 15
   b.   22 – 25 – 43

10. Which of the following are Pythagorean triples? Explain your answer.
    a.   8 – 15 – 17
    b.   10 – 24 – 26
    c.   6 – 8 – 12
    d.   1 – 2 – 3

11. Test any two triples to see if they are Pythagorean triples.

12. Determine whether or not the following triples are Pythagorean triples. Explain your answer.
    a.   30 – 40 – 50
    b.   40 – 76 – 86
    c.   9 – 40 – 41

13. State the converse of the Pythagorean Theorem.

14. State the contrapositive of the Pythagorean Theorem.

Exercises 15–20: Determine whether the triple is a Pythagorean triple.

15. 4 – 5 – 6

16. 25 – 60 – 65

17. 11 – 60 – 61

18. 8 – 15 – 17

19. 32 – 44 – 56

20. 10 – 15 – 25

21. a)   Show that $a = \dfrac{3}{2}$, $b = 2$, $c = \dfrac{5}{2}$ can be the sides of a right triangle.

    b)   Explain why the values for a, b, and c above do not form a Pythagorean triple.

    c)   Find a Pythagorean triple that is similar to the triangle in a).

22. a)   Show that 12 – 16 – 20 is a Pythagorean triple.

    b)   Find two Pythagorean triangles similar to 12 – 16 – 20 one whose corresponding sides are longer, and one whose corresponding sides are shorter.

23. a)   Show that 10 – 24 – 26 is a Pythagorean triple.

    b)   Find all possible similar Pythagorean triples with corresponding sides shorter than 10 – 24 – 26.

    c)   Find one similar Pythagorean triple with corresponding sides longer than 10 – 24 – 26.

24. Find a Pythagorean triple with $c > 250$.

25. Find a Pythagorean triple with $b > 100$.

Exercises 26–35: Find the gcd of the triples below.

26. 10, 20, 25   31. 11, 21, 31

27. 4, 8, 15   32. 21, 33, 66

28. 6, 8, 12   33. 14, 28, 42

29. 385, 435, 660   34. 15, 45, 54

30. 6, 8, 12   35. 231, 273, 399

36. Rewrite the proof of **Theorem 2.2** in the column format introduced in Section 1.5.

37. Determine if this conjecture is true: If $\gcd(a, b) = d$ and $d \mid c$, then $\gcd(a, b, c) = d$.

    a)   Test the conjecture on three different choices for a, b, and c.

    b)   Either prove the conjecture true or clearly explain how you know it is false.

38. Prove that if $\gcd(a, b) = d$ and $\gcd(b, c) = d$, then $\gcd(a, b, c) = d$

Section 2.2   Primitive Pythagorean Triples

Since we know that there are an infinite number of similar Pythagorean triangles with integer sides, what happens if we exclude those triangles whose sides have a common divisor greater than 1? The goal now is to answer the question of how many *non-similar* Pythagorean triangles there are. In this section we will study Pythagorean triples $a-b-c$, where $\gcd(a, b, c) = 1$. Pythagorean triples of this type are called *primitive* Pythagorean triples. Here is the formal definition.

> **Definition 2.3** The triple of positive integers $a - b - c$ is a **primitive Pythagorean triple** if and only if $a^2 + b^2 = c^2$ and the greatest common divisor of a, b, and c is 1, written as $\gcd(a, b, c) = 1$. A primitive Pythagorean triple is abbreviated as PPT.

A **primitive Pythagorean triple** is sometimes called a *primitive Pythagorean triangle*.

Example 2.6. The 3 – 4 – 5 triangle is a primitive Pythagorean triangle.

From Theorem 2.2, we know that if two sides of a Pythagorean triangle share a common factor, so does the third side. This leads us to conclude:

> **Corollary 2.1** If $a - b - c$ is a PPT, then no two of the natural numbers share a common factor other than 1.

This is a very useful corollary. For instance, if one of the sides has even length, the other two sides must have odd lengths in a PPT. The fact that "no two of the integers share a common factor" is frequently expressed as "the integers $\{a, b, c, etc.\}$ are *relatively prime in pairs.*"

Example 2.7. Find a primitive Pythagorean triple that is similar to the Pythagorean triple 144 – 42 – 150.

Solution:

Since gcd (144, 42) = 6, and 6|150, we have gcd (144, 42, 150) = 6, the triple 24 – 7 – 25 obtained by dividing each side by 6 is a similar triangle and is primitive Pythagorean triple.

Since Theorem 2.2 tells us that 7 – 24 – 25 is a Pythagorean triple, we do not have to check the statement.

Notice that *Questions* 2 and 3 from the last section can now be rephrased as:

Question 2: How many primitive Pythagorean triples are there?

Question 3: Are there formulas that will always produce primitive Pythagorean triples?

Table 2.1 provides more examples of primitive Pythagorean triples.

a	b	c
3	4	5
5	12	13
21	20	29
15	8	17
7	24	25

Table 2.1

Test each of the new examples to confirm that they are in fact primitive Pythagorean triples.

Can you find another primitive Pythagorean triple? What about two more? Ten more? How will we know when all of them have been found? In order to know whether we have all primitive Pythagorean triples, a systematic approach to finding them is needed. Here are some questions to answer. The first two are the questions from the end of the previous section.

Question 1: How many primitive Pythagorean triples are there? If there is a fixed number of possible primitive Pythagorean triples—maybe 100 or 1000 or 12,000,000—mathematicians call the set *finitely many*. If that is the case, then perhaps we can actually write them all down.

No matter how large the set, the list will eventually come to an end. On the other hand, if the list of different primitive Pythagorean triples is endless, there are *infinitely many*. In which case, we cannot write them all down.

Question 2: Are there formulas that will always produce primitive Pythagorean triples? (Is it possible to find formulas for a, b, and c so that the formulas always produce values that form a PPT?)

Question 3: If the answer to **Question 2** above is "yes," then is there a set of formulas that will produce all possible primitive Pythagorean triples?

Question 4: Do the primitive Pythagorean triples follow any patterns? From the definition, if $a-b-c$ is a PPT, then $a^2 + b^2 = c^2$ and $\gcd(a, b, c) = 1$, but are there any other common properties that all PPTs share?

Starting with the last question, let us look for patterns in Table 2.1. If there is a pattern that all primitive Pythagorean triples must follow, we may be able to use it to define formulas. Having equations that always give primitive Pythagorean triples makes it easier to find more.

Here are some examples of possible conjectures based on the PPTs in Table 2.1.

Conjecture 2.1: The hypotenuse of a PPT is always odd.

Conjecture 2.2: At least one side of a PPT must be prime.

Conjecture 2.3: The greatest common divisor of any two sides of a PPT is 1.

Notice that **Conjecture 2.3** is not the same as the definition which says that the greatest common divisor of all three sides is 1. Exercise 19 asks you to find an example where $\gcd(a, b, c) = 1$, but none of $\gcd(a, b)$, $\gcd(b, c)$, and $\gcd(a, c)$ are 1.

Conjecture 2.4: One side of a PPT is even, and the other two sides are odd.

Conjecture 2.5: The even side of a PPT is always divisible by 4.

Before using these conjectures to try to find formulas for PPTs, we need to know whether they are true or false. To prove any of these conjectures false, we need a counterexample. To prove a conjecture true requires a general proof showing that the statement is true for all primitive Pythagorean triples. Although additional examples will never give us a proof, they can provide support for suspecting it is true.

Example 2.8.

    a) Verify that the triple 63 – 16 – 65 is a primitive Pythagorean triple.

    b) Test each of the five conjectures above to see if they are true or false for the PPT 63 – 16 – 65.

Solution:

    a) Since $63^2 + 16^2 = 4225$ and $65^2 = 4225$, $63 - 16 - 65$ is a Pythagorean triple.

       Now, to show $\gcd(63, 16, 65) = 1$. Starting with 16 (because it is the smallest) the positive divisors of 16 are 1, 2, 4, 8, and 16. Only 1 divides 63 and 65, so the only common divisor for all three numbers is 1. Therefore, $\gcd(63, 16, 65) = 1$.

    b) Now we will test each conjecture on the PPT $63 - 16 - 65$.

Conjecture 2.1: This conjecture is true for this example since the hypotenuse, 65, is odd.

Conjecture 2.2: This conjecture is **false**, since none of 63, 16, or 65 are prime numbers. Therefore, we have found a counterexample for *Conjecture 2.2*.

Conjecture 2.3: Checking every pair of sides, $\gcd(63, 16) = 1$, $\gcd(16, 65) = 1$, and $\gcd(63, 65) = 1$, so this conjecture is true in this example.

Conjecture 2.4: This conjecture is true for this example since 16 is even while 63 and 65 are both odd.

Conjecture 2.5: Since 16 is divisible by 4, this conjecture is true for this example.

In the next section we will prove that the answers to both **Question 2** and **Question 3** are yes: There are formulas which always produce PPTs and every primitive Pythagorean triple can be found using these formulas. This will also give us the answer to **Question 1**: Since each time a different value is substituted into the formulas, we obtain a different primitive Pythagorean triple, there are infinitely many.

Before that, we will introduce two formulas that generate primitive Pythagorean triples so that you can see how useful they are. One is very specific and the second one is general. For the remainder of this section, we will work with these formulas. There are two components to the formulas to generate primitive Pythagorean triples: the actual equations for a, b, and c and the rules explaining what integers can be substituted into the equations to produce PPTs.

Formulas for Primitive Pythagorean Triples

Choose integers s and t using the following rules:

    i s and t are odd integers,

   ii $s > t > 0$, and

  iii s and t are relatively prime)

    If $a = st$, $b = \dfrac{s^2 - t^2}{2}$, $c = \dfrac{s^2 + t^2}{2}$,   then $a - b - c$ is a primitive Pythagorean triple.

For now, we confirm that values chosen in this way form a Pythagorean triple.

> **Theorem 2.4** With s and t defined above, $a - b - c$ is a primitive Pythagorean triangle.

Proof: Let s and t be odd, positive integers such that $\gcd(s, t) = 1$ and $s > t$.

Let a, b and c be integers such that $a = st$, $b = \dfrac{s^2 - t^2}{2}$, and $c = \dfrac{s^2 + t^2}{2}$.

Step 1: Show that a, b and c are all positive integers.

Since s and t are both odd integers, s^2 and t^2 are also odd, so the sum $s^2 + t^2$ and the difference $s^2 - t^2$ are even integers. Thus, b and c will both be integers. Since a is just the product of two integers, a is also an integer.

Also, since $s > t$, $s^2 - t^2 > 0$, b will be positive. Since s and t are both positive, they are both at least 1, so a and c will also be positive.

Step 2: Substituting the formulas for a and b into $a^2 + b^2$ gives the following:

$$
\begin{aligned}
a^2 + b^2 &= (st)^2 + \left(\frac{s^2 - t^2}{2}\right)^2 \\
&= \frac{4s^2t^2 + s^4 - 2s^2t^2 + t^4}{4} \\
&= \frac{s^4 + 2s^2t^2 + t^4}{4} \\
&= \frac{\left(s^2 + t^2\right)^2}{4} \\
&= \left(\frac{s^2 + t^2}{2}\right)^2 \\
&= c^2
\end{aligned}
$$

∎

Notice that only two of the three conditions on s and t have been used: We needed both to be odd so that b and c are integers, and we needed $s > t > 0$ so that a, b and c, the sides of the triangle, are all positive. (If t were larger than s, then b would be negative.)

What about the condition that $\gcd(s, t) = 1$? In fact, if we choose $s = 9$ and $t = 3$, which has a gcd greater than 1, and apply the formulas, the results are the following triple:

$$
a = 27, \quad b = \frac{81 - 9}{2} = 36, \quad c = \frac{81 + 9}{2} = 45.
$$

This is a Pythagorean triple, but not a ***primitive*** Pythagorean triple, because $\gcd(27, 36, 45) = 9$.

Now, on to some examples of how these formulas can be used.

Example 2.9. Find the PPT corresponding to the values $s=11$ and $t=7$.

Solution:

Using the PPT formulas, we have $a=11\cdot 7=77$, $b=\dfrac{11^2-7^2}{2}=\dfrac{72}{3}=36$ and $c=\dfrac{11^2+7^2}{2}=\dfrac{170}{2}=85$. Therefore, the PPT is $77-36-85$.

Example 2.10. Find all values of s and t that make $a=21$. Then, find the corresponding PPTs.

Solution:

Since $a=21=7\times 3=1\times 21$, there are two choices for s and t: either $s=7$, $t=3$ or $s=21$, $t=1$. Using the values $s=7$ and $t=3$, the resulting PPT is the triple is $21-20-29$. Using $s=21$ and $t=1$, the PPT is the triple $21-120-121$.

Example 2.11. Find all values of s and t that make $a=75$, and find the corresponding PPTs.

Solution:

Even though $75=1\cdot 75=5\cdot 15=3\cdot 25$, there are still only two choices for s and t that produce PPTs. If $s=15$ and $t=5$, then $\gcd(s,t)=5\neq 1$. So this choice will not produce a PPT. The two resulting PPTs are:

$75-2812-2813$ (when $s=75$, $t=1$), and
$75-308-317$ (when $s=25$, $t=3$).

Example 2.12. Suppose that you choose the values $s=2$ and $t=1$.

    a) Which rule for s and t does this choice break?
    b) What happens if you substitute $s=2$ and $t=1$ into the PPT formulas? Do you get a Pythagorean triple? Is it primitive?

Solution:

    a) This breaks the first rule which states that both s and t must be odd.

    b) Applying the PPT formulas, we have $a=2$, $b=\dfrac{3}{2}$, and $c=\dfrac{5}{2}$. The first thing to notice is that this is definitely not a PPT; in fact, it is not even a Pythagorean triple. (Why not? Look back at the definition to see.) But, it does specify the sides of a right triangle because the values satisfy the Pythagorean Theorem, that is: $2^2+\left(\dfrac{3}{2}\right)^2=4+\dfrac{9}{4}=\dfrac{25}{4}=\left(\dfrac{5}{2}\right)^2$. This emphasizes why we must have both s and t odd in the PPT formulas.

Example 2.13. Find an example of a PPT with $c > 50$.

Solution:

The formula for computing c is $c = \dfrac{s^2 + t^2}{2}$. To make c greater than 50, choose s and t so that $s^2 + t^2$ is greater than 100. Suppose $t = 5$. Then $s^2 + t^2 = s^2 + 25$, so we need an odd integer s not divisible by 5 so that s^2 is greater than 75. One possible choice is $s = 9$. Using $s = 9$, $t = 5$ to compute the PPT we have that:

$$a = 45, \quad b = 28, \quad c = 53$$

Table 2.2 provides a list of corresponding values of t and s for reference.

s	t	a	b	c
3	1	3	4	5
5	1	5	12	13
7	1	7	24	25
9	1	9	40	41
11	1	11	60	61
5	3	15	8	17
7	3	21	20	29
9	3	27	36	45
11	3	33	56	65
13	3	39	80	89
7	5	35	12	37
9	5	45	28	53
11	5	55	48	73
13	5	65	72	97
15	5	75	100	125

Table 2.2

Exercise Set 2.2

Exercises 1–14: Determine whether or not the given triple is (a) a Pythagorean triple and if so is it (b) a primitive Pythagorean triple. Explain your answer.

1. $10 - 24 - 26$
2. $6 - 8 - 12$
3. $1 - 2 - 3$
4. $30 - 40 - 50$
5. $40 - 76 - 86$
6. $9 - 40 - 41$
7. $3 - 4 - 7$

8. $6 - 8 - 10$
9. $45 - 28 - 53$
10. $5 - 12 - 13$
11. $6 - 9 - 12$
12. $15 - 20 - 25$
13. $100 - 621 - 629$
14. $15 - 20 - 25$

Exercises 15–20: For each of the following Pythagorean triples, find a similar triangle whose sides form a primitive Pythagorean triple (PPT).

15. 27 – 36 – 45

16. 45 – 24 – 51

17. 350 – 120 – 370

18. 126 – 120 – 174

19. 135 – 72 – 153

20. 25 – 60 – 65

21. Give an example of integers a, b, and c such that $\gcd(a, b, c) = 1$ but none of $\gcd(a, b)$, $\gcd(b, c)$, and $\gcd(a, c)$ are 1.

Exercises 22–25: Find the PPT corresponding to the choice of s and t.

22. $s = 11$, $t = 5$

23. $s = 27$, $t = 1$

24. $s = 13$, $t = 11$

25. $s = 91$, $t = 1$

26. Find all pairs s and t that make $a = 11$, and find the corresponding PPT for each set of values.

27. Find all pairs s and t that make $a = 19$, and find the corresponding PPT for each set of values.

28. Find s and t that yield the PPT $9 - 40 - 41$.

29. Find s and t that yield the PPT $25 - 312 - 313$.

30. a) Create a table of PPTs with $t = 1$ and different values of s. Make a conjecture about the relationship between t and the PPT.

   b) Test the conjecture from part a) on $t = 3$ using several values of s. If your conjecture is not true in this case, revise it.

   c) Test your latest conjecture when $t = 5$. Is either the original or the revised conjecture still true?

31. Prove that if $t = 1$ and $s > t$, then a PPT generated by s. and t has the property $c = b + 1$.

32. a) List three PPTs with $c = b + 9$.

   b) Develop a conjecture about when c is 9 more than b.

   c) Prove your conjecture in b) is true, or provide a counterexample to show it is false.

33. Find a primitive Pythagorean triple with $b > 100$.

34. Find all primitive Pythagorean triples with $c < 50$.

35. Find all primitive Pythagorean triples with $a < 20$.

36. Find all Pythagorean triples containing 12. (Note: they do not have to be primitive).

37. Prove that any odd positive integer greater than 1 can be a leg of a PPT.

38. Prove that if $a - b - c$ is a PPT with one odd leg and one even leg, then the hypotenuse c must be odd.

Section 2.3   The Proof of the Primitive Pythagorean Triples Formula

In the last section, we stated rules for finding primitive Pythagorean triples. Now we will outline the proof of the claims about the formulas that were made. For reference, the formulas are included below.

Formulas for Primitive Pythagorean Triples

Choose integers s and t using the following rules:

i s and t are odd integers,

ii s $> t > 0$, and

iii s and t are relatively prime)

If $a = st$, $b = \dfrac{s^2 - t^2}{2}$, $c = \dfrac{s^2 + t^2}{2}$, then $a - b - c$ is a primitive Pythagorean triple.

In Section 2.2, it was verified that these formulas produce Pythagorean triples. Now, there are two remaining statements to prove:

1. If s and t are chosen according to the given rules, the resulting values for a, b, and c will be a primitive Pythagorean triple. Since Theorem 2.3 shows that they form a Pythagorean triple, it remains to show that $\gcd(a, b, c) = 1$.

2. For any primitive Pythagorean triple, there are values for s and t meeting the conditions given above such that substituting them into the formulas produces that exact PPT. This means that the formulas above generate all possible primitive Pythagorean triples.

Parts of the proofs of these statements can be proven now, but some parts use tools to be developed in Chapters 3 and 4. At the end of Chapter 4, we will return to these results and fill in the details of the proofs.

Theorem 2.4 states the first result listed above: that the formulas produce primitive Pythagorean triples.

Theorem 2.4 If positive integers s and t are selected such that $s > t$, s, and t are odd, and $\gcd(s, t) = 1$, and if $a = st$, $b = \dfrac{s^2 - t^2}{2}$, and $c = \dfrac{s^2 + t^2}{2}$ then the integers a, b, and c form a primitive Pythagorean triple.

The proof that the Pythagorean triples will be primitive relies on properties of prime numbers which will be studied in Chapter 3. (We proved the formulas produced Pythagorean triples in Theorem 2.3). We will return to this proof at the end of Chapter 4.

We begin by outlining a proof of the second claim: If $a - b - c$ is a PPT, then there are values $s > t > 0$ with s and t both odd and $\gcd(s, t) = 1$ such that $a = st$, $b = \dfrac{s^2 - t^2}{2}$, and $c = \dfrac{s^2 + t^2}{2}$.

We will start with one additional property of the sides of a primitive Pythagorean triple. Lemma 2.1 is **Conjecture 2.3** from Section 2.2, and the Lemma 2.2 (below) comes from **Conjecture 2.4**. The smaller results that contribute to the proof of a major result, or Theorem, are called Lemmas.

> **Lemma 2.2** If $a - b - c$ is a PPT, then one of the legs, a or b is odd and the other is even.

Proof:

There are three possibilities for the legs of the triangle. Either:

   i) both legs are even,
   ii) both legs are odd, or
   iii) one is odd and one is even.

The third option is the one we want to show is true. To do this, we will show that both of the other cases are impossible. (Since we are going to show something is impossible, we will use a proof by contradiction in each case.) Then, because one of these cases must be true, it will have to be iii).

Proof that i) cannot happen: Suppose that both legs of the PPT are even, so a and b are both even. Then these two legs share a common divisor of 2. But, by Lemma 2.1, $\gcd(a, b) = 1$. Therefore, 2 cannot divide both a and b, and so a and b cannot both be even.

Proof that ii) cannot happen: Suppose that both legs of the PPT are odd, so a and b are both odd. Then a^2 and b^2 are also odd. Therefore, since $c^2 = a^2 + b^2$, c^2 is even, so c is even.

Therefore, 2 cannot divide both a and b, and so a and b cannot both be even.

From the definitions of odd and even, there are integers k, l, and m such that $a = 2k+1$, $b = 2l+1$, $c = 2m$

Then, substituting these expressions into $a^2 + b^2 = c^2$ and simplifying, we obtain the following:

$$(2k+1)^2 + (2l+1)^2 = (2m)^2$$
$$4k^2 + 4k + 1 + 4l^2 + 4l + 1 = 4m^2$$
$$4k^2 + 4k + 4l^2 + 4l + 2 = 4m^2$$
$$2(2k^2 + 2k + 2l^2 + 2l + 1) = 2(2m^2)$$

$$\therefore \ 2k^2 + 2k + 2l^2 + 2l + 1 = 2m^2$$
$$2(k^2 + 2 + l^2 + l) + 1 = 2m^2$$

But this equation cannot be true because the left side is odd, while the right side is even. Therefore, it is not possible for both legs of a PPT to be odd.

Since we have shown that both i) and ii) are impossible, so iii) must be true, and all PPTs have one odd leg and one even leg.

∎

To match the formulas for primitive Pythagorean triples stated in Section 2.2, we will label the odd leg of a PPT as a, and the even leg as b.

Notice that since one leg is even and the other is odd, the hypotenuse c must be odd. The proof of this fact is Exercise 41 in Section 2.2. This exercise proves the last claim from **Conjecture 2.4**. We include the result here as a Lemma, with a proof using Lemmas 2.1 and 2.2.

Lemma 2.3 The hypotenuse of a primitive Pythagorean triangle is always odd.

Proof: Let $a-b-c$ be a PPT, with c the hypotenuse. By Lemma 2.2, one leg is odd and one leg is even. We will call the odd leg a and the even leg b. Since b is even, $b=2m$ for $m \in \mathbb{Z}$, and so $2 \mid b$. Now, by Lemma 2.1, $\gcd(b, c)=1$. Therefore, 2 cannot divide c since if it did, it is also a common divisor of b and c. Therefore, c must be odd.

■

Now, suppose $a-b-c$ is a primitive Pythagorean triple. Then $\gcd(a,b,c)=1$, and $a^2+b^2=c^2$. By Lemma 2.2, one of the legs of the PPT must be odd (a) and the other must be even (b). Finally, the hypotenuse, c, is also odd by Lemma 2.3.

In order to show that a, b, and c can be expressed in terms of the PPT formulas, we need to find an alternate equation for a, b, or c that we can work with.

One way to start is to solve the equation $a^2+b^2=c^2$ to get another expression for a^2:

$$a^2 = c^2 - b^2$$
$$a^2 = (c+b)(c-b)$$

From this equation for a^2, you can see that if s and t are chosen so that $c+b=s^2$ and $c-b=t^2$, then $a = st$. We will prove this is possible in a series of steps proving facts about $(c+b)$ and $(c-b)$. To see what properties may be true about $(c+b)$ and $(c-b)$, we will look at some examples of PPTs in Table 2.1.

One of the first things to notice is that $(c+b)$ and $(c-b)$ are both always odd. Here are some conjectures based on Table 2.1.

Conjecture 2.6: If $a-b-c$ is a PPT, then $(c+b)$ and $(c-b)$ are both odd.

Conjecture 2.7: If $a-b-c$ is a PPT, then $(c+b)$ and $(c-b)$ are relatively prime.

Conjecture 2.8: If $a-b-c$ is a PPT, then $(c+b)$ and $(c-b)$ are both perfect squares.

Each of these conjectures is true for all PPTs, and they are used to show that the PPT formulas stated at the beginning of this chapter to generate any PPT. To prove the second two conjectures, we need tools from Chapters 3 and 4. We are ready to prove the first conjecture now, and it is stated in the Lemma 2.4 below.

Lemma 2.4 If $a-b-c$ is a primitive Pythagorean triple, then n $(c+b)$ and $(c-b)$ are both odd.

Proof.

Let $a-b-c$ be a PPT. By Lemma 2.2, one of the legs is odd. Call the odd leg a and the even leg b. By Lemma 2.3, the hypotenuse, c, must be odd. Since an odd integer plus or minus an even integer is odd, both $(c+b)$ and $(c-b)$ are odd integers.

∎

Lemma 2.5 If $a-b-c$ is a primitive Pythagorean triple, then $(c+b)$ and $(c-b)$ are relatively prime.

The proof of Lemma 2.5 requires results to be studied in Chapter 4. We will return to this Lemma at the end of Chapter 4.

Lemma 2.6 If $a-b-c$ is a primitive Pythagorean triple, then $(c+b)$ and $(c-b)$ are both squares.

The proof of Lemma 2.6 depends on the material covered later. We will return to the proof at the end of Chapter 4.

The results above are summarized here in Theorem 2.5.

Theorem 2.5 Let $a-b-c$ be a PPT. Then there exist integers $s > t \geq 1$ with s and t odd and $\gcd(s, t)=1$ such that

$$a = st, \quad b = \frac{s^2 - t^2}{2}, \quad c = \frac{s^2 + t^2}{2}$$

In addition to using the Lemmas in this section, the proof of Theorem 2.5 uses tools developed in Chapter 3 when we study primes. We will return to the proof at the end of Chapter 4.

Combining Theorems 2.4 and 2.5 we obtain the following result.

Theorem 2.6 The triple of integers a, b, c forms a PPT if and only if $a = st$, $b = \frac{s^2 - t^2}{2}$, and $c = \frac{s^2 + t^2}{2}$ where s and t are odd integers such that $s > t \geq t$ and $\gcd(s, t)=1$.

Proof.

The proof of Theorem 2.5 proves the one direction of this if and only if statement.

The proof of Theorem 2.6 proves the converse direction of this if and only if statement.

∎

Section 2.4   Summary and Review Exercises

Vocabulary and Symbols

Pythagorean Theorem

Pythagorean triangle

Pythagorean triple, $a - b - c$

Similar triangles

primitive Pythagorean triple

primitive Pythagorean triangle

finitely many

infinitely many

relatively prime in pairs

Suggested Readings

"Andrew Wiles on Solving Fermat," and interview with NOVA, http://www.pbs.org/wgbh/nova/physics/andrew-wiles-fermat.html

Cox, David A. "Introduction to Fermat's Last Theorem," *The American Mathematical Monthly* 101 (January, 1994): 3–14.

Chapter 2 Review Exercises

1. Explain what $a-b-c$ represents.

2. Explain the difference between Pythagorean triples and primitive Pythagorean triples.

3. What is the relationship between a primitive Pythagorean triangle and a primitive Pythagorean triple?

4. For each of the triples of numbers given below, determine if the numbers are a primitive Pythagorean triple. Explain your answer.
   a. $78-120-340$
   b. $9-12-15$
   c. $12-35-37$
   d. $7-15-35$

5. For each of the primitive Pythagorean triples, find the integers s and t from which a, b, and c are found.
   a) $119-120-169$
   b) $69-260-269$
   c) $13-84-85$
   d) $45-28-53$

6. For each of the pairs of values, s and t, find the corresponding primitive Pythagorean triple.
   a) $s=15,\ t=7$
   b) $s=25,\ t=3$
   c) $s=27,\ t=11$
   d) $s=31,\ t=1$

7. Find a Pythagorean triple $a-b-c$ with side b larger than 1000.

8. Find a PPT $a-b-c$ with side b larger than 1000.

9. Find a PPT with $a = 11$.

10. Find a PPT with $a = 101$.

11. Find five primitive Pythagorean triples such that the length of the hypotenuse is one more than the length of one of the legs.

12. How many primitive Pythagorean triples with $a = 45$ are there, and what are they?

13. Is there a primitive Pythagorean triple such that $a = 23$? If so, find one. If not, why not?

14. Is there a primitive Pythagorean triple such that $a = 31$? If so, find one. If not, why not?

15. Show that for every odd number $a \geq 3$, there is a PPT with a side of length a.

16. Give four new examples of primitive Pythagorean triples $a - b - c$ where a is odd and b is even. In your examples, determine the remainders when b is divided by 4 and make a conjecture based on what you observe.

17. Determine how many PPTs have $b < 75$?

18. Find all pairs s and t that make $a = 45$, and find the corresponding PPT for each set of values.

19. Find all pairs s and t that make $a = 65$, and find the corresponding PPT for each set of values.

20. Find all pairs s and t that make $a = 63$, and find the corresponding PPT for each set of values.

21. Find all pairs s and t that make $a = 27$, and find the corresponding PPT for each set of values.

22. If s and t are odd integers with $s > t \geq 1$, prove that $\dfrac{s^2 - t^2}{2}$ is always a positive integer.

23. Prove: $t = 1 \Rightarrow b$ and c differ by 1.

Section 2.5   Activities

1. Find the formula for the length of the third side of a triangle that is not a right triangle. What additional mathematics do you need to solve for the length?
2. The area of a right triangle is easy to find. What additional information do you need to find the area of an oblique triangle?
3. There are other formulas for finding primitive Pythagorean triples. Find at least two of these.
4. Surveyors use a process call "triangulation." What is this concept and how is it used?

Pierre de Fermat

1601–1665

Pierre de Fermat was an amateur mathematician and the first person to consider the theory of numbers to be an independent discipline in mathematics.

By profession, Fermat was a lawyer, but his hobby was the study of mathematics.

Fermat lived in France through the Black Plague that killed many of his colleagues in the parliament, and he became a prominent lawyer in the Parliament of Toulouse. He enjoyed mathematics and spent much of his spare time working on mathematics.

Some of Blaise Pascal's friends were poker players and they asked Pascal to help them figure out the likelihood of certain winning poker hands. Pascal struck up a correspondence with Fermat. Through this correspondence, they laid the foundation for probability theory. While Fermat made great contributions to other fields in mathematics, analytic geometry and calculus primarily, he is most remembered for his outstanding contributions to number theory and is frequently referred to as the *founder of number theory*. Because he did not have the notation and symbolism that we have today, most of his arguments were lengthy and awkward.

Among Fermat's friends were noteworthy French mathematicians, Blaise Pascal and Martin Mersenne. Pascal is well known for his work in probability, the binomial theorem and *Pascal's Triangle*. Mersenne was a monk with whom many mathematicians corresponded. He passed information from one mathematician to another. Both Fermat and Mersenne were honored for their work by having their names attached to problems and theorems in number theory problems.

Fermat's last theorem states that if $n > 2$, there is no natural number solution to the equation

$$x^n + y^n = z^n$$

He proofed the statement for $n = 4$ and claimed to have a general proof of the statement but that the margin of the book he was reading was not large enough to write it down. In fact, the statement was not proven until the twentieth century when Andrew Wiles created a correct proof.

CHAPTER 3

Prime Numbers and Unique Factorization

"And perhaps, posterity will thank me for having shown it that the ancients did not know everything."

– Pierre de Fermat

Section 3.1   Why Are Prime Numbers Important?

While prime numbers were introduced in Chapter 1, this chapter will provide a more in-depth study of primes. Let us begin by reviewing two definitions.

Definition 3.1 An integer $p > 1$ is **prime** if and only if the only positive divisors of p are 1 and p.

Definition 3.2 An integer $m > 1$ is **composite** if and only if $m = a \cdot b$ where both $1 < a < m$ and $1 < b < m$.

An integer greater than 1 that is not prime is **composite**. Notice that both definitions specify an integer greater than 1, the integer 1 is neither prime nor composite.

Example 3.1. Determine whether each number below is prime or composite.

- a) 28
- b) 29
- c) 12
- d) 4921

Solution:

- a) 28 is composite, because 28 can be written as $28 = 7 \cdot 4$ or $2 \cdot 2 \cdot 7$.
- b) 29 is prime, because 29 can only be factored as $29 = 1 \cdot 29$, which means the only positive divisors of 29 are 1 and 29.
- c) 123 is composite, because $123 = 3 \cdot 41$.
- d) 259 is composite, because $259 = 7 \cdot 37$.

Prime numbers produce intriguing mathematical problems, but also allow one to create large integers that are prime or if not prime at least difficult to factor. One extremely important application of finding large prime numbers occurs in cryptography, the study of secret codes that we will study in Chapter 7.

Notice from Example 3.1 that determining if a number is prime tends to take longer as numbers get larger. To determine if 2591 or 7429 are primes, (Exercise 25) may take longer than the examples above, even given the divisibility rules in Chapter 1. You can determine if a number has any divisors by checking all positive integers less than or equal to the number, but this becomes incredibly time-consuming when the number is large. Short-cuts for finding divisors will be helpful.

In each of the examples above, notice that each time a number was composite, one of the divisors was always smaller than or equal to the square root of the number. For example, $\sqrt{20} \approx 4.47$, and 20 factored as $2 \cdot 10$ and $4 \cdot 5$. To convince yourself of this, think about a perfect square such as $64 = 8 \cdot 8$. The divisors or factors of 64 are: 1, 2, 4, 8, 16, 32, and 64. Notice that each factor larger than 8 (the square root of 64) is paired with a factor less than eight: $64 = 64 \cdot 1 = 32 \cdot 2 = 16 \cdot 4 = 8 \cdot 8$. We can prove that this property is always true. However, as numbers get larger even testing *all* numbers less than the square root can be daunting, even with the use of computers.

To simplify the problem of finding primes, mathematicians have developed tests for primes, called *Primality Tests*. Primality Tests provide shortcuts to test if a number is prime, without having to check all the possible divisors. One of the simplest Primality Tests uses prime divisors of a number. First, let us confirm that every integer greater than 1 has a prime divisor. This fact is stated in the following Lemma.

Lemma 3.1 Every integer greater than 1 has at least one prime divisor.

Proof: Let k be an integer greater than 1. Then, there are two cases: k is either a prime number or a composite number.

Case 1: If k is prime: Since every integer divides itself, k is its own prime divisor.
Case 2: If k is composite, we use a proof by contradiction to prove k has a prime divisor. Suppose that there is at least one composite integer greater than 1 with no prime divisors. Choose the smallest of these integers, and call it n. Then $n = ab$ with both a and b greater than 1 and less than n. Now, since n was chosen to be the smallest integer with no prime divisor, and $a < n$, a must have a prime divisor, p. But, since $p \mid a$ and $a \mid n$, it is also true that $p \mid n$, a contradiction. Therefore, there is no integer greater than 1 with no prime divisors.

∎

Remark: Choosing the smallest number of a set is a special property of the integers called the **Well-Ordering Principle**: Every non-empty set of positive integers has a smallest element. This is not true for all sets of numbers. For example, the Well-Ordering Principle is not true for the set of real numbers.

Using this lemma, we can now prove one Primality test, the fact stated earlier about $\sqrt{n}$.

Theorem 3.1 If n is a composite number, then n must have a prime divisor p such that $p \leq \sqrt{n}$.

Proof: Let n be a composite number. Then, $n = ab$, where $a \leq b$ and both a and b are greater than 1 and less than n. In symbols, $1 < a < n$ and $1 < b < n$. By Lemma 3.1, a has a prime divisor p.

Since $a \leq b$ there are two possibilities: either $a = b$, or $a < b$. If they are equal, then $a \leq \sqrt{n}$; otherwise, if $a > \sqrt{n}$, then $ab > \sqrt{n} \cdot \sqrt{n} = n$, (i.e. $ab > n$) which is a contradiction since $ab = n$. Then, since $p \mid a$ and $a \mid n$ imply that $p \mid n$, p is a prime divisor of n, and $p \leq \sqrt{n}$.

∎

Now, suppose we want to test an integer $n > 1$ to see whether it is prime or composite. By Theorem 3.1, if n is composite, then n must have a prime divisor $p \leq \sqrt{n}$. Using the contrapositive of Theorem 3.1, if n does not have a prime divisor $p \leq \sqrt{n}$, then n must not be composite, which means n is prime. Therefore, to test to see if a number is prime, it is sufficient to check to see if any prime less than or equal to the square root of the number is a divisor. If none of these are divisors, then the number is prime. This leads to the following statement.

Primality Test 1 If a natural number $n > 1$ has no prime divisor p such that $p \leq \sqrt{n}$, then n is prime.

Example 3.2. Use the Primality Test to determine whether each positive integer below is prime or composite.
   a) 149
   b) 161

Solution:

   a) 149

   Since $\sqrt{149} \approx 12.2$, by the Primality Test, just check to see if any of the primes 2, 3, 5, 7, or 11 divide 149. The first three (2, 3, and 5) can be ruled out quickly using the Divisibility Tests from Section 1.9. Checking 7 and 11 shows that neither of these is a divisor of 149, either. Therefore, 149 is prime.

   b) 161

   Since $\sqrt{161} \approx 12.7$, once again check the primes less than 12.7 to see if they divide 161. These primes are 2, 3, 5, 7, or 11. Again, the first three (2, 3, and 5) can be ruled out quickly. Checking 7 shows that $161 = 7 \cdot 23$. Therefore 161 is composite, not prime.

eratosthenes

The Greek mathematician Eratosthenes (276–194 BC) was well-known for his work in many fields. One of his famous contributions is that he developed a method for finding all primes less than a given natural number n, based on Primality Test 1. Even today, this is one of the most efficient methods to find "small primes" (primes less than 1 million).

Eratosthenes' method for finding primes is known as the ***Sieve of Eratosthenes***. We will find all primes less than the number 50. By the Primality Test, any composite number less than or equal to 50 has a prime divisor less than or equal to $\sqrt{50}$, or about 7.1. The primes less than 7.1 are 2, 3, 5, and 7. Therefore, by deleting all multiples of these prime numbers (not including the primes themselves) from the collection of numbers from 2 to 50, we will have deleted all composite numbers, and the remaining numbers are prime. Table 3.1 shows the results of the completed Sieve of Eratosthenes for $n = 50$. The shaded numbers are the primes whose multiples we had to check. The different colors are to distinguish why numbers were removed.

☐   Number removed because it was a multiple of 2

☐   Number removed because it was a multiple of 3

☐   Number removed because it was a multiple of 5

☐   Number removed because it was a multiple of 7

Sieve of Eratosthenes

	2	3	4	5	6	7	8	9	10
11	12	13	14	15	16	17	18	19	20
21	22	23	24	25	26	27	28	29	30
31	32	33	34	35	36	37	38	39	40
41	42	43	44	45	46	47	48	49	50

Table 3.1

This process filters or "sieves" out the composite numbers, and any remaining number that has not been crossed off is prime. In Table 3.2, the primes less than 50 are circled. They are: 2, 3, 5, 7, 11, 13, 17, 19, 23, 29, 31, 37, 41, 43, and 47.

	②	③	4	⑤	6	⑦	8	9	10
⑪	12	⑬	14	15	16	⑰	18	⑲	20
21	22	㉓	24	25	26	27	28	㉙	30
㉛	32	33	34	35	36	㊲	38	39	40
㊶	42	㊸	44	45	46	㊼	48	49	50

Table 3.2

Exercise Set 3.1

1. Find the smallest prime factor of each of the following numbers. (The Divisibility Tests in Section 1.9 may be helpful).
   a) 1234566
   b) 135795

Exercises 2–5: When using the Primality Test on the given number, what is the largest value that has to be checked to confirm whether or not the number is prime?

2. 461
3. 127
4. 449
5. 517

Exercises 6–25: Use the Primality Test to determine whether the number is prime or composite.

6. 461	11. 101	16. 143	21. 441
7. 127	12. 113	17. 213	22. 127
8. 449	13. 119	18. 221	23. 131
9. 517	14. 139	19. 754	24. 289
10. 91	15. 361	20. 3649	25. 1331

26. Show that 997 is prime, but 7429 is not.
27. Find all primes less than 30 using the Sieve of Eratosthenes.
28. Find all primes less than 70 using the Sieve of Eratosthenes.
29. Find all primes less than 100 using the Sieve of Eratosthenes. (A grid of integers from 1 to 100 is included below in Table 3.3.)

Sieve of Eratosthenes

	2	3	4	5	6	7	8	9	10
11	12	13	14	15	16	17	18	19	20
21	22	23	24	25	26	27	28	29	30
31	32	33	34	35	36	37	38	39	40
41	42	43	44	45	46	47	48	49	50
51	52	53	54	55	56	57	58	59	60
61	62	63	64	65	66	67	68	69	70
71	72	73	74	75	76	77	78	79	80
81	82	83	84	85	86	87	88	89	90
91	92	93	94	95	96	97	98	99	100

Table 3.3

30. Ryann goes to the gym every Monday. On the main level, there are 30 lockers available (for free). The problem is that each time she goes to the gym she ends up in a different locker and has trouble remembering where she put her jacket. Suppose she always puts her jacket in a locker that is identified with a prime number. What is the maximum number of lockers she would have to check before finding her jacket?

31. In the ladies' locker room, there are 151 lockers available for day use. Using the same strategy as in problem # 29, what is the maximum number of lockers she would have to check?

32. Suppose you want to find all primes less than 250 using the Sieve of Eratosthenes. What are the dimensions of the number grid you would need? What are the primes whose multiples you would have to cross off, to guarantee that you have found all the primes less than 250?

33. Prove or disprove the following conjecture: If p and q are odd primes, then $pq+1$ is never prime.

Section 3.2   The Unique Factorization Theorem

The *Unique Factorization Theorem* is also called the *Fundamental Theorem of Arithmetic*. The theorem states that every integer greater than 1 can be written as a product of primes in exactly one way, except for the order in which they are written. In other words, $28 = 2 \cdot 2 \cdot 7$, which also can be written as $2 \cdot 7 \cdot 2$, but since the lists contain exactly the same primes, they are not considered different factorizations. This is why primes are called the "building blocks" of natural numbers – each natural number can be "built" from a collection of prime numbers.

This section explains the Fundamental Theorem of Arithmetic and provides examples of how prime factorizations are used. Then, in Section 3.3, we will finally prove that the Unique Factorization Theorem is true in the set of integers. Since we will be talking about many primes, we will use p to represent a prime number, and subscripts to distinguish among them, for example p_1, p_2, p_3 represent three distinct primes.

> **Theorem 3.2 The Unique Factorization Theorem** Every integer $n \geq 2$ can be factored into a product of primes $n = p_1 p_2 ... p_r$ in exactly one way. (Note: arranging the factors in a different order is not a new factorization.)

The product $p_1 p_2 ... p_r$ is called the ***prime factorization of n***. Each of the symbols p_1, p_2, and so on represents a prime number in the factorization of n. For example, if $n = 28$ then $28 = 2 \cdot 2 \cdot 7$, so $p_1 = 2$, $p_2 = 2$ and $p_3 = 7$. A general term of the prime factorization (not necessarily the first or second prime in the product) is commonly represented by p_i. The Unique Factorization Theorem tells us that this factorization is unique, except for the order of the primes. In other words, $28 = 2 \cdot 2 \cdot 7$, which also can be written as $2 \cdot 7 \cdot 2$, but since the lists contain exactly the same primes, they are not considered different factorizations.

> **Definition 3.3** In general notation, a ***prime power factorization of n*** is written as $n = p_1^{n_1} p_2^{n_2} ... p_r^{n_r}$.

Prime factorizations are usually written with like primes grouped together, to make it easier to see the components of the number. So, the factorization of $28 = 2^2 \cdot 7$.

In this case, $p_1 = 2$, $p_2 = 7$, and the exponents are $n_1 = 2$ and $n_2 = 1$. In this case, since repeated primes are grouped in powers, each of the p_i's will be different. Also, note that a prime is considered its own factorization, so the prime factorization of 5 is 5.

Example 3.3. Find the prime power factorization of 320.

Solution:

Since prime factorizations are unique, starting with any factors of 320 will produce the same final answer. Here is one way to get to the prime factorization.

$$320 = 10 \cdot 32 = (2 \cdot 5)(2^5) = 2^6 \cdot 5$$

Note that starting with different factors still yields the same prime factorization:

$$320 = 2 \cdot 160 = 2 \cdot (8 \cdot 20) = 2 \cdot 2^3 \cdot (4 \cdot 5) = 2 \cdot 2^3 \cdot 2^2 \cdot 5 = 2^6 \cdot 5$$

Example 3.4. Find the prime factorization of 1134.

Solution:

From the Divisibility Tests, you may notice that 1134 is divisible by 2, 3, and 9. Starting with any one of these factors will lead to the same final prime factorization. Here are two ways to get to the prime factorization of 1134.

$$1134 = 3 \cdot 378 = 3 \cdot 2 \cdot 189 = 3 \cdot 2 \cdot 9 \cdot 21 = 3 \cdot 2 \cdot 3 \cdot 3 \cdot 3 \cdot 7 = 2 \cdot 3^4 \cdot 7$$

$$1134 = 2 \cdot 567 = 2 \cdot 9 \cdot 63 = 2 \cdot 3 \cdot 3 \cdot 7 \cdot 9 = 2 \cdot 3 \cdot 3 \cdot 7 \cdot 3 \cdot 3 = 2 \cdot 3^4 \cdot 7$$

Example 3.5. Find the prime factorization of 113.

Solution:

In this example, the Divisibility Rules are not very helpful. However, the Primality Test will reduce the work of looking for divisors. If 113 is composite, then it must have at least one prime divisor less than or equal to $\sqrt{113} \approx 10.6$. Check to see if one of 2, 3, 5, or 7 is a divisor of 113. Since none of these divides 113, 113 is prime.

Example 3.6. Find the prime factorization of 143.

Solution:

Again, the divisors that are easy to check using the Divisibility Tests do not evenly divide 143. According to the Primality Test, since $\sqrt{143} \approx 11.9$, check the primes 2, 3, 5, 7, and 11 to see if any of them divide 143. From this list, only 11 divides 143, and this gives us the prime factorization of 143.

$$143 = 11 \cdot 13$$

Example 3.7. Find all positive divisors of 315.

Solution:

We will use the prime factorization $315 = 3^2 \cdot 5 \cdot 7$ to keep track of all of the divisors. The divisors of 315 are made up of all combinations of these prime factors (as well as the number 1, which doesn't show up in the prime factorization). Here is a list of the all positive divisors:

1	$3 \cdot 3 = 9$	$3 \cdot 3 \cdot 5 = 45$	$3 \cdot 3 \cdot 5 \cdot 7 = 315$
3	$3 \cdot 5 = 15$	$3 \cdot 3 \cdot 7 = 63$	
5	$3 \cdot 7 = 21$	$3 \cdot 5 \cdot 7 = 105$	
7	$5 \cdot 7 = 35$		

Example 3.8. Find a and b such that $a > 1000$, $b > 1000$, and $\gcd(a, b) = 15$.

Solution:

If $\gcd(a, b) = 15 = 3 \cdot 5$, then $3 \cdot 5$ must be part of the prime factorization of both a and b. Also, since 15 is the greatest common divisor of a and b, they cannot have any other prime factors in common. One way to choose a and b is to multiply each one by different prime factors to make each number large enough. For example, $a = 3 \cdot 5 \cdot 7 \cdot 11 = 1155$ and $b = 3 \cdot 5 \cdot 13 \cdot 17 = 3315$. Now, $\gcd(a, b) = 15$ and both a and b are greater than 1000, as required. Can you find another correct solution?

The last part of this section contains examples of ways to use unique prime factorizations, which are useful in proving general statements about a number, and also to do calculations with specific numbers. We will start with a familiar example: Find the greatest common divisor of two integers. In Chapter 2, the greatest common divisors were used to determine if a particular Pythagorean triple is a primitive Pythagorean triple. Prime factorizations provide a more systematic way to find the greatest common divisors.

Example 3.9. Find $\gcd(126, 540)$.

Solution:

First, find the prime factorizations for 126 and 540.

$$126 = 2 \cdot 3^2 \cdot 7$$
$$540 = 2^2 \cdot 3^3 \cdot 5$$

The primes 2 and 3 are in the prime factorizations of both 126 and 540, but 126 and 540 do not share any other prime factors. Now, 540 is divisible by $2^2 = 4$, but 126 is divisible only by 2, so 2 will be a factor of the greatest common divisor. Also, 540 is divisible by 3^3 but 126 is divisible only by 3^2, so 3^2 will be a factor of the greatest common divisor. Thus, the greatest common divisor is $\gcd(126, 540) = 2 \cdot 3^2 = 18$.

The primes appearing in the prime factorizations of two numbers can be used to find the prime factorization of the greatest common divisor of those two numbers. This technique is summarized below.

Using Prime Power Factorizations to find gcd(a, b)
1. Write the prime power factorizations for both a and b.
2. Find the prime factors that a and b have in common.
3. The greatest common divisor of a and b will be the product of the prime factors shared by a and b, with the smaller exponent from the prime factorizations of a and b.

Example 3.10. Find gcd$(4200, 720)$.

Solution:

First, find the prime factorizations of 4200 and 720.

$$4200 = 2^3 \cdot 3 \cdot 5^2 \cdot 7$$
$$720 = 2^4 \cdot 3^2 \cdot 5$$

Both numbers have prime factors of 2, 3, and 5. The smallest exponent for the factor of 2 is 3, the smallest exponent for the factor of 3 is 1, and the smallest exponent for the factor of 5 is 1. The prime 7 is not included in the greatest common divisor since 7 is not a factor of 720. Therefore, $\gcd\left(4200, 720\right) = 2^3 \cdot 3 \cdot 5 = 120$.

Example 3.11. Is $100 - 621 - 629$ a primitive Pythagorean triple?

Solution:

To answer this question, two things need to be checked: first that the numbers given satisfy the Pythagorean Theorem, and second that $\gcd\left(100,\ 621,\ 629\right) = 1$.

Since $100^2 + 621^2 = 395641$ and $629^2 = 395641$, these numbers represent a Pythagorean triple.

Now, use prime factorizations to find the $\gcd\left(100,\ 621,\ 629\right)$. (Remember the Primality Test may be helpful in finding prime factorizations).

$$100 = 2^2 \cdot 5^2$$
$$621 = 3^3 \cdot 23$$
$$629 = 17 \cdot 37$$

Since these three numbers don't share any prime factors, they have no divisors in common except for 1, so $\gcd\left(100,\ 621,\ 629\right) = 1$.

Note: This question is Exercise 34 from Section 2.2, before a systematic method for finding greatest common divisors. If you did this problem before, compare the two solutions.

Using Prime Power Factorizations to find lcm (a, b)

1. Write the prime power factorizations for both a and b.
2. List all of the prime factors in a and b.
3. The least common multiple of a and b will be the product of the prime factors of a and b, with the larger exponent from the prime factorizations of a and b.

Example 3.12. Find lcm (4200, 720).

Solution:

From example 3.8 we have the prime factorizations:

$$4200 = 2^3 \cdot 3 \cdot 5^2 \cdot 7$$
$$720 = 2^4 \cdot 3^2 \cdot 5$$

Using the prime factorization, the lcm is $2^4 \cdot 3^2 \cdot 5 \cdot 7 = 5040$.

Remember that the least common multiple or lcm of two integers is the smallest number that both integers divide. Prime factorizations can also be used to find the least common multiple of two numbers.

Example 3.13. Find lcm (60, 126).

Solution:

For this example, look at the prime factorizations of 60 and 126.

$$60 = 2^2 \cdot 3 \cdot 5$$
$$126 = 2 \cdot 3^2 \cdot 7$$

If 60 divides a number, that number must also be divisible by 2^2, 3 and 5. Likewise, if 126 divides a number, it must be divisible by 2, 3^2, and 7. To find the smallest number both 60 and 126 divide, include the largest power of each prime factor appearing in either number's factorization. Therefore:

$$\text{lcm}(60, 126) = 2^2 \cdot 3^2 \cdot 5 \cdot 7 = 1260$$

Prime factorizations can be useful in proving results about divisibility. The next two theorems use prime factorizations in their proofs. Theorem 3.3 is used again at the end of Chapter 4, to prove the PPT formulas from Chapter 2 do produce all primitive Pythagorean triples. Before the theorems are introduced, we introduce Lemma 3.2 which is useful in the proof.

Lemma 3.2 If $a|b$ then the prime factors of a are prime factors of b.

Proof: Let $a|b$ and let p be a prime factor of a. Then, $p|a$. Therefore, since $p|a$ and $a|b$, we have that $p|b$. (This was proved in Example 1.40). Therefore, p is also a prime factor of b.

■

Notice that this means that if $a \mid b$, then each prime factor of a must be contained in the prime factorization of b.

Theorem 3.3 If $c^2 \mid d^2$ then $c \mid d$.

Proof: Let $c^2 \mid d^2$. Let $c = p_1^{c_1} \cdot p_2^{c_2} \cdot p_3^{c_3} \cdot p_4^{c_4} \cdots p_k^{c_k}$ and let $d = q_1^{d_1} \cdot q_2^{d_2} \cdot q_3^{d_3} \cdot q_4^{d_4} \cdots q_m^{d_m}$. Then the prime factorizations of c^2 and d^2 are:

$$c^2 = p_1^{2c_1} \cdot p_2^{2c_2} \cdot p_3^{2c_3} \cdot p_4^{2c_4} \cdots p_k^{2c_k},$$

$$d^2 = q_1^{2d_1} \cdot q_2^{2d_2} \cdot q_3^{2d_3} \cdot q_4^{2d_4} \cdots q_m^{2d_m}.$$

Since $c^2 \mid d^2$, the prime factorization of c^2 must be contained in the prime factorization of d^2 by Lemma 3.2. Therefore, we can rearrange the factors of d^2 to write the factors common to c^2 first, obtaining

$$d^2 = p_1^{2c_1} \cdot p_2^{2c_2} \cdot p_3^{2c_3} \cdot p_4^{2c_4} \cdots p_k^{2c_k} \cdots q_m^{2d_m}.$$

Using this factorization to find d, we see that

$$d = p_1^{c_1} \cdot p_2^{c_2} \cdot p_3^{c_3} \cdot p_4^{c_4} \cdots p_k^{c_k} \cdots q_m^{d_m}.$$

Notice that the first part is just the prime factorization of c, so

$$d = c \cdots q_m^{d_m}.$$

Therefore, $c \mid d$.

■

Theorem 3.4 If $\gcd(s, t) = 1$ then $\gcd\left(s^2, t^2\right) = 1$.

Proof. Let $\gcd(s, t) = 1$. Then there are no primes in both the prime factorization of s and the prime factorization of t. Writing the prime power factorizations we use p_i's to represent the primes in the factorization of s and q_i's to represent the primes in the factorization of t:

$$s = p_1^{s_1} \cdot p_2^{s_2} \cdots p_m^{s_m}$$

and

$$t = q_1^{t_1} \cdot q_2^{t_2} \cdots q_n^{t_n}$$

where none of the p_i's are equal to the q_j's. Now, square s and t to obtain the following:

$$s^2 = (p_1^{s_1} \cdot p_2^{s_2} \cdots p_m^{s_m})^2 = p_1^{2s_1} \cdot p_2^{2s_2} \cdots p_m^{2s_m}$$

and

$$t^2 = (q_1^{t_1} \cdot q_2^{t_2} \cdots \cdots q_n^{t_n})^2 = q_1^{2t_1} \cdot q_2^{2t_2} \cdots \cdots q_n^{2t_n}$$

Since no new primes were introduced into the prime factorizations of s^2 and t^2, the greatest common divisor is still 1.

∎

Not every collection of numbers has this property. In the Activities section, you are asked to find a set of integers that does not obey the Unique Factorization Theorem.

The next theorem is useful for finding any of the values, ab, $\gcd(a, b)$ and $\operatorname{lcm}(a, b)$ when the other two are known.

> **Theorem 3.5** Let $a, b \in N$ Then $ab = \gcd(a, b) \cdot \operatorname{lcm}(a, b)$

Proof: First consider the case that a and b are relatively prime. Then $\gcd(a, b) = 1$

$$a = p_1^{s_1} \cdot p_2^{s_2} \cdots p_m^{s_m}$$

and

$$b = q_1^{t_1} \cdot q_2^{t_2} \cdots q_n^{t_n}$$

$$\text{then } ab = p_1^{s_1} \cdot p_2^{s_2} \cdots p_m^{s_m} q_1^{t_1} \cdot q_2^{t_2} \cdots q_n^{t_n}$$

$$= 1 \cdot p_1^{s_1} \cdot p_2^{s_2} \cdots p_m^{s_m} q_1^{t_1} \cdot q_2^{t_2} \cdots q_n^{t_n}$$

Using the rule for the least common multiple, the highest power every prime appearing in either list appears in the least common multiple. In this case, that is ab.

The notation is more complicated when the integers are not relatively prime. We will sketch the proof and leave out some of the messy notation.

List all of the primes appearing in either list in one long list. If a prime in one of the two integers does not appear in the other one, we write it as p^0.

$$a = p_1^{s_1} \cdot p_2^{s_2} \cdots p_m^{s_m}$$
$$b = p_1^{t_1} \cdot p_2^{t_2} \cdots p_m^{t_m}$$

Remember that the rule for multiplication of integers with exponents is to keep the base and add the exponents.

$$ab = p_1^{s_1 + t_1} \cdot p_2^{s_2 + t_2} \cdots p_m^{s_m + t_m}$$

Next, separate the primes into two parts so that the smaller of s or t appears in the first group and the larger appears in the second group.

$ab =$ (collection of p_i s where i is the smaller value) (collections of p_k s where k is the larger of the two values). The first group is the $\gcd(a, b)$ and the second group is the $\operatorname{lcm}(a, b)$.

$$\therefore ab = \gcd(a, b) \cdot \operatorname{lcm}(a, b).$$

∎

Example 3.14. Find the least common multiple of 245 and 370 using theorem 3.5.

Solution:

245·370 = 90650 and gcd(245, 370) = 5. So, 90650 = 5·lcm (245, 370)
Dividing by 5, we have lcm (245, 370) – 18130.

Exercise Set 3.2

1. Explain why the Unique Factorization Theorem would not be true if 1 were a prime number.
2. Find the prime factorization of 294, and then use it to list all the divisors of 294.
3. Find the prime factorization of 140 and then use it to list all the divisors of 140.

Exercises 4–9: Find the prime factorization of the following integers. Write the prime power factorization, with the smallest primes first, grouped in powers. (For example, write $3·2·2$ as $2^2·3$).

4. 108
5. 315
6. 1040

7. 7429
8. 561
9. 12012

10. Determine whether 3649 is prime. If not, find its prime factorization.
11. Describe all integers with exactly two positive divisors. Provide some specific examples and a general formula.
12. Describe all integers with exactly three positive divisors. Provide some specific examples and a general formula.
13. Describe all integers with exactly four positive divisors. Provide some specific examples and a general formula.
14. Find all positive divisors of the integer n if $n = p^3$ where p is prime.
15. Find all positive divisors of the integer n if $n = 5q$ where q is prime.

Exercises 16–21: Find the gcd of each pair.

16. $(44, 130)$
17. $(2^4·5^3·7^3·11, 2^5·7^2·11^3·13)$
18. $(561, 3289)$

19. $(221, 323)$
20. $(2^2·3^3·5·7, 2^2·3^2·5·7^2)$
21. $(15, 421)$

22. Find two numbers a and b such that gcd$(a, b)=14$, $a > 1200$, and $b > 4000$.
23. Find two numbers a and b such that gcd$(a, b)=14$, $a > 1200$, and $b > 4000$, and the only prime divisors of a and b are 2 and 7.

Exercises 24–29: Find an integer that is relatively prime to the given integer.

24. 840

25. 1260

26. 12,870

27. 2310

28. 273

29. 56,595

30. Write a step-by-step process for finding the least common multiple of two integers using their prime power factorizations. Test the process on at least two pairs of integers.

31. Consider the following conjecture: If a divides b and p is part of the prime factorization of a, then p divides b.
    a) Rewrite the conjecture using symbols when possible.
    b) Choose two sets of values for a, b, and p and show that the statement is true in both cases.
    c) Prove that the conjecture is true.

32. Explain how to get the prime factorization of c^2 from the prime factorization of c that was used in the proof of **Theorem 3.3**.

33. Look at the prime factorizations of several perfect squares. Organize your examples in a table. Include at least two perfect squares that have more than one prime factor (for example,

34. Make a conjecture about the properties of prime factorizations of perfect squares, based on your examples. Can you prove your conjecture?

35. The following statement is false. Find a counterexample, and explain your example.

$$\text{If } \gcd\left(s,\, t\right) = 4, \text{ then } \gcd\left(s^2,\, t^2\right) = 4.$$

36. Prove the converse of **Theorem 3.3**: If $\gcd\left(s^2,\, t^2\right) = 1$, then $\gcd\left(s,\, t\right) = 1$.

37. Test the following conjecture using several examples. Then, try to either prove or disprove the conjecture: If $\gcd\left(s,\, t\right) = n$, then $\gcd\left(s^2,\, t^2\right) = n^2$.

38. Prove or disprove: If $a > 0$ and $a \mid b$, then $\gcd(a, b) = a$. **Hint:** To prove this statement, you need a general proof. To disprove the statement, find a counterexample. Try several examples first to decide whether you think it is true or false.

Section 3.3   Proof of the Unique Factorization Theorem

> "…there is no apparent reason why one number is prime and another not. To the contrary, upon looking at these numbers one has the feeling of being in the presence of one of the inexplicable secrets of creation."
>
> *D. Zagier*

Knowing that the property of unique factorization into primes is not automatic in all number systems, we will return to $\mathbb{Z}$ and look at why it is true in this case. The Unique Factorization Theorem actually has two parts: first, that each integer greater than 1 has a prime factorization, and second that each number has only one prime factorization—that prime factorizations are unique. (Remember that the prime factorization of a prime is just the prime itself). This theorem, originally stated as Theorem 3.2, is restated below.

> **Theorem 3.6 The Unique Factorization Theorem** Every integer $n \geq 2$ can be factored into a product of primes $n = p_1 p_2 \ldots p_n$ in exactly one way. (Note: arranging the factors in a different order does not count as a new factorization.

Proof: First prove that every integer $n > 1$ has a prime factorization, using a proof by contradiction. So, suppose that there exists at least one integer greater than 1 that cannot be written as a product of primes. Pick the smallest of these integers and call it k.

Then k cannot be prime, because if it were, it would be its own prime factorization. Therefore, k must be composite. Then k can be written as $k = ab$, where both a and b are greater than 1 and less than k. Now, k was chosen to be the smallest integer greater than 1 not having a prime factorization, so since a and b are both greater than 1 and less than k, a and b must both have prime factorizations. But since $k = ab$, k has a prime factorization also. This contradicts the choice of k. Therefore, there are no integers greater than 1 that do not have a prime factorization.

To prove the second part of the theorem, we must prove that prime factorizations are unique. To prove this part of the theorem, write out two prime factorizations for an integer, and then show that they have to contain the same primes. Start by assuming that there is an integer $n > 1$ such that $n = p_1 p_2 p_3 \ldots p_k = q_1 q_2 q_3 \ldots q_r$, where each of the p_i and q_i are primes. Now, by the definition of divides, $p_1 \mid q_1 q_2 q_3 \ldots q_r$, $p_2 \mid q_1 q_2 q_3 \ldots q_r$, and so on. Since p_1 is prime, it must be true that p_1 divides one of the q_i's, so relabel them so that $p_1 \mid q_1$. (We will examine this result more closely in Chapter 4. For now, see if you can convince yourself that it is reasonable by looking at a few examples). Since p_1 and q_1 are both prime, and the only divisors of q_1 are 1 and q_1 itself, p_1 and q_1 must be equal. Similarly, p_2 must divide one of the q_i's, so relabel so that $p_2 \mid q_2$, which implies that $p_2 = q_2$. Continuing in this manner, we will get that $p_i = q_i$ for each of the primes, and therefore there is only one way to factor n into primes.

∎

Unique factorization is a very special property that applies to natural numbers. This property does not hold in the set of integers. For example, $6 = 2 \cdot 3 = (-2)(-3)$. Similarly, in the rational numbers $2 = 2 \cdot 1 = (1/2)(4)$ and many other choices of pairs.

Section 3.4   The Search for Primes

> "Mathematicians have tried in vain to this day to discover some order in the sequence of prime numbers, and we have reason to believe that it is a mystery into which the human mind will never penetrate."
>
> — *Leonhard Euler, 1707–1783*

One question that we have not yet answered is: "How many primes are there?" If there is a fixed number of primes – maybe 1,000 or even 50,000,000 – then there are *finitely many* primes. If that is the case, then they can be written down, and the list of primes would come to an end. There would be a biggest prime out there, and no integer larger than it is prime. On the other hand, if the list of primes goes on forever, with no largest prime, then there are *infinitely many* primes.

Mathematicians are searching for larger and larger primes, and they keep track of the largest integers that have been proven to be primes. In 2008, mathematicians confirmed that the nearly 13 million digit number $2^{43112609} - 1$ was prime, and this number held the honor of being the largest known prime until 2013 when it was overshadowed by $2^{57885161} - 1$, with over 17 million digits. Primes of this form $(2^p - 1)$ are called Mersenne primes. Can we be sure that primes larger than this one exist, even if we haven't actually found them? Thanks to Euclid, we know that the answer is yes!

Definition 3.4 *Mersenne primes* are primes that can be written in the form $2^p - 1$.

Euclid's proof that there must be infinitely many primes is one of the most famous proofs in Number Theory. This proof is a good example of an ideal time to use a proof by contradiction, because the statement of the theorem does not contain any given information. The proof depends on a fact proved in Lemma 3.1: Every integer greater than 1 must have at least one prime divisor. Euclid showed that if there is a finite number of primes, it is always possible to create a number that couldn't possibly be divisible by any of them. Theorem 3.5 says it all.

Theorem 3.7 There are infinitely many primes.

Proof (by contradiction):
Suppose that there are finitely many primes, say n of them. Then they can be listed in order as follows: $p_1, p_2, p_3, \ldots, p_n$. Now, consider the natural number $n = p_1 p_2 p_3 \ldots p_n + 1$. Then, since n is a positive integer greater than 1, n must have a prime divisor by Lemma 3.1. But, on the other hand, when we divide each of the primes into n there is a remainder of 1. Therefore, n is a new prime. This is a contradiction since we claimed to have listed all the primes. Therefore, there must be infinitely many primes.

∎

Since we now know that there are infinitely many primes, here are some questions about the occurrence of these primes:

1. Is there a pattern to the occurrence of primes?
2. Do primes occur regularly throughout the integers? (Is every 10th, or 100th, or k^{th} integer a prime?)
3. Is there a formula that will generate all primes?
4. Is there a formula that will always yield a prime number?
5. If a formula that always yields a prime is not possible, then is it possible to find a formula that will give a prime number infinitely often? (In other words, is there a formula that will result in a prime number when infinitely many integers are substituted into the formula?

To answer the first question, think about finding a sequence of two consecutive composite integers. This is not hard to do; for example, 8 and 9 or 9 and 10 both work. To find three consecutive composite integers, we can put together 8, 9, 10. To find a longer string of consecutive composites, say seven in a row, the smallest sequence of numbers that works is 90, 91, 92, 93, 94, 95, 96. To find even longer strings of consecutive composites, we would have to use larger numbers. This illustrates that as numbers get bigger, the primes get more spread out.

In fact, we can generate a list of consecutive composite numbers of any length, although this method will not necessarily provide the sequence of the smallest possible integers that work. This method uses factorials.

Definition 3.5 The *factorial of a natural number n* is the product of that number and the positive integers less than that number, denoted $n!$

For example, $3! = 3 \cdot 2 \cdot 1$, and $10! = 10 \cdot 9 \cdot 8 \cdot 7 \cdot 6 \cdot 5 \cdot 4 \cdot 3 \cdot 2 \cdot 1$. Notice that each positive integer less than or equal to n will be a divisor of $n!$ Suppose you want to find 4 consecutive composite integers. Since $4! = 4 \cdot 3 \cdot 2 \cdot 1$. To construct the set, begin with $5! = 5 \cdot 4 \cdot 3 \cdot 2 \cdot 1$ so that 2, 3, 4 and 5 are divisors. To make consecutive numbers, form the sequence $5! + 2$, $5! + 3$, $5! + 4$, $5! + 5$, or 122, 123, 124, 125. Notice that the first number will be divisible by 2 since it divides both terms of the sum, the second will be divisible by 3, and so on.

Example 3.15. Find eight consecutive composite natural numbers.

Solution:

To get eight consecutive integers, start with $9! + 2$ and work up to $9! + 9$. The list of integers is:

$$9! + 2,\ 9! + 3,\ 9! + 4,\ 9! + 5,\ 9! + 6,\ 9! + 7,\ 9! + 8,\ 9! + 9$$

Then, the first integer is divisible by 2, the second by 3, the third by 4, and so on, guaranteeing that all values on this list are composite.

From these examples, we see that a set of n consecutive natural numbers form the sequence

$$n! + 2,\ n! + 3,\ n! + 4,\ \ldots n! + n$$

Reiterating, one can find a list of n consecutive composite natural numbers, for any natural number n. So, we can find a gap between primes of any length. This answers questions 1 and 2. Incidentally, do you know why the list does not start with $n! + 1$?

Question 3: Is there a formula that will always generate primes?

No one has been able to find a practical formula which generates only primes. The next best thing is a formula that will generate primes infinitely often; such a formula may not produce a prime every time a natural number is substituted, but there is a never-ending collection of integers that will result in a prime when substituted into the formula. Several formulas or types of formulas which generate primes infinitely often have been found. In some cases, it has been proven that the formula will generate infinitely many primes, and in other cases it is still a conjecture. Below are some examples of conjectures about primes.

Landau Problems

At the 1912 International Congress of Mathematicians, a large mathematics conference held every four years, the German mathematician Edmund Landau listed four statements that are conjectures about primes that sound simple, but have not yet been proven true or false. As of 2012, no one has yet been able to definitively answer the question of whether each of these statements is true or false. The list below includes the Landau Problems.

1. **Goldbach's Conjecture:** Every even integer greater than 2 can be written as the sum of two primes. This statement is very approachable – Start checking even integers now: $4 = 2 + 2$, $6 = 3 + 3$, $8 = 5 + 3$. Notice that repeated primes are acceptable.

2. **Twin Prime Conjecture:** There are infinitely many twin primes p such that p and $p + 2$ are both prime.

   People have found very large pairs of twin primes, but no proof.

3. **Legendre's Conjecture:** There is always at least one prime between two consecutive perfect squares (n^2 and $(n+1)^2$).

   This is another conjecture you can test immediately. For example, if $n = 2$, then we are looking for a prime between 4 and 9. There are two in this case: 5 and 7.

4. **Near-square Prime Conjecture:** There are infinitely many primes of the form $n^2 +1$.

   We can find some primes of this form: if $n = 1$, then $n^2 +1 = 2$, and if $n = 2$, then $n^2 +1 = 5$. Primes of this form are called *near-square primes*, because if $p = n^2 +1$, then $p - 1 = n^2$, a perfect square.

5. There are infinitely many primes of the form $2^p -1$, called **Mersenne primes.**

   The French mathematician Marin Mersenne (1588–1648) searched for a formula to generate prime numbers and studied numbers of the form $2^p -1$. Mersenne proved that if $2^n -1$ was prime, then n was necessarily prime, and also that the converse was false: a prime value of n does not guarantee that $2^n -1$ is prime. Mathematicians believe that there are infinitely many Mersenne primes, but this has not been proven although as mentioned at the beginning of this section, extremely large Mersenne primes have been found.

6. There are infinitely many primes of the form $2^{2^n} +1$, for $n \geq 0$, called **Fermat primes.**

   The French mathematician Pierre de Fermat (of Fermat's Last Theorem fame) studied numbers of the form $2^{2^n} +1$, for $n \geq 0$. Numbers with this form are called *Fermat numbers* since Fermat was the first person to study them. The first three Fermat numbers are 3, 5, 17. A Fermat number which is prime is called a *Fermat prime*. From the list above, one can see that the first three Fermat numbers are prime. The fourth and fifth Fermat numbers, 257 and 65537, are prime as well. In fact, in 1650 Fermat made the conjecture that all Fermat numbers are prime. Unfortunately, every Fermat number larger than the first five that has been tested has turned out to be composite. This proves Fermat's claim false, and it seems unlikely that more Fermat primes will be found.

7. **Unnamed primes:** Is it possible to find a value of $a \neq 2$, so that $a^n -1$ will be a prime number for infinitely many values of n?

Exercise Set 3.4

1. a) Find 10 consecutive composite integers.
   b) It is possible to find any number of consecutive composite numbers. What does this tell you about the placement of primes in the integers?

2. Explain how to find 100 consecutive composite integers. (Note: you do not need to write out all the numbers, but explain how to construct them).

3. Test the following conjecture and develop a hypothesis about whether it is true or false. Are you able to prove your hypothesis?

   Conjecture: The expression $2n^2 +11$ is prime for all positive integers n.

4. The French mathematician Joseph Bertrand made the following conjecture in 1845: For every positive integer n, there is a prime p such that $n < p < 2n$.

   a) Test the conjecture for $n = 3$, $n = 7$ and $n = 10$.

   b) Find the smallest prime satisfying the conjecture for $n = 73$, and verify that the p you found is prime.

5. Consider the formula $9n + 16$, where n is a positive integer. What is the smallest prime that can be expressed in this way? What value of n gives this prime?

6. Do an Internet search to find the largest known prime and the largest known Mersenne prime. Are they the same? How were they found?

Exercises 7–15: Test the conjecture and make a hypothesis about whether it is true or false. If possible, prove your hypothesis. (Remember that a counterexample can prove a conjecture is false, but a general proof is needed to prove it is true. Conjectures:

7. There are infinitely many primes of the form $n^2 + 1$.

8. There are infinitely many primes of the form $n^2 - 1$.

9. There are infinitely many primes of the form $n^2 - 2$.

10. There are infinitely many primes of the form $n^2 + 5n + 6$.

11. There are infinitely many primes of the form $n^2 - 9$.

12. There are infinitely many primes of the form $n^2 + 9$.

13. There are infinitely many primes of the form $n^2 + n + 1$.

14. There are infinitely many primes of the form $n^2 + 2n + 1$.

15. There are infinitely many primes of the form $n^2 + 3n + 2$.

16. Cousin primes are primes that differ by 4. Find two pairs of cousin primes.

17. Goldbach's conjecture states that every even number greater than 2 is a sum of two primes.

    a) Show that the conjecture holds true for 26 and for 40.

    b) Although Goldbach's conjecture only specifies that an even number can be written as the sum of two primes in one way, often there is more than one way. Find all the ways that 60 can be written as the sum of two primes.

    c) Show that 11 cannot be written as the sum of two primes. Explain why this is not a counterexample for Goldbach's conjecture.

Section 3.5   Summary and Review Exercises

Vocabulary and Symbols

prime

composite

Primality test

Sieve of Eratosthenes

prime power factorization

Well-Ordering Principle

Near-prime factorization

Fermat primes

Mersenne primes

Fundamental Theorem of Arithmetic

Unique Factorization Theorem

Suggested Readings

Devlin, Keith. "World's Largest Prime," *Focus* (The newsletter of the Mathematical Association of America) 17 (December, 1997): 1.

Doxiadis, Apostolos. *Uncle Petros and Goldbach's Conjecture: A Novel of Mathematical Obsession*. New York, NY: Bloomsbury, 2001.

Granville, Andrew. "Prime Number Patterns," *The American Mathematical Monthly* 115 (April, 2008): 279–296.

Schwartz, Richard Evan. *You Can Count on Monsters*. Natick, MA: A. K. Peters, Ltd., 2010.

Chapter 3 Review Exercises

1. When using the Primality Test to see if 754 is prime, what primes must be tested to see if they are divisors of 754? Is 754 prime or composite?

2. Determine which of the following integers are prime: 113, 201, 213, 221, 259.

Exercises 3–12: Find the prime power factorization.

3. 3465

4. 40320

5. 369655

6. 36465

7. 34890

8. 16281

9. 14641

10. 135762

11. 13392

12. 24578

13. Determine if 1,111,111,111 is prime. If not, find its prime factorization.

14. Determine if 13579 is prime. If it is not, factor it into the product of primes.

15. Determine if 123456789 is prime. If it is not, find its prime factorization.

16. Determine if 987654321 is prime. If it is not, find its prime factorization.

17. Given two integers m and n the prime factorization of these is $m = 2^2 \cdot 3^3 \cdot 5 \cdot 7 \cdot 11$ and $n = 2 \cdot 3 \cdot 11$.
    a) Find $\gcd(m, n)$.
    b) Find $\operatorname{lcm}(m, n)$

18. True or False. If false, give a counterexample:
    a) There are infinitely many primes of the type $n^2 - 49$.
    b) If p is prime, then $2^p - 1$ is prime.
       There is an infinite number of primes.

19. Twin Primes
    a) Find the first 8 twin prime pairs $(p, p+2)$.
    b) Using (a), find the values you obtain when you add 1 to the product of each pair of twin primes.
    c) Use (b) to make a conjecture/generalization about twin primes p and $p+2$.

20. Prove or disprove: If p, q and r are odd primes, then $pqr + 1$ is composite.

21. If p and q are distinct primes, find all divisors of pq.

22. Find all integers with exactly five factors. Provide some examples and a general formula.

23. Consider the following three integers in prime factorization form:

$$a = 2^2 \cdot 3^2 \cdot 5^2 \cdot 11; \quad b = 2 \cdot 5^3 \cdot 11 \cdot 17; \quad c = 2^2 \cdot 3^2 \cdot 11^2 \cdot 17$$

    a) Use the above prime factorizations to determine $\gcd(a, b, c)$.

    b) Use the above prime factorization to determine $\operatorname{lcm}(a, b, c)$.

Exercises 24–29: Use prime power factorization to find the greatest common divisor.

24. $(756, 2205)$

25. $(4725, 17460)$

26. $(465, 3861)$

27. $(4600, 2116)$

28. $(630, 990)$

29. $(96, 144)$

Exercises 30–35: Use prime power factorization to find the least common multiple.

30. $(756, 2205)$

31. $(4725, 17460)$

32. $(465, 3861)$

33. $(96, 144)$

Section 3.6   Activities

1. What is the largest pair of twin primes found since 2012?

2. Look up Eratosthenes and find out about his contributions to mathematics and other fields.

3. What is the largest known prime number?

4. Research the topic *even integers* to see an example of a collection of integers that does not obey the Unique Factorization Theorem. A starting place is "The Even World" in *The Whole Truth about Whole Numbers* by Forman and Rash, Springer, 2015. What is the largest known prime number?

5. In the *MAA Focus* journal, June/July 2019 there is a short article on p. 6 "Proof of The Sheldon Conjecture" about episode 73 in which "Sheldon Cooper claims that 73 is the 'best number'." The rationale for this claim is given and in October, 2019, a proof of this conjecture was published in the fall. Read the article, view, and summarize the episode.

6. There are many powerful computer software programs that can solve difficult mathematical problems. Some of these also show step-by-step solutions. One of these is Wolfram Alpha, which is available on the iPad and other devices for little or no cost. Try Wolfram Alpha yourself.

Sophie Germain

(1776–1831)

Sophie Germain was born in Paris and was in her teen years during the French Revolution. Her parents were concerned for her safety and were reluctant to let her leave the house during these years. So, she spent long hours reading books in her father's home library.

Sophie discovered that mathematics can be captivating and decided to become a mathematician. Unfortunately, her parents did not consider mathematics to be suitable for a female and made it impossible for her to work on mathematics in the evening (Pommershiem, 703). But Sophie persisted and finally her parents relented, and supported here while she was doing mathematical research as an adult.

Since she was not allowed to study at the science and engineering university, she used an assumed name (Antoine-August Le Blanc) to obtain lecture notes and otherwise was self-taught. Germain gravitated to number theory and corresponded frequently with Lagrange who was well-known among number theorists. Lagrange was very impressed with the creativity of the work that she sent to him and wanted to meet her. He was even more impressed when he found out that Le Blanc was a woman. She also corresponded with Karl F. Gauss, whom we will meet in Chapter 5.

Germain made many contributions to the solution of Fermat's Last Theorem. Her approach was to divide the problem into cases. Case I considers when n is an odd prime:

$$x^p + y^p = z^p$$

Germain proved that this statement is true for all odd primes $p < 100$. Case II considers the possibility that at least one of the values x, y, or z is divisible by p. Her approach to the problem was used for more than 100 years.

NOTES TO MYSELF

Euclid

347–287 BC

Euclid of Alexandria provided great insights into mathematics and is well known for his long treatise *Euclid's Elements* which has 13 volumes. It has been in print continuously for over 2000 years.

Little is known about Euclid's life but evidently, he had a school in Alexandria. He is known for organizing and publishing the geometry of his day and contributing new ideas of his own. He led a team of mathematicians in Alexandria who all contributed to the creation of the *Elements* (Krantz, 7). The name "Euclid" was very common and was even used to describe a group of men. Their inspiration came from Euclid of Megara. However, there is significant agreement among scholars that Euclid of Alexandria created the *Elements* with the assistance of his students. The *Elements* have appeared in at least 1000 editions (Krantz, 7–9).

There is speculation that Euclid studied in Plato's Academy in Athens because there was no other place that he could have amassed his knowledge of geometry. Euclid organized the topics in geometry so that it would be easier to study. For example, the concept of lines, whether parallel or intersecting, are studied together. The study of circles, arcs, and tangents, concentric or intersecting are grouped. He constructed precise figures using only a straight edge and compass. Euclid taught at the University of Alexandria, Euclid solved the problem of finding all right triangles whose sides are integers (Chapter 2).

Euclid's proofs use basic assumptions including undefined terms, such as "point" and "line," that are described but not defined. On these basics, he constructed definitions, axioms, and postulates. Proofs of theorems are based on the connection of these constructs (undefined terms, definitions, etc.) using logic.

Euclid was interested in number theory, and books 7 through 9 of the *Elements* deal with this topic. One of his creations is the Euclidean algorithm, which is of great importance today, and is the main topic of this chapter. He developed a rigorous proof that the algorithm is actually a theorem. Euclid was an important and influential mathematics teacher whose work has stood the test of time.

CHAPTER 4

The Euclidean Algorithm

"An algorithm must be seen to be believed."

--Donald Knuth, 1938–

Section 4.1   The Division Algorithm

In Section 1.11, we defined the greatest common divisor of two (or more) integers. This concept was used in Chapter 2 in order to determine whether or not a particular right triangle was primitive. In Exercise 13 of Section 2.2, you were asked to determine whether or not $100 - 621 - 629$ was a primitive Pythagorean triple. This concept turns out to be very important in modern applications of mathematics in a variety of settings, including secret codes, and thus will be a recurring theme in this book. In this chapter, we explore some properties of the gcd and find an algorithm that will calculate the value for any pair of integers, no matter how large. This problem came up in Chapter 3, where prime factorizations were used to make it easier to find the greatest common divisor of these three numbers.

Factoring an integer into its prime factors helps to find the greatest common divisor of a set of integers quickly. In Chapter 1 we discussed several divisibility rules. Here are two more examples of the less frequently used divisibility tests.

1. $7|a$ if and only if when you double the last digit of a and subtract that from the number that remains after removing the last digit, the value is divisible by 7
2. $11|a$ if and only if the number formed by alternately subtracting and adding the digits of a is divisible by 11.

Example 4.1. Determine if 882 is divisible by 7.

Solution:

Step 1: The last digit of 882 is 2: $2 \cdot 2 = 4$

Step 2: Removing the last digit leaves 88

Step 3: $88 - 4 = 84$

Step 4: $84 = 7(12)$

$\therefore$ 882 is divisible by 7.

Example 4.2. Determine if 121345 is divisible by 11.

Solution:

Using the rule on the digits from left to right, we have

$$1 - 2 + 1 - 3 + 4 - 5 = -4$$

$$\therefore 121345 \text{ is not divisible by } 11.$$

While we have the Primality Tests developed in Section 3.1, as numbers get larger factoring becomes laborious and impractical even using super computers. This fact is the basis for one of the encryption techniques discussed in Chapter 7. Frequently, it is desirable to have an *algorithm* or procedure to apply to solve a problem.

> **Definition 4.1** An *algorithm* is a procedure for solving a mathematical problem in a finite number of steps that frequently involves repetition of an operation or a step.

An *algorithm* is a process that concludes with the solution of a problem or an answer to the question it is meant to solve in a finite number of steps. An example of this is the process of finding the greatest common divisor of two natural numbers by making a factor tree.

In this section, we describe the *Division Algorithm*, which leads to the very useful *Euclidean Algorithm*, discussed in the next section, for finding the greatest common divisor of two numbers, no matter how large. Each step of the Euclidean Algorithm is based on the division of integers.

Remark: Mathematics books commonly use d to mean *divisor*, q to represent *quotient*, and r to represent *remainder*.

If an integer c is divided by a positive integer d, there are two possible outcomes:

1. c is a multiple of d, which means d divides c, OR
2. c falls between two consecutive multiples of d, that is, c leaves a remainder when divided by d. Consecutive multiples are numbers that differ by d. For example, if $d = 4$, then the pair 8, 12 or the pair 16, 20 are examples of consecutive multiples of 4. The numbers in between consecutive pairs leave a remainder when divided by 4, as shown on the number line below.

Example 4.3. For instance, divide 34 by 4. Then $c = 34$ and $d = 4$. Rewrite the dividend in terms of the divisor and a remainder.

Solution:

$$
\begin{array}{r}
8 \\
4\overline{)34} \\
32 \\
\hline
2
\end{array}
$$

So, the remainder is 2. (When learning long division, you may have written "R2" to indicate that the remainder is 2.) The integer 34 falls *between* two consecutive multiples of 4: $8(4) = 32$ and $9(4) = 36$. Rewriting 34 in terms of the divisor and remainder, $34 = 8(4) + 2$, the remainder is 2 when 34 is divided by 8, as shown in the division above.

In general, if m is a multiple of d, then the next multiple is obtained by adding d: $m + d$. These are consecutive multiples. Continuing with this example, $d = 4$. Then, if $m = 20$, m is a multiple of 4 since $20 = 5(4)$. If $c = 17$, then c is not a multiple of 4, but c falls between the two multiples $16 = 4(4)$ and $20 = 5(4)$. And, if $c = 3$, then c falls between the multiples $0 = 0(4)$ and $4 = 1(4)$.

Let's look more closely at two intervals 4 through 8 and -4 through 0 and the integers in these intervals.

4	5	6	7	8
4(1)	4(1) + 1	4(1) + 2	4(1) + 3	4(2)

also

-4	-3	-2	-1	0
4(−1)	4(−1) + 1	4(−1) + 2	4(−1) + 3	4(0)

If you start on a multiple of 4, you will get to another multiple of 4 by adding 4, for example:

$$0 + 4 = 4 \text{ and } -8 + 4 = -4$$

A number between two consecutive multiples of 4 leaves a remainder when divided by 4. This remainder is recorded as a positive number. Notice that $-3 = -2(1) + (-1)$ or $4(0) - 3$ as well as being expressed as $4(-1) + 1$. We will always choose the expression with a positive remainder.

Slightly more general, any integer c can be written as $c = q \cdot 4 + r$, where q is an integer and r is either 0, 1, 2, or 3. Notice that the remainder is always less than the divisor.

The pattern for the integer 4 illustrated above will work for any positive integer. So, if d is any positive integer and c is any integer, then either c is divisible by d (in which case $c = qd$ for some integer q) or c is between consecutive multiples qd and $(q+1)d$ for some integer q. Combining these two possibilities we get the following equation:

$$c = qd + r \text{ where } r \text{ is one of the natural numbers } 0, 1, 2, \ldots, d-1.$$

This relationship is called the Division Algorithm, and is stated below:

> **The Division Algorithm** If d if a positive integer, then for any integer c, $c = qd + r$ where $q \in \mathbb{Z}$ and $0 \leq r < d$. In this equation, q is called the **quotient**, d is the **divisor**, r is the **remainder**, and c is called the **dividend**. If $r = 0$, then $d|c$.

Here are some examples using the Division Algorithm.

Example 4.4. In each example, divide c by d and then use the Division Algorithm to express the result:

   a) $d = 5, c = 9$
   b) $d = 256, c = 1024$

Solution:

   a) $d = 5$ and $c = 9$
        $9 = 1(5) + 4$. (The quotient, q is 1 and the remainder, r is 4).
   b) $d = 256$ and $c = 1024$
        $1024 = 4(256) + 0$
        Since 1024 is a multiple of 256, the remainder is zero.

Example 4.5. In each example, divide c by d and then use the Division Algorithm to express the result:

   a) $d = 7, c = 555$
   b) $d = 8, c = 6$
   c) $d = 4, c = -22$

Solution:

   a) $d = 7$ and $c = 555$
        $555 = 79(7) + 2$

        Note: To find the quotient, in this case 79, you are looking for the largest multiple of 7 that is less than 555. If you divide 555 by 7 on the calculator, the whole number part of the answer is the quotient. Then to find the remainder, subtract $555 - 79(7) = 2$.

   b) $d = 8$ and $c = 6$
        Here, 6 is being divided by 8, but since 8 is bigger than 6, 8 does not divide 6 a natural number of times. Notice that 6 is between the multiples $0(8) = 0$ and $1(8) = 8$, so the quotient is 0 and the remainder is 6.
        $$6 = 0(8) + 6$$

c) $d = 4$ and $c = -22$

Since 4 does not divide –22 evenly, to find the quotient and remainder, we need the largest multiple of 4 that is less than –22, and the remainder must be positive. In this case, this $q = -6$. So,

$$-22 = -6(4) + 2.$$

When performing division, we are frequently interested in the quotient: how many times one integer divided another integer. The Division Algorithm also displays the remainder, which is very useful in grouping or classifying numbers. A few examples when the divisor is 4 appear in Table 4.1. In Chapter 5, useful applications using remainders are covered in more detail.

Suppose that we are dividing integers by the number 4. Because the multiples of 4 are spaced 4 apart, the possible remainders when dividing by 4 are 0, 1, 2, or 3. Every integer has to have one of these remainders when divided by 4. Table 4.1 below contains a few examples.

c	Division algorithm	Remainder
4	$4 = 4(1) + 0$	0
7	$7 = 4(1) + 3$	3
45	$45 = 4(11) + 1$	1
10	$10 = 4(2) + 2$	2
17	$17 = 4(4) + 1$	1
54	$53 = 4(13) + 2$	2
–31	$-31 = 4(-8) + 1$	1

Table 4.1

Notice that each possible remainder shows up at least once in the table above, and 45 and 17 both have a remainder of 1 when divided by 4 while 10 and 54 both have a remainder of 2.

Question: What other integers have a remainder of 1?

From the Division Algorithm, if c is going to have a remainder of 1 when divided by 4, then c must satisfy the equation $c = 4q + 1$, for some integer q. By substituting different values for q, we generate an infinite list of all integers that have a remainder of 1. Choosing the values 1, 2, 3, and –3 for q, shows that 5, 9, 13, and –11 all have a remainder of 1 when divided by 4. (Check these and confirm that their remainder is 1.)

Example 4.6. Write a formula to represent all integers n that have a remainder of 3 when divided by 7. Then, find two negative integers and two positive integers that have a remainder of 3 when divided by 7.

Solution:

From the Division Algorithm, if the integer n has a remainder of 3 when divided by 7, then n can be written as $n = 7q + 3$, where q is an integer. Picking different values for q shows that there are both positive and negative values for n. Also notice that when we increase q by 1, n increases by 7.

q	n
−2	$7(-2)+3=-11$
−1	$7(-1)+3=-4$
0	$7(0)+3=7$
1	$7(1)+3=10$
2	$7(2)+3=17$
3	$7(3)+3=24$

Table 4.2

From Table 4.2, two negative values with a remainder of 3 when divided by 7 are −11 and −4 and two positive values are 10 and 17, but this list goes on indefinitely, as the value if q changes.

Exercise Set 4.1

Exercises 1–14: For each value of d and c, find the quotient and remainder when dividing c by d, and then write the result in the form $c=qd+r$ from the Division Algorithm.

1. $d=4,\quad c=160$
2. $d=7,\quad c=47$
3. $d=7,\quad c=28$
4. $d=11,\ c=567$
5. $d=18,\ c=9$
6. $d=15,\ c=7$
7. $d=8,\quad c=6$

8. $d=6,\quad c=138$
9. $d=12,\ c=-34$
10. $d=14,\ c=1567$
11. $d=4,\quad c=8k$
12. $d=3,\quad c=21k$
13. $d=6,\quad c=6k+15$
14. $d=5,\quad c=5k+32$

15. Explain why knowing the remainder when a number is divided by 7 is important? What about 12? Think of an example of how each of these can be used.

16. Explain what is wrong with the following if the Division Algorithm is being applied, and correct it: Suppose you want to divide 37 by 7. Since 4(7) = 28, we can say 7 evenly divides 37 four times, with a remainder of 9, or $37=4(7)+9$.

17. List each possible remainder when dividing an integer by 7. Find several different integers that have each remainder. What patterns do you notice?

18. List every possible remainder when dividing an integer by 6. Find several different integers that have each remainder. What patterns do you notice?

19. Write a formula to represent all integers that have a remainder of 4 when divided by 7.

20. Write a formula to represent all integers that have a remainder of 3 when divided by 6.

21. Prove the following conjecture true or false. (First test the conjecture on several examples). Conjecture: Two consecutive odd integers can never both be divisible by 3.

22. Prove that if $n \in \mathbb{Z}$, then n^2 is divisible by 4, or has a remainder of 1 when divided by 4. (Hint: Look at the cases when n is even and when n is odd separately.)

Section 4.2   The Euclidean Algorithm

The division algorithm can be extended as described in this section. Before proceeding, we provide a lemma that will be used repeatedly in this section.

Lemma 4.1 If a and b are integers and r is the remainder when b is divided by a, then any common divisor of a and b will also divide r.

Proof:

The proof of this fact is Exercise 18.

The ***Euclidean Algorithm*** is a method for finding the greatest common divisor of any two integers. In contrast to the methods we have already developed to find the greatest common divisor of two integers, the Euclidean Algorithm is not more labor-intensive as the numbers involved get larger. Each step of the Euclidean Algorithm is an application of the Division Algorithm. While not complicated, the Euclidean Algorithm requires careful algebra and some patience. We begin with two specific examples to see *how* the Euclidean Algorithm works. Then, the general form for the Euclidean Algorithm is given, followed by an analysis of *why* it works.

Example 4.7. Find $\gcd(146, 60)$ using the Euclidean Algorithm.

Solution:

We will illustrate the steps of the Euclidean Algorithm for this example. The divisors and remainders in each step are color-coded to emphasize the relationships between the steps of the algorithm.

Step 1: Use the Division Algorithm to write the result of dividing the larger of the two numbers (in this case, 146) by the smaller number.

$$146 = 2(60) + 26$$

Note that by Lemma 4.1, the $\gcd(146, 60)$ divides 26.

Step 2: Apply the Division Algorithm again, to divide the divisor from Step 1 (in this case, 60) by the remainder from Step 1 (in this case 26).

$$60 = 2(26) + 8$$

Similarly, the $\gcd(60, 26)|8$.

Step 3: Apply the Division Algorithm to divide the divisor from Step 2 (26, in this example) by the remainder in Step 2 (8, in this example).

$$26 = 3(8) + 2$$

Continue to repeat this process until the remainder is 0.

Step 4: Since the remainder is non-zero, divide the divisor from Step 3 (8, in this example) from remainder in Step 3 (2, in this example).

$$8 = 4(2) + 0$$

This 0 remainder means that the Euclidean Algorithm is complete. The last non-zero remainder is the greatest common divisor of the original two integers, so $\gcd(146, 60) = 2$. (Prime factorization can be used to confirm that this is correct).

The next example illustrates the usefulness of the Euclidean Algorithm. It is possible to find the greatest common divisor of 2059 and 2581 by listing all of their factors or finding their prime factorizations, but this is laborious.

Example 4.8. Find gcd(2059, 2581) using the Euclidean Algorithm.

Solution:

The first step of the Euclidean Algorithm is again to find the quotient and remainder when the larger of the two integers is divided by the smaller one, and then write the result using the Division Algorithm.

$$2581 = 1(2059) + 522$$

Repeat the same process, dividing the divisor by the remainder.

$$2059 = 3(522) + 493$$

Repeat until the remainder is zero.

$$522 = 1(493) + 29$$
$$493 = 17(29) + 0$$

Therefore, according to the Euclidean Algorithm, $\gcd(2059, 2581) = 29$.

To describe the process used in the Euclidean Algorithm in general, we use letters with subscripts to represent the steps. In order to make it easier to follow, the remainders will be designated by $r_1, r_2, \cdots$. The first remainder is r_1. The number of remainders depends on how many lines are used to arrive at a zero remainder. This happens since the remainders get smaller each time, but they can never be negative.

The quotients in each step are designated by $q_1, q_2, \ldots$ and so on. Below is a general statement of the Euclidean algorithm. When you look at the steps, notice that both the divisor and the remainder from the previous line carry down to the next line and are shifted to the left. Again, these values are shown in color to clearly explain the process.

The Euclidean Algorithm: Let a and b be two positive integers, with b the larger of the two integers. To find the greatest common divisor of a and b, apply the Division Algorithm repeatedly as shown below. The last non-zero remainder, r_n, is the greatest common divisor of a and b.

$$b = q_1 a + r_1 \qquad 0 \le r_1 < a,$$
$$a = q_2 r_1 + r_2 \qquad 0 \le r_2 < r_1,$$
$$r_1 = q_3 r_2 + r_3 \qquad 0 \le r_3 < r_2,$$
$$r_2 = q_4 r_3 + r_4 \qquad 0 \le r_4 < r_3,$$
$$\vdots \qquad\qquad \vdots$$
$$r_{n-2} = q_n r_{n-1} + \boldsymbol{r_n} \qquad 0 \le \boldsymbol{r_n} < r_{n-1},$$
$$r_{n-1} = q_{n+1} \boldsymbol{r_n} + 0$$

$$\text{Then, } \gcd(a, b) = r_n.$$

Example 4.9. Use the Euclidean Algorithm to find $\gcd(3829, 561)$.

Solution:

$$3829 = 6(561) + 463$$
$$561 = 1(463) + 98$$
$$463 = 4(98) + 71$$
$$98 = 1(71) + 27$$
$$71 = 2(27) + 17$$
$$27 = 1(17) + 10$$
$$17 = 1(10) + 7$$
$$10 = 1(7) + \mathbf{3}$$
$$7 = 2(\mathbf{3}) + 1$$
$$\mathbf{3} = 3(1) + 0$$

Therefore, according to the Euclidean Algorithm, $\gcd(3829, 561) = 1$.

Notice that not only does the last non-zero remainder divide both a and b, but that it is **the greatest common divisor of a and b**. To verify that this is always true, start from the first line.

The first step of the Euclidean Algorithm is

$$b = q_1 a + r_1$$

Rewrite this as

$$b - q_1 a = r_1$$

This argument is used to prove Lemma 4.1 and can be continued through each line in the algorithm, as indicated in Example 4.9. Since we are interested in finding the greatest common divisor of a and b, the following lemma will be useful.

> **Lemma 4.2** If a and b are integers, and r is the remainder when b is divided by a, then $\gcd(a, b) = \gcd(a, r)$.

Proof.

Let a and b be integers and let r be the remainder when b is divided by a. From the Division Algorithm, $b = qa + r$. Also, by Lemma 4.1, any common divisor of a and b also divides r. Now, suppose that m is a common divisor of a and r. Since $m \mid a$ and $m \mid r$, there are integers k and l such that $a = mk$ and $r = ml$. Substituting these values into the Division Algorithm produces the following equation:

$$b = q(mk) + ml$$
$$b = m(qk + l)$$

Since $qk + l \in \mathbb{Z}$, this says that $m \mid b$. Therefore, any common divisor of a and r is also a common divisor of a and b. Since the two pairs of integers share exactly the same common divisors, the greatest common divisor must be the same. Therefore, $\gcd(a, b) = \gcd(a, r)$.

∎

Now we can use Lemma 4.2 to show that the Euclidean Algorithm produces the correct result for the greatest common divisor of a and b.

	Steps of the Euclidean Algorithm	**Using Lemma 4.2 in each step**
Step 1	$b = q_1 a + r_1$	$\gcd(a, b) = \gcd(a, r_1)$.
Step 2	$a = q_2 r_1 + r_2$	Rewrite, $\gcd(a, r_1) = \gcd(r_1, r_2)$.
Step 3	$r_1 = q_3 r_2 + r_3$	$\gcd(r_1, r_2) = \gcd(r_2, r_3)$.
Step 4	$r_2 = q_4 r_3 + r_4$	$\gcd(r_2, r_3) = \gcd(r_3, r_4)$.
⋮	⋮	⋮
Step n	$r_{n-2} = q_n r_{n-1} + r_n$	$\gcd(r_{n-2}, r_{n-1}) = \gcd(r_{n-1}, r_n)$.
Step $n+1$	$r_{n-1} = q_{n+1} r_n + 0$	$\gcd(r_{n-1}, r_n) = \gcd(r_n, 0) = r_n$.

Looking at the steps above, notice the pattern in the results from Lemma 4.2. Through these equations, we see that the sequence $\gcd(a, b) = \gcd(r_1, r_2) = \gcd(r_2, r_3) = \gcd(r_3, r_4) = \cdots = \gcd(r_{n-1}, r_n) = \gcd(r_n, 0) = r_n$. shows that the algorithm works in general.

If you still are not convinced of the usefulness of the Euclidean Algorithm, try finding the answer to the next example using another method before applying the Euclidean Algorithm.

Example 4.10. Find gcd(54516, 25830).

Solution:

Step 1: Use the Division Algorithm to write the result of dividing 54516 by 25830.

Since 25830 divides 54516 evenly twice, the remainder will be $\text{remainder} = 54516 - 2(25830) = 2856$. Therefore, the first step of the Euclidean Algorithm is:

$$54516 = 2\left(25830\right) + 2856$$

Step 2: Since the remainder is not zero, repeat the process, dividing 25830 by 2856.

$$25830 = 9\left(2856\right) + 126$$

Step 3: Continue dividing the divisor by the remainder, until you reach a remainder of zero.

$$2856 = 22\left(126\right) + 84$$

Since the last remainder is not zero, repeat:

$$126 = 1\left(84\right) + 42$$

Repeat again:

$$84 = 2\left(42\right) + 0$$

The last nonzero remainder is 42.
Hence, $42 = \gcd(54516, 25830)$. (Check to see that 42 divides both of these integers.)

Before finishing this section, here is one more example.

Example 4.11. Find gcd(24, 192) using the Euclidean Algorithm.

Solution:

Applying the Division Algorithm produces the equation $192 = 8(24) + 0$ for the first step of the Euclidean Algorithm. There is no line with a non-zero remainder since 24 divides 192 evenly. This means that 24 is the greatest common divisor of these two integers since 24 is the largest integer that can divide itself, and 24 also divides 192.

Theorem 4.1 states that the result from Example 4.11 is true in general.

> **Theorem 4.1** If a is a positive integer and $a \mid b$ then $\gcd(a, b) = a$.

The proof of Theorem 4.1 is left as Exercise 19.

Exercise Set 4.2

Exercises 1–12: Use the Euclidean Algorithm to find the greatest common divisor.

1. (693, 231)
2. (294, 588)
3. (1045, 1265)
4. (693, 165)
5. (2145, 345)
6. (266, 644)
7. (595, 1463)
8. (2059, 581)
9. (8898, 72720)
10. (12, 1812705)
11. (543, 123456)
12. (963, 657)

13. Think of another algorithm you have learned in a mathematics class or other course. Carefully write down the steps of the algorithm.

14. a) By testing several values for m, develop a conjecture about $\gcd(m, m+1)$.
    b) Either prove that your conjecture is true, or find a counterexample to show it is false. If the conjecture is false, revise it so that it is true. (Hint: try the Euclidean Algorithm to prove the conjecture true.)

15. Form a conjecture about the greatest common divisor of two consecutive even integers. Then either prove that your conjecture is true, or find a counterexample to show it is false. If the conjecture is false, revise it so that it is true, and prove it.

16. Form a conjecture about the greatest common divisor of two consecutive odd integers. Then either prove that your conjecture is true, or find a counterexample to show it is false. If the conjecture is false, revise it so that it is true, and prove it.

17. Prove or disprove: If $k > 1$ then the integers $3k+1$ and $5k+1$, are relatively prime.

18. Prove **Lemma 4.1**

19. Prove **Theorem 4.1**.

Section 4.3   Solving Linear Equations in Two Variables and the Euclidean Algorithm Backwards

The Euclidean Algorithm can be used to find the greatest common divisor of any two integers. For example, we know that there are always integers x and y such that $ax + by = \gcd(a, b)$. Now we are interested in finding a method that will produce solutions to the equation $ax + by = \gcd(a, b)$.

Definition 4.2 The expression $ax + by$ is called a **linear combination of a and b.**

Solving the equation $ax + by = c$ for y, we obtain the familiar slope-intercept form of a line.

$$ax + by = c$$
$$by = -ax + c$$
$$y = \frac{-a}{b}x + \frac{c}{b}$$

The last equation shows that $ax + by = c$ represents a line with slope $\frac{-a}{b}$ and y-intercept $\frac{c}{b}$.

To graph the line represented by the equation $ax + by = c$, choose a value for x, and then solve for y to see what value makes the equation true. This pair of values (x, y) represents both a solution to the equation as well as a point on the graph of the line. Substitute another value for x to get a second point to plot, and then construct the line.

Example 4.12. Find solutions to the equation $3x + 4y = 1$.

Solution:

Choosing $x = 1$, and then solving for y, we obtain $y = \frac{-1}{2}$. So, $x = 1$, $y = \frac{-1}{2}$ is a solution to the equation $3x + 4y = 1$, and the point $\left(1, \frac{-1}{2}\right)$ is on the graph of the equation, shown in Figure 4.1. Similarly, if $x = -1$, solving for y shows that $y = 1$, so $x = -1$, $y = 1$ is a solution of the equation, and $(-1, 1)$ is a point on the graph. Notice that in the first case, the value for y is not an integer, but in the second case, both x and y have integer values. Every linear equation of the form $ax + by = c$ will have infinitely many solutions, since each point on the line represents a solution.

In Algebra, we generally expressed y in terms of x and for each value substituted for x one can find the corresponding value of y. However, this technique does not always lead to integer solutions. Let us explore the answers to these two questions:

Question 1: When does the linear equation $ax + by = c$ have integer values for both x and y solutions?

Question 2: If there is one pair of integer values, are there also other integer solutions?
To answer Question 1, suppose the coefficients on the left side of the linear equation have a common divisor. Let d be the greatest common divisor, $\gcd(a, b) = d$. Then there will not be a solution to the equation if d does not divide c.

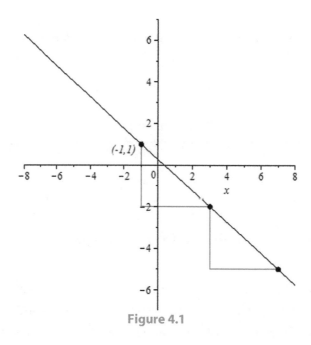

Figure 4.1

Definition 4.3 The triple of positive integers $a-b-c$ is a **Pythagorean triple** if and only if $a^2 + b^2 = c^2$.

Example 4.13. Find an integer solution to the linear equation $12x + 20y = \gcd(12, 20)$.

Solution:

First, $\gcd(12, 20) = 4$, so we are looking for an integer solution to the equation $12x + 20y = 4$. Divide the equation of 4 to find the equivalent equation

$$3x + 5y = 1$$

Let's test a couple of values for x: 1 and 2. When $x = 1$, y is fraction $= -2/5$. However, when $x = 2$, $y = -1$ is a solution to the equation. Notice that $x = -3$, $y = 2$ is also a solution.

In Examples 4.12 and 4.13, we guessed some solutions to the equation, by finding solutions by trial and error is more difficult with larger integers. However, the question of which equations of this type have integer solutions and how to find them is related to the Euclidean Algorithm. By using the Euclidean Algorithm backwards, we can find integer values for x and y that solve the equation $ax + by = \gcd(a, b)$. Since the Euclidean algorithm can always be used to find the greatest common divisor of a and b for any integers a and b, this also means that the equation $ax + by = \gcd(a, b)$ always has at least one integer solution. This method of using the Euclidean Algorithm backwards is demonstrated in the next example.

Example 4.14. Find an integer solution to the equation $345x + 285y = \gcd(345, 285)$.

Solution:

First, use the Euclidean Algorithm to find $\gcd(345, 285)$.

$$345 = 1(285) + 60$$
$$285 = 4(60) + 45$$
$$60 = 1(45) + 15$$
$$45 = 3(15) + 0$$

Therefore, $\gcd(345, 285) = 15$. The first step in working backwards through the Euclidean Algorithm is to solve each step with a non-zero remainder for its remainder. These steps are shown below, with the original Euclidean Algorithm on the left, and the equation solved for its remainder on the right.

Euclidean Algorithm Steps	**Work backwards to solve for the remainder**
$345 = 1(285) + 60$	$15 = 60 - 1(45)$
$285 = 4(60) + 45$	$45 = 285 - 4(60)$
$60 = 1(45) + 15$	$60 = 345 - 1(285)$
$45 = 3(15) + 0$	

Step 1. Notice that the first line in the "Work backwards to solve for the remainder" has the greatest common divisor on the left side. Starting at this point, substitute for the "45" using the next equation.

$$15 = 60 - 1(45) = 60 - 1(285 - 4(60))$$

Combining similar terms, $15 = 5(60) - 285$

Step 2. Move down one equation, and use it to substitute for the remainder from the previous line (in this case, 60).

$$15 = 5(345 - 1(285)) - 285$$

Combining similar terms, $15 = 5(345) - 6(285)$

Step 3. We now have the gcd written in terms of the original two values $15 = 5(345) - 6(285)$

Step 4. The original equation to solve is $345x + 285y = 15$, so a solution is $x = 5$, $y = -6$.

Example 4.15. Find an integer solution to the equation $1236x + 240y = \gcd(1236, 240)$.

Solution:

First, work through the Euclidean Algorithm to find $\gcd(1236, 240)$. These steps are shown below.

Euclidean Algorithm Steps

$$1236 = 5(240) + 36$$
$$240 = 6(36) + 24$$
$$36 = 1(24) + 12$$
$$24 = 2(12) + 0$$

The goal is to have the greatest common divisor (in this example, 12) in terms of 1236 and 240. To do this, substitute going from the bottom line on the right to the top line.

Step 1. $12 = 36 - 1(24)$

Step 2. Substitute using the next equation up, solved for the remainder:

$$24 = 240 - 6(36)$$
$$12 = 36 - 1(240 - 6(36))$$

Step 3. Combine similar terms

$$12 = 36 - 1(240) + 6(36)$$
$$12 = 7(36) - 1(240)$$

Step 4. Substitute using the next equation up, solved for the remainder:

$$36 = 1236 - 5(240)$$
$$12 = 7(1236 - 5(240)) - 1(240)$$

Step 5. Again, combine similar terms

$$12 = 7(1236) - 36(240)$$

The problem was: Find values of x and y so that $1236x + 240y = 12$.
Comparing this equation with the result in Step 5 shows that $x = 7$ and $y = -36$ is a solution.

The algorithm or steps used in this example to express $\gcd(a, b)$ as a linear combination of a and b will work for any problem, and are summarized here.

Expressing the gcd in terms of a and b

Step 1 Solve for the gcd using the Euclidean Algorithm.

Step 2 Begin with the last non-zero remainder and substitute the expression from the previous line for the remainder from the previous line.

Step 3 Combine like terms.

Step 4 Replace the next remainder above the current one.

Step 5 Combine like terms.

Repeat until all the equations have been used, and the greatest common divisor is expressed in terms of the original a and b.

Example 4.16. Find integer values of x and y so that $1457x + 1891y = \gcd(1457, 1891)$.

Solution:

To answer this question, first use the Euclidean Algorithm to find $\gcd(1457, 1891)$, and then work backwards to find values for x and y that solve the equation.

The Euclidean Algorithm and each step solved for its remainder are shown below.

Euclidean Algorithm Steps	Steps Solved for the Remainder
$1891 = 1(1457) + 434$	$31 = 155 - 1(124)$
$1457 = 3(434) + 155$	$124 = 434 - 2(155)$
$434 = 2(155) + 124$	$155 = 1457 - 3(434)$
$155 = 1(124) + 31$	$434 = 1891 - 1(1457)$
$124 = 4(31) + 0$	

Starting with the equation solved for 31, the greatest common divisor, work our way up substituting and then simplifying, until all the equations have been used and we have an expression for 31 in terms of 1457 and 1891.

$$
\begin{aligned}
31 &= 155 - 1(124) \\
&= 155 - 1\big(434 - 2(155)\big) \\
&= 3(155) - 1(434)
\end{aligned}
$$

$$= 155 - 1\left(434 - 2\left(155\right)\right)$$
$$= 3\left(155\right) - 1\left(434\right)$$
$$= 3\left(1457 - 3\left(434\right)\right) - 1\left(434\right)$$
$$= 3\left(1457\right) - 10\left(434\right)$$
$$= 3\left(1457\right) - 10\left(1891 - 1\left(1457\right)\right)$$
$$= 13\left(1457\right) - 10\left(1891\right)$$

This shows that a solution to the equation $1457x + 1891y = 31$ is $x = 13$, $y = -10$. Remember that you can always check the solution by substituting these values for x and y into the original equation.

The fact that the greatest common divisor of a and b can always be written as a linear combination of a and b is used to prove the next result, called Euclid's Lemma. This highlights an interesting divisibility property of prime numbers. This result was originally proved by Euclid in book VII of *Euclid's Elements*.

Theorem 4.2 (Euclid's Lemma) Suppose p is prime, and a, $b \in \mathbb{Z}$. If $p \mid ab$, then $p \mid a$ or $p \mid b$.

Proof. Let p be prime and suppose $p \mid ab$, and $p \nmid a$. Then, in order to show that the original statement is true, we must show that $p \mid b$. (Why?). Now, since $p \nmid a$ and p is prime, the only divisor a and p can have in common is 1. Therefore, a and p are relatively prime, $\gcd(a, p) = 1$. So, there is a pair of values $r, s \in \mathbb{Z}$ such that $ra + sp = 1$. Multiplying both sides of this equation by b gives $rab + spb = b$. Now, since $p \mid ab$, there is an $m \in \mathbb{Z}$ such that $pm = ab$. Replacing ab in the equation above yields $rpm + spb = b$, or $p(rm + sb) = b$. Since $rm + sb \in \mathbb{Z}$, we have that $p \mid b$.

■

Remark: This theorem is not true if p were composite instead of prime. To find a counterexample, find three integers a, b, and c such that $a \mid bc$, but $a \nmid b$ and $a \nmid c$.

Exercise Set 4.3

Exercises 1–12: In Exercises 1–12 of Section 4.2 you found the greatest common divisor of each pair of integers below. Now, use the Euclidean Algorithm backwards to express the greatest common divisor of the two integers as a linear combination of the two integers.

1. (693, 231)
2. (294, 588)
3. (1045, 1265)
4. (693, 165)
5. (2145, 345)
6. (266, 644)

7. (595, 1463)
8. (2059, 581)
9. (8898, 72720)
10. (12, 1812705)
11. (543, 123456)
12. (963, 657)

13. The greatest common divisor of 256 and 140 was found using the Euclidean Algorithm, and the steps are shown below. Use the Euclidean Algorithm backwards to find a solution of the equation $256x + 140y = 4$.

$$256 = 1(140) + 116$$
$$140 = 1(116) + 24$$
$$116 = 4(24) + 20$$
$$24 = 1(20) + 4$$
$$20 = 5(4) + 0$$

14. The greatest common divisor of 1234 and 24 was found using the Euclidean Algorithm, and the steps are shown below. Use the Euclidean Algorithm backwards to find a solution of the equation $1234x + 24y = 2$.

$$1234 = 51(24) + 10$$
$$24 = 2(10) + 4$$
$$10 = 2(4) + 2$$
$$4 = 2(2) + 0$$

15. Find a solution to the equation $156x + 40y = \gcd(156, 40)$.

16. Find a solution to the equation $8x + 120y = \gcd(8, 120)$.

17. The following statement is FALSE. Find a counterexample and explain your example.

$$\text{If } a \mid bc, \text{ then } a \mid b \text{ or } a \mid c.$$

18. Find a counterexample to the following statement and explain your example.

$$\text{If } a \mid c \text{ and } b \mid c \text{ then } ab \mid c.$$

19. In this problem, we will look at a more general version of Theorem 4.3.

    a) Prove: If p is prime and $p \mid abc$, then $p \mid a$ or $p \mid b$ or $p \mid c$. (Hint: you can write abc as $(ab)c$, a product of two numbers instead of three.)

    b) Prove: If p is prime and $p \mid abcd$, then either $p \mid a$ or $p \mid b$ or $p \mid c$ or $p \mid d$.

    c) Theorem 4.3 can be re-written with a prime p dividing the product of any number of integers. The result is still that the prime p must divide one term from the product. This general statement is given below. If $n = 2$ below, you will get Theorem 4.3 given in the section. Explain how you can generalize the technique from parts a) and b) to prove the statement below.

20. Prove: If $\gcd(a, b) = 1$, then there exist integers r and s such that $ra + sb = 1$.

21. Prove: Every integer can be expressed as a linear combination of 7 and 7.

22. Prove: If $\gcd(a, b) = 1$ and $a \mid bc$, then $a \mid c$. (Hint: Since $\gcd(a, b) = 1$, there is a solution to the equation $ax + by = 1$. This means that there are integers m and n such that $am + bn = 1$).

23. Prove: If $\gcd(a, b) = 1$, $a \mid c$ and $b \mid c$, then $ab \mid c$.

General form of Theorem 4.2 (Euclid's Lemma) If p is prime and $p \mid a_1 \cdot a_2 \cdot \ldots \cdot a_n$, then $p \mid a_i$ for a value of i with $1 \leq i \leq n$.

Section 4.4   More about Solutions to $ax + by = \gcd(a, b)$

In Section 4.3, the Euclidean Algorithm proved that the greatest common divisor of a and b can be written as a linear combination of a and b. Another way to phrase this is:

There is always an integer solution to the equation $ax + by = \gcd(a, b)$.

The steps of the Euclidean Algorithm backwards produce exactly one solution to this type of equation. However, in Example 4.13, two solutions to this type of linear equation were found by trial and error. In this section we will look for a systematic method of finding all integer solutions to linear equations of this type.

Example 4.17. We begin with an example of a simple equation. Find solution of

$$3x + 4y = \gcd(3, 4), \text{ or } 3x + 4y = 1.$$

Solution:

By testing values for x and y, one solution is $x = -1$, $y = 1$. Now, the graph of the equation $3x + 4y = 1$ is made up of all the points that are solutions to the equation, so $(-1, 1)$ is a point on the graph. Also, remember that the graph of $3x + 4y = 1$ is a straight line.

Solving $3x + 4y = 1$ for y shows that the slope-intercept form of the line is $y = \dfrac{-3}{4}x + \dfrac{1}{4}$, so the slope of this line is $\dfrac{-3}{4}$. The slope of a line represents the *rise* over the *run*. Once you know one point on the line, the slope provides instructions to get to another point on the line. Remember that the *rise* is measured in the vertical (y) direction, so the rise indicates how far up or down to move from one point get to another point on the line. The run is measured in the horizontal (x) direction, so the *run* indicates how far to move to right or left to get to another point on the line.

In this example, since the rise is -3 and the run is 4, starting at a point on the line, moving down 3 units and to the right 4 units, will take us to another point on the line. This is true for any point on the line, but if we start at a point with integer coordinates, we will reach another point with integer coordinates. Since $(-1, 1)$ is an integer solution to the equation, we can find another integer solution by moving down 3 units in the vertical direction and 4 units to the right in the horizontal direction. This takes us to the point $((3, -2)$, so $x = 3$, $y = -2$ is another integer solution to $3x + 4y = 1$. Repeating this procedure produces the point $(7, -5)$, so $x = 7$, $y = -5$ is yet another integer solution to the equation. This process of using the slope to move from one point on the line to the next is illustrated on the graph in Figure 4.1.

Repeating this process produces more integer solutions to the equation $3x + 4y = 1$. In fact, using this method we can write general formulas for integer solutions. Starting at the first integer solution we found, $\left(-1, 1\right)$, repeatedly moving down three units and then to the right 4 units will produce another point on the line. Therefore, points with coordinates

$$x = -1 + 4n, \text{ for } n \in \mathbb{Z}$$
$$y = 1 - 3n, \text{ for } n \in \mathbb{Z}$$

are on the line and are therefore also integer solutions to $3x + 4y = 1$.

In general, when solving an equation of the form $ax + by = \gcd(a, b)$, the Euclidean Algorithm can always be used to find one solution. Solving the equation for y shows that $y = \dfrac{-a}{b}x + \dfrac{\gcd(a, b)}{b}$. Therefore, the slope is $\dfrac{-a}{b}$. The theorem below shows a general formula for solutions to $ax + by = \gcd(a, b)$.

> **Theorem 4.3** Let $ax + by = \gcd(a, b)$. If $x = x_0$, $y = y_0$ is one solution to this equation, then $x = x_0 + bn$, $y = y_0 - an$ is also a solution, for any integer n.

Proof.

Let $x = x_0$, $y = y_0$ be a solution of the equation $ax + by = \gcd(a, b)$. Then $ax_0 + by_0 = \gcd(a, b)$. Now, to show that the new values for x and y given in Theorem 4.4 also form a solution to this equation, show that when these values are substituted into $ax + by$, the result is equal to $\gcd(a, b)$.

Substituting and simplifying,

$$a(x_0 + bn) + b(y_0 - an) = ax_0 + abn + by_0 - abn$$
$$= ax_0 + by_0$$
$$= \gcd(a, b),$$

since (x_0, y_0) is a solution to the equation. Therefore, the new pair of values for x and y also gives a solution to the equation.

■

Theorem 4.4 provides the formulas to generate all solutions to equations of the form $ax + by = \gcd(a, b)$.

> **Theorem 4.4** Suppose that $x = x_0$, $y = y_0$ is a solution of the equation $ax + by = \gcd(a, b)$. Then, if $d = \gcd(a, b)$, all solutions have the form
>
> $$x = x_0 + \frac{b}{d}n, \quad y = y_0 - \frac{a}{d}n,$$
>
> where n is an integer.

Remark: The formulas in Theorem 4.4 produce infinitely many integer solutions to $ax + by = \gcd(a, b)$, ,but they do not always produce all possible solutions. For example, $x = 2$, $y = -1$ is a solution to the equation $9x + 15y = 3$ from Example 4.13, since $9(2) + 15(-1) = 3$, but there is no integer value of n that will produce this solution using the equations from Theorem 4.4. (Use the equations in Example 4.13 for x and y to convince yourself this is true.)

We can show that if x and y have the form specified in this theorem, they form a solution of the equation $ax + by = \gcd(a, b)$. The proof that all solutions have this form is beyond the scope of this course and is not included.

Partial Proof of Theorem 4.4.

Let $x = x_0$, $y = y_0$ be a solution to the equation $ax + by = \gcd(a, b)$, and let $\gcd(a, b) = d$. Then $ax_0 + by_0 = d$. Now, to show the x and y given in the theorem form a solution, substitute into the equation and simplify to verify that the result is $d = \gcd(a, b)$.

$$ax + by = a\left(x_0 + \frac{b}{d}n\right) + b\left(y_0 - \frac{a}{d}n\right)$$

$$= ax_0 + \frac{ab}{d}n + by_0 - \frac{ab}{d}n$$

$$= ax_0 + by_0$$

$$= d$$

since (x_0, y_0) was a solution to the equation. Therefore, the equations given for x and y in the theorem provide a solution to $ax + by = \gcd(a, b)$.

■

Example 4.18. One solution to the equation $9x + 15y = 3$ is $x = -3$, $y = 2$. Find four more solutions.

Solution:

According to Theorem 4.4, we can find more solutions using the formulas $x = -3 + 15n$, $y = 2 - 9n$.

Notice that if $n = 0$, $x = -3$ and $y = 2$, and this is the solution we started with. Table 4.3 shows some solutions for different values of n. Remember you can always check a solution by substituting the values of x and y back into the equation.

n	$x = -3 + 15n$	$y = 2 - 9n$
-2	-33	20
-1	-18	11
1	12	-7
2	27	-16

Table 4.3

Example 4.19. Find all solutions to the equation $12x + 20y = 4$ from Example 4.9.

Solution:

From Example 4.13, one of the solutions to this equation is $x = 2$, $y = -1$. By Theorem 4.5, since $\gcd(12, 20) = 4$, all solutions will have the form:

$$x = 2 + \frac{20}{4}n = 2 + 5n,$$

$$y = -1 - \frac{12}{4}n = -1 - 3n,$$

where n is any integer. Notice that $n = -1$, gives the solution $x = -3$, $y = 2$ which is the second solution found in Example 4.13.

Exercise Set 4.4

1. When do the equations for x and y in **Theorem 4.4** produce all possible solutions to the linear equation $ax + by = \gcd(a, b)$? (Hint: Use **Theorem 4.5**.)

Exercises 2–13: Use the Euclidean Algorithm to find one solution to each of the equations below.

2. $416x + 614y = \gcd(416, 614)$

3. $12x + 510y = \gcd(12, 510)$

4. $45x + 46y = \gcd(45, 46)$

5. $14x - 42y = \gcd(14, 42)$

6. $147x + 258y = \gcd(147, 258)$

7. $10x + 17y = \gcd(10, 17)$

8. $99x - 49y = \gcd(99, 49)$

9. $14x + 42y = \gcd(14, 42)$

10. $16x + 31y = \gcd(16, 31)$

11. $41x + 19y = 131$

12. $21x + 18y = 300$

13. $123x + 57y = 393$

Exercises 14–25: Find all solutions to the equation from Exercises 2–13.

26. How many positive integer pairs satisfy the equation $20x + 14y = 2014$?

Section 4.5   What if $ax + by \neq \gcd(a, b)$?

A natural question to ask now is what happens if $ax + by = c$ where c can be any integer? If c happens to be equal to $\gcd(a, b)$, then the question is already answered: There are infinitely many solutions, and after finding one solution, there are formulas to find them all. But what if $c \neq \gcd(a, b)$? Some questions that come up are:

1. Will there still always be integer solutions to the equation?

2. If there are any integer solutions, will there be infinitely many?

3. If there are integer solutions, are there formulas to find all of them?

Note that the equation $ax + by = c$ will always have infinitely many *real number* solutions, since the coordinates of each point on the graph form a solution to the equation. We are interested in **integer** solutions in particular. One way to rephrase the first question stated above is: "Must every line contain at least one point with integer coordinates?" In terms of the graph, the second question can then be stated as: "If the line does contain a point with integer coordinates, will there be infinitely many such points?"

So, consider the equation $ax + by = c$ and let $d = \gcd(a, b)$. Then by Theorem 1.2, since $d \mid a$ and $d \mid b$, $d \mid (ax + by)$. Therefore, if the equation has an integer solutions then $d \mid c$ as well. Forming the contrapositive of this statement gives us an answer to the first question: if $d \nmid c$, then the equation $ax + by = c$ cannot have any integer solutions.

Example 4.20. Explain why the equation $2x + 4y = 3$ cannot have any integer solutions.

Solution:

Since $\gcd(2,4) = 2$, the left-hand-side can be written as $2(x+2y)$. If x and y are integers, this represents an even integer. Since 3 is an odd integer, there are no integer solutions.

However, this equation does have (non-integer) solutions. Since every point on the line represents a solution, the values $x = \dfrac{1}{2}$, $y = \dfrac{1}{2}$ as well as $x = 1$, $y = \dfrac{1}{4}$ represent examples of non-integer solutions to the equation.

Theorem 4.5 formally states the explanation above.

> **Theorem 4.5** Let $d = \gcd(a, b)$. If $d \nmid c$, then there is no integer solution to $ax = by = c$.

The proof of this Theorem is left as Exercise 35.

Now, suppose that $d = \gcd(a, b)$, and d divides c. Does $ax + by = c$ have solutions in this case?

If $d \mid c$, then by the definition of divides, $c = dk$ for an integer k. Therefore, we can write the equation as $ax + by = dk$.

From Section 4.3, a solution to $ax + by = d$ can be found using the Euclidean Algorithm backwards. Let $x = x_0$, $y = y_0$ be the solution found with this method. Then,

$$ax_0 + by_0 = d.$$

Multiplying both sides of this equation by k:

$$k(ax_0 + by_0) = kd$$
$$a(kx_0) + b(ky_0) = c.$$

This shows that $x = kx_0$, $y = ky_0$ is an integer solution to $ax + by = c$ in this case. This result is summarized in Theorem 4.6.

> **Theorem 4.6** Consider the equation $ax + by = c$. Let $d = \gcd(a, b)$. If $d \mid c$ then this equation has at least one integer solution. If (x_0, y_0) is a solution to $ax + by = \gcd(a, b)$ and $c = dk$, then a solution is given by $x = kx_0$, $y = ky_0$.

The proof of this theorem is left as Exercise 36.

Example 4.21. Find an integer solution to the equation $345x + 285y = 60$.

Solution:

In Example 4.10, we found that $x = 5$, $y = -6$ is a solution to the equation $345x + 285y = 15$ where $15 = \gcd(345, 285)$. Since $60 = 4 \cdot 15$, then $x = 4 \cdot 5$, $y = 4 \cdot -6$, or $x = 20$, $y = -24$ is a solution to $345x + 285y = 60$.

Now we will consider the remaining questions: (1) if there is one integer solution, are there infinitely many, and (2) is there a formula to find them?

Theorem 4.7 $ax + bc = c$ has integer solutions when $d = \gcd(a, b)$ and $d \mid c$, then $ax + by = c$ has at least one integer solution.

Proof.

Suppose that $d \mid c$ so that there is at least one integer solution to $ax + by = c$. If one solution is $x = x_0$, $y = y_0$, then the same technique used in Section 4.4 will work to find more. Solving $ax + by = c$ for y, we see that $y = \frac{-a}{b}x + \frac{c}{b}$, so the slope is $\frac{-a}{b}$. Notice that changing the right side of the equation did not affect the slope. Therefore, just as before, $x = x_0 + bn$ and $y = y_0 - an$ will be a solution to the equation for any integer n.

∎

The next Theorem shows the most general form that gives all integer solutions to $ax + by = c$.

Theorem 4.8 Let $ax + by = c$, where $d = \gcd(a, b)$ and $d \mid c$. Then if $x = x_0$, $y = y_0$ is one solution of this equation, all solutions have the form $x = x_0 + \frac{b}{d}n$, $y = y_0 - \frac{a}{d}n$, where n is an integer.

Exercise 37 Prove that if x and y have this form then they will be a solution to the equation $ax + by = c$.

Example 4.22. Find all integer solutions to the equation $345x + 285y = 60$.

Solution:

In Example 4.14, we found that one solution to this equation is $x = 20$, $y = -24$. Using the formulas in Theorem 4.8, all solutions are

$$x = 20 + \frac{285}{15}n = 20 + 19n,$$

$$y = -24 - \frac{345}{15}n = -24 - 23n,$$

where any integer can be substituted for n. So, for example, if $n = 2$, we obtain the solution $x = 20 + 19(2) = 58$ and $y = -24 - 23(2) = -70$.

Remark: There are other linear equations in two variables that do not quite fit the pattern described so far in this chapter, but the ideas that we have developed up to this point are very useful. The next example shows how these ideas can be used in other situations, similar to the cicada problem in Chapter 0. These equations are of the type $ax - by = 0$, or $ax = by$.

Remark: There are other linear equations in two variables that do not quite fit the pattern described in this chapter, but the ideas that we have developed up to this point are very useful. The next example shows how these ideas can be used in other situations, similar to the cicada problem in Chapter 0. These equations are of the type $ax - by = 0$, or $ax = by$.

Example 4.23. Ethan and Gavin are brothers who both play baseball. Ethan is three years older than Gavin, hence his gait is longer and he takes fewer steps to run the bases. Ethan can run the bases in 37 steps, while Gavin takes 45 steps to run the bases. If they both leave the home plate at the same time, how many steps will each of them take before they are back at the home plate at the same time?

Solution:

Let x represent the number of times Ethan touches the home plate, and y represents the number of times Gavin touches the home plate until they are there at the same time. Then, $37x = 45y$ when they are both at the home plate. Since $\gcd(37, 45) = 1$, for this equation to be true $x = 45$, $y = 37$. This solution says that Ethan will run the bases 45 times and Gavin will run the bases 37 times when they both arrive at the home plate at the same time.

Exercise Set 4.5

Exercises 1–8: Determine if the linear equation in two variables has an integer solution. Explain your answer.

1. $15x + 21y = 3$
2. $4x + 6y = 35$
3. $28x - 21y = 100$
4. $12x + 18y = 50$

5. $315x + 513y = 6$
6. $235x + 5665y = 5$
7. $40x + 63y = 521$
8. $147x + 258y = 369$

Exercises 9–16: Find an integer solution of the equation.

9. $154x + 91y = 42$
10. $8x + 23y = 4$
11. $97x + 98y = 13$
12. $12x + 18y = 48$

13. $4x + 6y = 72$
14. $9x - 5y = 2$
15. $15x - 21y = 12$
16. $15x + 91y = 42$

Exercises 17–24: Find all integer solutions to the equation in Exercises 9–16.

25. Find all solutions to the linear equation $8x + 64y = 16$. Is there a shortcut for finding the first solution?

26. Find all solutions to the linear equation $9x + 54y = 27$. Is there a shortcut for finding the first solution?

27. Given the equation $ax + 12y = 21$.

    a) Find a value for a so that this equation will have no solutions. Explain your choice.
    b) Find a value for a so that this equation will have a solution. Explain your choice.

28. What conditions on a and b will guarantee that the equation $ax + by = c$ has a solution for any value of c?

29. Form the equation $ax + by = c$ with the values given below, and then find a value for the missing number so that the equation will have a solution. Explain your choice.

    a) $a = 4, \ b = ?, \ c = -37$
    b) $a = ?, \ b = -9, \ c = 54$
    c) $a = -16, \ b = 48, \ c = ?$

30. Find a value for c so that the equation $ax + 8y = c$ will have integer solutions for any value of a.

31. Find a value for c so that the equation $6x + by = c$ will have integer solutions for any value of b.

32. The following statement is FALSE. Find a counterexample to the statement and explain the example: If $3|a$, $3|b$, and $3|c$ then the equation $ax + by = c$ has an integer solution.

33. You bought a new 49-gallon aquarium and some exotic fish to go with it. On your way up to the counter, the saleswoman mentions that your fish cannot survive in regular tap water, and you need to fill the tank with special fish-tropic Artesian water, sold in 5-gallon and 8-gallon containers. How many containers of each size do you need to fill the tank exactly?

34. Due to various postage increases, you have a small collection of 6 cent and 15 cent stamps. If you have a letter to mail that costs 85 cents, is it possible to use your stamps to get the exact postage?

35. Prove **Theorem 4.5**. (Hint: try a proof by contradiction).

36. Prove that if x and y are as specified in **Theorem 4.6**, they are a solution of the equation $ax + by = c$.

37. Prove that if x and y are as specified in **Theorem 4.8**, they form a solution of the equation $ax + by = c$.

38. Prove that the integer $+6$ cannot be written as a linear combination of the integers 4 and 12. (Hint: A linear combination of 4 and 12 has the form $4x + 12y$ where x and y are integers.

Section 4.6   Return to Primitive Pythagorean Triples (Optional)

In this section, the details of the proof of the claims about the primitive Pythagorean triple formulas that were made in Section 2.2 are given. For reference, the formulas are included below.

Formulas for primitive Pythagorean triples

Choose integers s and t using the following rules:

   i. s and t are odd,

   ii. $s > t \geq 1$, and

   iii. $\gcd(s, t) = 1$ (in other words, s and t have NO common divisors other than 1, so they are relatively prime)

Then, if

$$a = st, \qquad b = \frac{s^2 - t^2}{2}, \qquad c = \frac{s^2 + t^2}{2}$$

$a - b - c$ is a primitive Pythagorean triple.

In Section 2.2, it was verified that these formulas produce Pythagorean triples, and in Section 2.3 the proof that the formulas produce all primitive Pythagorean triples was outlined.

The first result we must now prove is Theorem 2.4, restated below.

Theorem 4.9 If integers s and t are selected such that $s > t$, s and t are odd, and $\gcd(s, t) = 1$, and if $a = st$, $b = \dfrac{s^2 - t^2}{2}$, and $c = \dfrac{s^2 + t^2}{2}$ then the integers a, b, and c are a primitive Pythagorean triple.

Proof. (by contradiction)

Since we showed in Theorem 2.3 that a, b, and c computed as above to form a Pythagorean triple, it remains to show that $\gcd(a, b, c) = 1$. Suppose instead that $\gcd(a, b, c) = d$ where $d > 1$. Now $d \mid a$, $d \mid b$, and $d \mid c$, so it is also true that $d \mid (b+c)$ and $d \mid (b-c)$.

Since $b + c = \dfrac{s^2 - t^2}{2} + \dfrac{s^2 + t^2}{2} = \dfrac{2s^2}{2} = s^2$, it must be true that $d \mid s^2$.

Since $b - c = \dfrac{s^2 - t^2}{2} - \dfrac{s^2 + t^2}{2} = \dfrac{-2t^2}{2} = -t^2$, it must be true that $d \mid -t^2$, and therefore also $d \mid t^2$.

By Theorem 3.3, since $\gcd(s, t) = 1$, $\gcd(s^2, t^2) = 1$ as well. This means that $d = 1$, which is a contradiction. Therefore, it must be true that $\gcd(a, b, c) = 1$.

∎

Now we are ready to prove the second claim: if we start with a PPT $a - b - c$, then there are integers s and t, $s > t$, with s and t both odd and $\gcd(s, t) = 1$ such that $a = st$, $b = \dfrac{s^2 - t^2}{2}$, and $c = \dfrac{s^2 + t^2}{2}$.

Two properties of primitive Pythagorean triples will be proved. The first Lemma is **Conjecture 2.3** from Section 2.2, and the second Lemma is a proof of part of **Conjecture 2.4**.

Lemma 4.3 If $a-b-c$ is a primitive Pythagorean triple, then the greatest common divisor of any two of these integers is 1.

Proof (by contradiction):
There are two possible ways to contradict this statement. Either:

1. the two legs of the Pythagorean triangle share a common divisor larger than 1, or
2. one of the legs and the hypotenuse of the Pythagorean triangle share a common divisor larger than 1.

To complete the proof, we will show that both of these assumptions lead to a contradiction of the premise that we began with a **primitive** Pythagorean triple.

(1) Suppose there is a integer $d>1$ that divides a and b, the two legs of the Pythagorean triangle. Then, $a=de$ and $b=df$ for integers e and f. Substituting in the Pythagorean Theorem,

$$c^2 = a^2 + b^2 = (de)^2 + (df)^2 = d^2e^2 + d^2f^2 = d^2(e^2 + f^2)$$

This equation shows that d^2 divides c^2, or $d^2 \mid c^2$. Therefore, by Theorem 3.3, $d \mid c$.

Hence all three sides share a factor of d. Since $d>1$, this contradicts the fact that $a-b-c$ forms a primitive Pythagorean triple.

(2) Now suppose there is a integer $d>1$ such that $d \mid a$, , one of the legs, and $d \mid c$, the hypotenuse.

Then for integers k and m, $a=kd$ and $c=dm$. Substituting into the Pythagorean Theorem,

$$c^2 = a^2 + b^2$$
$$(dm)^2 = (kd)^2 + b^2$$
$$d^2m^2 = k^2d^2 + b^2$$
$$b^2 = k^2d^2 - d^2m^2$$
$$b^2 = d^2(k^2 - m^2).$$

Therefore, $d^2 \mid b^2$. Again, by Theorem 3.3, $d \mid b$. This means that d is a common factor of a, b, and c, which contradicts the fact that $a-b-c$ forms a primitive Pythagorean triple since $d>1$.

■

Then, by Exercise 35 of Section 2.1, since $\gcd(a, b)=1$ and $\gcd(b, c)=1$, it is true that $\gcd(a, b, c)=1$.

Lemma 4.4 If $a-b-c$ is a primitive Pythagorean triple, then $(c+b)$ and $(c-b)$ are relatively prime.

Proof.

Let $a-b-c$ be a PPT. To show that $(c+b)$ and $(c-b)$ are relatively prime, we must show that their greatest common divisor is 1. Suppose that d is a common divisor, so $d\,|\,(c+b)$ and $d\,|\,(c-b)$. Then there exist integers x and y such that $dx=(c+b)$ and $dy=(c-b)$.

Adding these two equations, we obtain:

$$dx+dy=(c+b)+(c-b)$$
$$d(x+y)=2c$$

Since $x+y\in\mathbb{Z}$ this means that $d\,|\,2c$.

Subtracting these two equations we obtain:

$$dx-dy=(c+b)-(c-b)$$
$$d(x-y)=2b$$

Since $x+y\in\mathbb{Z}$ this means that $d\,|\,2b$.

Now, since $(c+b)$ and $(c-b)$ are both odd by Lemma 2.3, $d\neq2$. Therefore $d\,|\,b$ and $d\,|\,c$. By Lemma 2.1, $\gcd(b,c)=1$ so d must be 1, and therefore $(c+b)$ and $(c-b)$ are relatively prime.

∎

> **Lemma 4.5** If $a-b-c$ is a primitive Pythagorean triple, then $(c+b)$ and $(c-b)$ are both perfect squares.

Proof:

There are two cases to consider: $(c-b)=1$ or $(c-b)\geq2$. (Why?)

Case 1: $(c-b)=1$. Then $a^2=c+b$, so $c+b$ is a perfect square.

Case 2: $(c-b)\geq2$. Factor both $(c-b)$ and $(c+b)$ as much as possible. No factor in the list of $(c-b)$ is also in the list of $(c+b)$ by Lemma 4.2. But since a^2 has two copies of each factor ($a^2=s^2t^2$) we must have the list of factors in $(c-b)$ consist of all squares, and the list of factors in $(c+b)$ must all appear twice. Hence both are perfect squares.

Let $s^2=c+b$ and $t^2=c-b$. We can find b and c in terms of s and t as follows.

$s^2+t^2=2c$ and $s^2-t^2=2b$

which gives us

$c = (s^2 + t^2)/2$ and $b = (s^2 - t^2)/2$

Using these values for b and c, $a^2 = s^2 t^2$, so $a = st$.

■

By summarizing the above results, we have arrived at the following theorem.

> **Theorem 4.10** If $a - b - c$ be a PPT, then there exist integers $s > t \geq 1$ with s and t odd and $\gcd(s, t) = 1$ such that $a = st$, $\quad b = \dfrac{s^2 - t^2}{2}$, $\quad c = \dfrac{s^2 + t^2}{2}$

Proof:

Let $a - b - c$ be a PPT. Then $a^2 + b^2 = c^2$, and $a^2 = c^2 - b^2 = (c + b)(c - b)$.

By Lemma 2.3, $(c + b)$ and $(c - b)$ are both odd.

By Lemma 2.4, $(c + b)$ and $(c - b)$ are relatively prime.

By Lemma 2.5, $(c + b)$ and $(c - b)$ are both squares.

Therefore, we can write $(c + b) = s^2$ and $(c - b) = t^2$, for integers s and t. Since $(c + b)$ and $(c - b)$ are both odd, s^2 and t^2 must be odd, which means s and t are each odd.

Also, since $(c + b)$ and $(c - b)$ are relatively prime, s^2 and t^2 are relatively prime. By a Theorem in Chapter 3, this means that s and t are also relatively prime, so $\gcd(s, t) = 1$.

Since $a^2 = (c + b)(c - b) = s^2 t^2$, we have that $a = st$.

Now, we can write b and c in terms of s and t as follows:

$$s^2 + t^2 = (c + b) + (c - b) = 2c$$
$$s^2 - t^2 = (c + b) - (c - b) = 2b$$

Solving the first equation for c yields $c = \dfrac{s^2 + t^2}{2}$.

Solving the second equation for b yields $b = \dfrac{s^2 - t^2}{2}$.

Therefore, the PPT $a - b - c$ can be expressed in terms of s and t satisfying the conditions given in the PPT formulas.

■

Combining Theorems 2.4 and 2.5 we obtain the following result.

Theorem 4.11 The triple of integers a, b, c forms a PPT if and only if $a = st$, $b = \dfrac{s^2 - t^2}{2}$, and $c = \dfrac{s^2 + t^2}{2}$ where s and t are odd integers such that $s > t \geq t$ and $\gcd(s, t) = 1$.

Proof:

The proof of Theorem 2.4 proves the reverse direction of this if and only if statement.

The proof of Theorem 2.5 proves the forward direction of this if and only if statement.

■

Section 4.7   Summary and Review Exercises

Vocabulary and Symbols

Division algorithm

quotient

divisor

remainder

dividend

Euclidean algorithm

linear combination of a and b

Euclid's lemma

Suggested Readings

Bell, Eric Temple, *Men of Mathematics*. New York: Simon and Schuster, 1986.

Guy, Richard K. "Nothing's New in Number Theory?" *The American Mathematical Monthly* 105 (December, 1998): 951–954.

Osen, Lynn M, *Women in Mathematics*. Cambridge: MIT Press, 1975.

Chapter 4 Review Exercises

Exercises 1–6: Find each greatest common divisor using the Euclidean algorithm.

1. $(12098, 78943)$

2. $(235490, 789685)$

3. $(156, 12705)$

4. $(2345, 12346)$

5. $(1050, 12705)$

6. $(165, 12750)$

Exercises 7–13: Find the least common multiple of each pair in #1–6.

7. Is it possible to have the greatest common divisor of two integers as zero? Explain.

8. Find the least common multiple of each pair of integers.

   a) 22 and 33

   b) 127 and 81

   c) 12750 and 165

9. Consider the equation $ax + 15y = 18$. Find a value for a so that the equation has no solutions and a value for a so that the equation does have solutions.

10. Determine whether each equation below has solutions. If so, find the general form of the solution. If not, explain why not.

    a) $16x + 31y = 1$

    b) $25x + 15y = 9$

    c) $22x + 33y = 44$

11. In how many ways can change be made for one dollar using only dimes and quarters?

12. Below is an example of the Euclidean algorithm to find the gcd of 92 and 49. Use this result to work backwards and find the values of x and y so that $92x + 49y = 1$.

$$92 = 49(1) + 43$$
$$49 = 43(1) + 6$$
$$43 = 6(7) + 1$$
$$7 = 7(1) + 0$$

13. In Chapter 2, there is a table of PPTs. We looked for patterns in the integers and made many conjectures. Some of these are actually theorems but we were unable to prove them before getting to this chapter. The following problems refer to primitive Pythagorean triples.

    a) Show that one of integers, a, b, or c is divisible by 3.

    b) Show that b is divisible by 4.

    c) Show that one of a, b or c is divisible by 5.

Section 4.8   Activities

1. Check your calculator or cell phone to see if it can find the greatest common divisor of two integers for you. Note that even if your phone can do this, it may not show the steps.

2. Write an algorithm that describes how to use your calculator to find the remainder in the Division Algorithm.

3. Use any computer algebra system (such as Wolfram Alpha, Maple, or Mathematica) to find the greatest common divisor of a set of four natural numbers.

4. Using the set of numbers from #3, and the greatest common divisor, find the least common multiple of the same natural numbers.

5. Euclid's work is primarily in geometry. Besides Number Theory, in what other areas of mathematics and science did Euclid have an impact?

6. What do you think motivated Euclid to create the Euclidean Algorithm?

Karl Friedrich Gauß.

Karl Friedrich Gauss

(1777–1855)

Karl Friedrich Gauss (1777–1855) is called *The Prince of Mathematics* for his outstanding contributions to many fields of mathematics.

Karl Friedrich Gauss was born in Brunswick, Germany and died in Göttingen, Germany. He was a child prodigy whose talents were recognized very early. Although he came from a poor family, he excelled at everything he studied. From the time he first went to school, his genius was recognized. He was given tutors who contributed to his learning; however, each reached the point where Gauss knew more than they did.

Gauss was given a stipend by the Duke of Brunswick to attend the Collegium Carolinium, a college of science. He began college at age 15 and finished his degree when he was 18 years old. He was fluent in Greek and Latin and published several of his works in these classical languages. After college, he worked on his doctoral degree at the very prestigious University of Göttingen from 1795 to 1798 and received his PhD from the University of Helmstedt.

Gauss joined the faculty at Göttingen as professor of astronomy and director of the observatory. He became a renowned mathematician and physicist. Some say that he is the last person to know all of the mathematics in existence at that time.

He is frequently quoted for saying "Mathematics is the queen of sciences and number theory is the queen of mathematics." Gauss' collective work comprises 12 volumes, but he had made extensive notes on many topics. Gauss knew more than he would say in public, probably because he was aware of the troubles Copernicus had with the Catholic church and other religious groups for his theory that the earth revolved around the sun, not the other way around.

CHAPTER 5

Congruences

"Mathematics is the Queen of the Sciences, and the theory of
numbers is the Queen of Mathematics."

--Carl Friedrich Gauss

Section 5.1   Introduction to Congruence

Classifying integers by their remainders when divided by a certain natural number helps in answering questions similar to these:

1. If it is Monday today, what day of the week will it be 23 days from now?

2. What day of the week is it 49 days from now?

You can answer both these questions without having to count ahead 23 or 49 days. Both have to do with division, and remainders. You know that every seven days, the day of the week repeats, so to figure out the day of the week, we just want to find out how many extra days over a full week there are. In other words, if we are interested in what day of the week it is some number of days from now, we will find the remainder when the number of days that have passed is divided by seven—it doesn't—matter how many full weeks have gone by. So, since $23 = 3(7) + 2$, if today is Monday it will be Wednesday in 23 days. And, since $49 = 7(7) + 0$, in 49 days it will be Monday.

The mathematical study of *congruences* generalizes this idea of paying attention to the remainder when one integer is divided by another integer. For example, since 23 has a remainder of 2 when divided by 7, we say that 23 and 2 are "congruent" with respect to 7. Thirty also has a remainder of 2 when divided by 7, so 30 is congruent to both 23 and 2 with respect 7. In fact, there are many choices: 30, 37, 44, 51, … that all have a remainder of 2 when divided by 7, so they are all "congruent" with respect to 7.

Question: Can you come up with examples of integers that are congruent to 2 when divided by 30?

The theory of congruences was introduced by the German mathematician Carl Friedrich Gauss (1777–1855) and was published when he was 24 years old. Congruences are a generalization of equations, and Gauss chose to use the symbol $\equiv$ in his congruence notation to emphasize this relationship. Gauss's definition:

Definition 5.1 Let $n > 1$ be a natural number. Two integers *a and b are congruent modulo n,* written as $a \equiv b \bmod n$, if and only if n divides $a - b$. We read as "*a* is congruent to *b* mod *n*." If *a* and *b* are not congruent, they are ***incongruent***.

Note: One divides every integer; so, every pair of integers will be congruent mod 1. Since this does not provide any information, 1 is not used as a modulus.

There are a few things to note in this definition:

1. n is a natural number, but a and b can be any integers.
2. The number n is called the **modulus** of the congruence and is abbreviated as **mod**.
3. If n divides $a-b$, then n also divides $b-a$, so one can subtract in either order.

From the example in the first paragraph, we said that 23 and 2 are congruent with respect to 7. We can now write this as $23 \equiv 2 \bmod 7$ and rephrase the sentence as: "23 is congruent to 2 mod 7." Applying the definition, we have $7 \mid (23-2)$, or $7 \mid 21$, which we know is true. Below are a few more examples of using the definition of **congruence**.

Example 5.1. Use the definition of congruence modulo n to determine whether the congruence is true or false.

   a) $10 \equiv 12 \bmod 3$
   b) $-6 \equiv 2 \bmod 4$
   c) $3 \equiv 7 \bmod 2$
   d) $2 \equiv -6 \bmod 4$.

Solution:

   a)   False, because $12-10 = 2$ and $3 \nmid 2$
   b)   True because $-6-2 = -8$ and $4 \mid -8$.
   c)   True because $7-3 = 4$ and $2 \mid 4$.
   d)   True because $2-(-6) = 8$ and $4 \mid 8$.

The only difference between the example in part b) and the one in part d) is that the congruence says that $4 \mid (-6-2)$. In the exercises you are asked to prove that if $a \equiv b \bmod m$, then $b \equiv a \bmod m$.

Example 5.2. Find all positive integers m such that $6 \equiv 12 \bmod m$.

Solution:

First, look at an example of one integer that works for m; for example, if $m = 2$, then $2 \mid (12-6)$. To ensure that we find all of the possibilities, we apply the definition to the congruence:

For the congruence $6 \equiv 12 \bmod m$ to be true, $m \mid (12-6)$, or $m \mid 6$. Therefore, the choices for m are $m = 2, 3$, or 6.

In addition to the definition of congruences, consider these two other useful ways to think of congruences. Begin with the definition, and then rearrange the resulting equation.

$$\text{If } a \equiv b \bmod m, \text{ then } m \mid a-b,$$

Therefore, $mk = a-b$ for some $k \in \mathbb{Z}$, which we can rewrite as $a = b + mk$.

Notice also that if $a = b + mk$, one can also write an equation of the form $b = a + m(-k)$.

These remarks are summarized in Theorem 5.1.

> **Theorem 5.1** Let $a, b, m \in \mathbb{Z}$, with $m > 1$. Then $a \equiv b \bmod m$ if and only if $a = b + mk$ for some $k \in \mathbb{Z}$.

The proof of Theorem 5.1 is mostly contained in the explanation above, but it is also included as an exercise, for practice with "if and only if" proofs.

Example 5.3. Find four numbers that are congruent to 4 modulo 7: two negative integers, and two positive integers.

Solution:

From Theorem 5.1 we know that $a \equiv 4 \bmod 7$ if and only if $a = 4 + 7k$, with $k \in \mathbb{Z}$. Since k can be any integer, we can add or subtract multiples of 7 to get more examples of integers congruent to 4. So, here are a few possibilities:

$$
\begin{aligned}
k &= -1 & a &= 4-7 = -3 \\
k &= -2 & a &= 4-2(7) = -10 \\
k &= 1 & a &= 4+7(1) = 11 \\
k &= 10 & a &= 4+7(10) = 74
\end{aligned}
$$

Therefore, $-3, -10, 11,$ and 74 are all congruent to 4 modulo 7. (If you aren't convinced, you can always check them using the definition).

Think of congruences in terms of remainders. For example, when 18 is divided by 7, the remainder is 4. Using the Division Algorithm, this can be written as $18 = 7(2) + 4$. So, $18 \equiv 4 \bmod 7$ by the definition of congruence. That is, 18 is congruent (modulo 7) to its remainder when divided by 7.

There is nothing special about 18 in this example. Since each integer is congruent to its remainder, if two integers have the same remainder when divided by m, they are congruent modulo m. These two results are listed below, in Theorems 5.2 and 5.3, with some examples of how each can be used.

> **Theorem 5.2** Let $a, m \in \mathbb{Z}$, with $m > 0$. Then, $a \equiv r \bmod m$, where $0 \leq r \leq m-1$, and r is the remainder when a is divided by m.

The general proof of this theorem is left as an exercise.

Theorem 5.2 is very useful, because in a given modulus m, it allows us to only work with integers from 0 to $m-1$. Every integer (positive or negative) is congruent to one of these. The values between 0 and $m-1$ inclusively form a set called the **least residue** that is defined below.

> **Definition 5.2** Let $b \in \mathbb{Z}$. The number r is the **least residue of b mod m** if and only if $0 \leq r \leq m-1$ and $b \equiv r \bmod m$.

Remark: Replacing an integer with its remainder when divided by m is called reducing the integer mod m. Using Theorem 5.1 allows one to add or subtract the modulus, m, until a value from 0 to $m-1$ is reached. Example 5.4 demonstrates how this theorem is used.

Example 5.4. Find the least residue of each integer in the given modulus.

a) 13 mod 12
b) 17 mod 3
c) 13 mod 26
d) 141 mod 6
e) −20 mod 11
f) 459 mod 5

Solution:

a) $13 \equiv 1 \bmod 12$, since both have a remainder of 1 when divided by 12. (Alternatively, since $13 - 12 = 1$, 13 and 1 are congruent modulo 12).
b) $17 \equiv 2 \bmod 3$, since $17 = 5(3) + 2$, so 2 is the remainder when 17 is divided by 3.
c) $13 \equiv 13 \bmod 26$, because 13 is less than 26, so it is already a least residue.
d) $141 \equiv 3 \bmod 6$, since $141 = 23(6) + 3$, so 3 is the remainder when 141 is divided by 6.
e) $-20 \equiv 2 \bmod 11$, since $-20 + 2(11) = 2$.
f) $459 \equiv 4 \bmod 5$, since 4 is the remainder when 459 is divided by 5.

Example 5.5. If a is an odd integer, what are the possible least residues of a modulo 4?

Solution:

First, since every integer must be congruent to its remainder, we know that there are four possibilities for a:

$$a \equiv 0 \bmod 4$$
$$a \equiv 1 \bmod 4$$
$$a \equiv 2 \bmod 4$$
$$a \equiv 3 \bmod 4$$

Rewriting each of these congruences as an equation, we get that either: $a = 0 + 4k$

$$a = 1 + 4k$$
$$a = 2 + 4k$$
$$a = 3 + 4k,$$

with $k \in \mathbb{Z}$ in each case.

Now, since 4 is even, $4k$ is always even. We have shown that the sum of two even numbers is even. Therefore, to make a odd, we get either $a = 1 + 4k$ or $a = 3 + 4k$. This corresponds to $a \equiv 1 \bmod 4$ or $a \equiv 3 \bmod 4$.

Theorem 5.3 Let $a, b, m \in \mathbb{Z}$, with $m > 0$. Then, $a \equiv b \bmod m$ if and only if a and b have the same remainder when divided by m.

Proof: $a \equiv b \bmod m$ if and only if $m \mid (a - b)$

$$\text{if and only if } a - b = km$$
$$\text{if and only if } a = b + mk$$

If $0 < b < m$, b is the remainder and the theorem is true.

If $b \geq m$, then $b \equiv r \bmod m$ where r is the least residue and $b = r + jm$.

Hence, if $a = b + mk = r + jm + km = r = (j + k)m$

Therefore, a and b have the same remainder when divided by m.

■

We can perform congruence arithmetic by first reducing integers to their least residues. Table 5.1 shows addition of integers in the least residue form.

+	0	1	2	3	4
0	0	1	2	3	4
1	1	2	3	4	4
2	2	3	4	0	1
3	3	4	0	1	2
4	4	0	1	2	3

Table 5.1 Addition of Least Residues Mod 5

Notice that in Table 5.1, each row and column has a "0" in it. This indicates that each integer has an additive inverse. For example, in row 2, column 3 we see a zero. Thus, $2 + 3 \equiv 0 \bmod 5$. So "3" is the additive inverse of "2." By the commutative property, 2 is the additive inverse of 3 also.

Table 5.2 shows multiplication of least residues mod 5.

×	0	1	2	3	4
0	0	0	0	0	0
1	0	1	2	3	4
2	0	2	4	1	3
3	0	3	1	4	2
4	0	4	3	2	1

Table 5.2 Multiplication of Least Residues Modulo 5

Notice that multiplication by zero always results in zero, so this least residue is often omitted from the multiplication table.

Exercise Set 5.1

1. Use the definition of congruence modulo n to determine whether the congruence is true or false.
   a) $0 \equiv 6 \bmod 3$
   b) $35 \equiv 55 \bmod 9$
   c) $-23 \equiv 20 \bmod 7$
   d) $-3 \equiv 3 \bmod 6$
   e) $-2 \equiv 2 \bmod 3$

2. Use the definition of congruence modulo n to determine whether the congruence is true or false.
   a) $37 \equiv -3 \bmod 5$
   b) $45 \equiv 9 \bmod 4$
   c) If n is composite, then $(n-1) \equiv 0 \pmod{n}$
   d) If p is a prime other than 2 or 5, then p is congruent to 1, 3, 7, or 9 (mod 10).
   e) $67 \equiv 1 \bmod 5$
   f) 3 and 6 are congruent modulo 5

3. Find all positive integers m such that $9 \equiv 15 \bmod m$.

4. Find all positive integers m such that $10 \equiv 12 \bmod m$.

5. Find all positive integers m such that $-5 \equiv 7 \bmod m$.

6. Rewrite each of the following statements using a congruence or congruences.

   Example: a is even can be written as $a \equiv 0 \bmod 2$.
   a) b is odd.
   b) c is divisible by 3.
   c) k has a remainder of 7 when divided by 11.
   d) a is odd, using the modulus 4.
   e) a is even, using the modulus 6.
   f) m is not divisible by 5.

7. Is it possible to rewrite the statement "a is odd" using the modulus 5? Explain why or why not.

8. Find 3 negative and 3 positive integers that are congruent to 5 mod 9.

9. Find 3 negative and 3 positive integers that are congruent to 11 mod 25.

10. Find an integer greater than 200 that is congruent to 8 mod 9.

11. Compute the value of $38^{11} \cdot 29^{11}$

12. Find all values of a such that $0 \le a \le 25$, and $a \equiv 42 \bmod 11$.

13. Find the least residue of each of the integers below in the given modulus.

    a) $10 \equiv$ _____ mod 3

    b) $14 \equiv$ _____ mod 28

    c) $-8 \equiv$ _____ mod 7

    d) $124 \equiv$ _____ mod 4

    e) $42 \equiv$ _____ mod 11

    f) $-15 \equiv$ _____ mod 9

14. Find the least residue of each of the following, in the given modulus.

    a) $10 \equiv$ _____ mod 5

    b) $-4 \equiv$ _____ mod 13

    c) $19 \equiv$ _____ mod 12

    d) $345 \equiv$ _____ mod 3

    e) $475 \equiv$ _____ mod 10

    f) $-1 \equiv$ _____ mod 13

15. True or false. If false, explain why:

    a) $37 \equiv -3 \bmod 6$

    b) $37 \equiv 2 \bmod 5$

    c) If a is an odd integer, then $a^2 \equiv 1 \bmod 8$

    d) $327 \equiv 19 \bmod 11$

    e) 2 and 4 are congruent modulo 5

    f) 7 and 37 are congruent modulo 5

16. Complete the iff statement below to make a true statement. Then, prove the statement.

    $$a \equiv 0 \bmod m \text{ iff } \underline{\hspace{5cm}}$$

17. Find the least residue of $2^{32} \bmod 47$.

18. Find the least residue of $17! \bmod 18$.

19. Find the least residue of $15! \bmod 16$.

20. Find the least residue of $2^{32} \bmod 47$.

21. Find the set of least residues modulo 6.

22. Find the set of least residues modulo 11.

23. Compute $35^{21} \bmod 11$

24. Prove **Theorem 5.1** from this section.

25. Prove **Theorem 5.2** from this section.

26. Prove that if $a \equiv b \bmod m$ then $b \equiv a \bmod m$.

27. Prove that $a \equiv a \bmod m$ for any integer $m > 0$.

28. If $a \equiv b \bmod m$ and c is a positive integer, prove that $ca \equiv cb \bmod m$.

Section 5.2   Congruences Versus Linear Equations

Now we consider the similarities and differences between congruences and equations. The next list contains the axioms used in arithmetic and algebra. They refer to the laws for addition and multiplication of real numbers. $a, b, c, d \in \mathbb{R}$

Axiom 1 Commutative properties $a + b = b + a$ and $ab = ba$

Axiom 2 $a = b \Leftrightarrow a \cdot c = b \cdot c$.

Axiom 3 $a = b \wedge c = d \Rightarrow a + c = b + d$ and $ac = ba$

Axiom 4 $a \cdot b = 0, \Leftrightarrow a = 0$ or $b = 0$.

Axiom 5 Associative properties: $(a + b) + c = a + (b + c)$ and $(ab)c = a(bc)$

Axiom 6 Identity elements: $a + 0 = 0 + a = a$ and $a \cdot 1 = 1 \cdot a = a$

Axiom 7 Distributive property: $a(b + c) = ab + ac$

Axiom 8 Transitive property: $a = b \wedge b = c \Rightarrow a = c$

The next lemma is a generalization of Axiom 1 and is true for congruences.

Lemma   5.1 Let $a \equiv b \bmod m$ and $c \equiv d \bmod m$ for $m > 0$,   and $a, b, c, d \in \mathbb{Z}$.   Then $a + c \equiv b + d \bmod m$.

Proof: Let $a, b, c, d \in \mathbb{Z}$ and let $m > 0$. Suppose that $a \equiv b \bmod m$ and $c \equiv d \bmod m.$. Then, by the definition of congruence, we know that $m \mid a - b$ and $m \mid c - d$. From the definition of divides, we know that there are integers k and n so that $mk = a - b$ and $mn = c - d$. We want to show that $m \mid (a + c) - (b + d)$. Adding the two equations above, we get that

$$mk + mn = m(k + n) = (a - b) + (c - d)$$
$$= a + c - b - d = (a + c) - (b + d)$$

Therefore, $m(k+n) = (a+c)-(b+d)$.

Hence, $m \mid [(a+c)-(b+d)]$, since $(k+n) \in \mathbb{Z}$.

By the definition of congruence, we conclude that $a+c \equiv b+d \bmod m$.

∎

Note: This lemma says that one can add *different* integers to each side, as long as they are congruent in the modulus of the congruence.

Example 5.6. Add the congruences: $5 \equiv 15 \bmod$ and $7 \equiv 27 \bmod 10$.

Solution:

By Lemma 5.1, $5+7 \equiv 15+27 \bmod 10$, or $12 \equiv 42 \bmod 10$.

We can check this by applying the definition of congruence or finding the least residue of each side. Using least residues makes the arithmetic easier.

Example 5.7. Find the sum: $15 + 7 + 4 + 36 \bmod 6$. Give your answer in the least residue form.

Solution:

We can add these numbers, and then find the remainder when the total is divided by 6. But, we can also replace each integer by a smaller integer congruent to it, mod 6. To make the arithmetic easier, we will replace each integer by its remainder, modulo 6. So, since 6 goes into 15 twice with a remainder of 2, $15 \equiv 2 \bmod 6$. Similarly, $7 \equiv 1 \bmod 6$, $4 \equiv 4 \bmod 6$ (since 4 is less than 6, it doesn't reduce at all), and $36 \equiv 0 \bmod 6$. Therefore, we get that

$$15+7+4+36 \equiv 2+1+4+0 \bmod 6$$
$$\equiv 7 \bmod 6$$
$$\equiv 1 \bmod 6$$

Lemma 5.1 applies to any addends, since subtraction is equivalent to adding a negative number. We will see an application of this idea to checking ID numbers in Section 5.4.

A generalization of Axiom 2 is also a property of congruences.

> **Lemma 5.2** Let $a \equiv b \bmod m$ and $c \equiv d \bmod m$ for $m > 0$, and $a, b, c, d \in \mathbb{Z}$. Then $a \cdot c \equiv b \cdot d \bmod m$.

Proof: Let $a, b, c, d, m \in \mathbb{Z}$ and $m > 0$.

Let $a \equiv b \bmod m$ and let $c \equiv d \bmod m$.

By the definition of congruence, we have that $m \mid a-b$ and $m \mid c-d$.

Now, by the definition of divides, there exist $k, l \in \mathbb{Z}$ such that $mk = a - b$ and $ml = c - d$. Here is where the proof gets creative. We want to conclude that $m \mid ac - bd$. We'll multiply the first equation above by c on both sides, and then the second equation by b on both sides. This gives us the two equations $mkc = (a - b)c = ac - bc$ and $mlb = (c - d)b = bc - bd$. Adding the two equations, we get $mkc + mlb = ac - bc + bc - bd = ac - bd$. Therefore, $m(kc + lb) = ac - bd$, which means that $m \mid ac - bd$, since $kc + lb \in \mathbb{Z}$. Finally, by the definition of congruence, we have that $a \cdot c \equiv b \cdot d \bmod m$.

∎

Example 5.8. Find the least residue of $18 \cdot 37 \bmod 4$.

Solution:

First replace each integer by its remainder and then multiply:

$$18 \equiv 2 \bmod 4$$
$$37 \equiv 1 \bmod 4$$
$$\therefore 18 \cdot 37 \bmod 4 \equiv 2 \cdot 1 \bmod 4 \equiv 2 \bmod 4$$

Lemma 5.2 is also useful when dealing with large integers, as shown in the next example.

Example 5.9. Find the remainder when 2^{50} is divided by 15.

Solution:

First, rewrite this question in terms of congruences. We are being asked to find the remainder of $2^{50} \bmod 15$.

Using a computer, we can probably calculate 2^{50}, but sometimes exponents are too large to calculate, so we will use properties of congruences to find another approach. Start raising 2 to

$$2 \equiv 2 \bmod 15$$
$$2^2 \equiv 4 \bmod 15$$
$$2^3 \equiv 8 \bmod 15$$
$$2^4 \equiv 16 \equiv 1 \bmod 15$$

Finally, we got to a power of 2 whose remainder is larger than 15, and we reduced this to its least residue. Now, every time we have a 2^4 in the product, we can replace it with 1. Use the division algorithm to rewrite the exponent 50 in the expression 2^{50}:

$$50 = 4(12) + 2$$

So that $2^{50} = (2^{(4(12)+2)}) = (2^{(4(12))}) \cdot 2^2$, by the law of exponents.

Reducing mod 15: $2^{50} \equiv (2^4)^{12} \cdot 2^2 \bmod 15 \equiv (1)^{12} \cdot 2^2 \bmod 15 \equiv 4 \bmod 15$.

When solving equations in algebra, such as $6x = 42$. Dividing both sides by 6 results in $x = 7$, the solution to the equation. Division of real numbers is actually multiplying by the reciprocal of the number, as long as $c \neq 0$.

$$6x = 42$$

$$\left(\frac{1}{6}\right)6x = \left(\frac{1}{6}\right)42$$

$$x = 7$$

Similarly, solving the equation $6x = 41$ leads to the result $x = 6\frac{5}{6}$. The result is a rational number but not an integer.

> **Caution** **Axiom 2 is not a property of congruences!** Counterexample: While it is true that $4 \equiv 12 \bmod 8$, because $12 - 4 = 8$ and $8 | 8$. But, dividing both sides of the congruence by 2 gives $2 \equiv 6 \bmod 8$ which is **false** because $6 - 2 = 4$ and $8 \nmid 4$.

Fortunately, there is a variation of this axiom that is true for congruences.

> **Theorem 5.4** If $a \equiv b \bmod m$ and c is a common factor of a, b and c, then c can be factored out from a, b and m.

Proof: Let $a = ck$, $b = cn$ and $m = cj$ from the hypothesis.

Then $a \equiv b \bmod m \Rightarrow m | (a - b) \Rightarrow a - b = mx$ for some integer $\Rightarrow ck - cn = cjx$ by substitution, and $\therefore k - n = jx \Rightarrow k \equiv n \bmod j$ which is what we were to prove.

■

Axiom 4 is used when solving quadratic equations by factoring. For example, if you are solving $x^2 - x - 6 = 0$, factor the left-hand side as $(x - 3)(x + 2) = 0$. Then, either $(x - 3) = 0$, or $(x + 2) = 0$, so the solutions are $x = 3, or -2$.

> **Caution** **Axiom 4 is not a property of congruences!** Counterexample: Suppose $ab \equiv 0 \bmod 12$. If $a = 0$ then the congruence will be true for any value of b, but it is also true when $a = 3$ and $b = 4$, and when $a = b = 6$.

There are other axioms of number systems (rational numbers, real numbers, etc.) that are theorems (properties) for congruences. These can be proven by using the definition of modulus and are listed below $a, b, c \in Z$. The proofs of these statements are left as exercises.

Commutative Properties: $a + c \equiv c + a \bmod m$ and $ab \equiv ba \bmod m$

Associative Properties: $a + (b + c) \equiv (a + b) + c \bmod m$ and $(ab)c \equiv a(bc) \bmod m$

Property of 0: $0 \in \mathbb{W} \Rightarrow 0 \cdot a \equiv 0 \bmod m$

Property of 1: $1 \in \mathbb{N} \Rightarrow 1 \cdot a \equiv a \bmod m$

Distributive Property: $a(b+c) \equiv ab + ac \bmod m$

Transitive Property: $a \equiv b \bmod m$ and $b \equiv c \bmod m \Rightarrow a \equiv c \bmod m$

Theorem 5.5 $a = b \Rightarrow a^k \equiv b^k \bmod m$

Proof: The proof is a direct consequence of Lemma 5.2.

The *divisibility tests* described in Chapter 1 can be proven using congruences. Example 5.10 reminds us of how a number can be written in place-value form. Following that, Theorem 5.6 proves the *divisibility test for 3* from Section 1.11.

Example 5.10. Before proving the theorem, write the integer 816 in the place-value form.

Solution:

If $a = 816$, then the unit's digit is 6, the tens digit is 1, and the hundreds digit is 8. So, the number 816 in expanded form is $8(100) + 1(10) + 6 = 8(10)^2 + 1(10) + 6$.

In general, we write the integer d in an expanded form, i.e. place-value form as follows:

If the integer a has units digit d_0, tens digit d_1, and so on, then in expanded notation,

$$d = d_0 + d_1 \cdot 10 + d_2 \cdot 100 + \cdots + d_n \cdot 10^n.$$

Notice that d_0 is the coefficient of $(10)^0$.

Theorem 5.6 3 divides an integer d if and only if 3 divides the sum of the digits of d.

Because the divisibility test is an "if and only if" statement, there are two parts to proving it is true. (1) Show that if 3 divides d, then 3 divides the sum of the digits of d. (2) prove that if 3 divides the sum of the digits of d, then 3 divides d.

Proof:

(1) Let d be an integer. Let $3 \mid d$. Then, in expanded notation,

$$d = d_0 + d_1 \cdot 10 + d_2 \cdot 100 + \cdots + d_n \cdot 10^n. \text{ Since } 3 \mid d, \ d \equiv 0 \bmod 3.$$

Now we want,

$$d_0 + d_1 \cdot 10 + d_2 \cdot 10^2 + \cdots + d_n \cdot 10^n \equiv 0 \bmod 3.$$

Also, since $10 \equiv 1 \bmod 3$ (Theorem 5.6, part 3), each 10 can be replaced by 1 in the congruence modulo 3. Therefore,

$$d_0 + d_1 \cdot 1 + d_2 \cdot 1 + \cdots + d_n \cdot 1 \equiv d_0 + d_1 + d_2 + \cdots + d_n \equiv 0 \bmod 3.$$

That is: $3 \mid d_0 + d_1 + d_2 + \cdots + d_n$, so 3 divides the sum of the digits of d.

(2) Let 3 divide the sum of the digits of d. In symbols,

$$3 \mid (d_0 + d_1 + d_2 + \cdots + d_n)$$

This means that $d_0 + d_1 + d_2 + \cdots + d_n \equiv 0 \bmod 3$. Since $10 \equiv 1 \bmod 3$, we can multiply any term by 1 or 10 as many times as we wish and maintain a true congruence modulo 3.

Therefore,

$$0 \equiv d_0 \cdot 1 + d_1 \cdot 1 + d_2 \cdot 1 + \cdots + d_n \cdot 1 \equiv d_0 + d_1 \cdot 10 + d_2 \cdot 10^2 + \cdots + d_n \cdot 10^n \bmod 3$$

The right-hand side of the congruence is the integer d written in expanded notation. Therefore, we can conclude that $0 \equiv d \bmod 3$ or $3 \mid d$.

■

The proofs of the other divisibility tests appear in the exercises. The proof of the more difficult divisibility test for divisibility by 7 is left as an activity.

Let us consider how the idea of congruences and least residues are helpful in classifying and organizing all integers by their least residues. Figure 5.1 is a Venn diagram of the integers grouped together by their least residues mod 5.

0	1	2	3	4
5	6	7	8	9
10	11	12	13	14
15	16	17	18	19
20	21	22	23	24
25	26	27	28	29
.	.	.	.	.
.	.	.	.	.
.	.	.	.	.
1000	1001	1002	1003	1004
.	.	.	.	.
.	.	.	.	.
.	.	.	.	.

Figure 5.1

There is a characteristic of rational and real numbers that we have not yet mentioned, the idea of multiplicative inverse. In the real number system, every nonzero element has a multiplicative inverse. The analogous definition for modular arithmetic is:

Definition 5.2 An integer *a* is the ***multiplicative inverse*** of *b* modulo *m* if and only iff $ab \equiv 1 \mod m$.

Example 5.11. If possible, find the multiplicative inverse of 12 mod 7.

Solution:

We are looking for an integer x that solves the congruence $12x \equiv 1 \mod 7$.

$$12x \equiv 5x \equiv 1 \mod 7$$

The nonzero residues mod 7 are 1, 2, 3, 4, 5, 6. Testing each of these, the only one that leads to a solution is $x = 3$.

$$5(3) \equiv 15 \equiv 1 \mod 7$$

Therefore, the multiplicative inverse of 12 mod 7 is 3.

Returning to the multiplication table for mod 5, Table 5.2, we see that in each non-zero row/column there is a "1." This indicates which elements are multiplicative inverses. For instance, $2 \cdot 3 \equiv 6 \equiv 1 \mod 5$. So, 2 and 3 are multiplicative inverses of each other. It is natural to ask if the rule for real numbers holds for modular arithmetic: Does every nonzero integer have a multiplicative inverse mod *m*? To answer this let us try another example.

Example 5.12. Construct a multiplication table for mod 6, and find the pairs are multiplicative inverses of each other.

Solution:

×	1	2	3	4	5
1	1	2	3	4	5
2	2	4	0	2	4
3	3	0	3	0	3
4	4	2	0	4	2
5	5	4	3	2	1

Table 5.3 Multiplication of Least Residues Mod 6

From Table 5.3, we see that $1 \cdot 1 \equiv 1 \mod 6$ and $5 \cdot 5 \equiv 1 \mod 6$ but no other least residue has a multiplicative inverse. Can you make a conjecture of why this is the case?

Exercise Set 5.2

1. Prove the commutative properties for congruences.

2. Find the following values, without using a calculator. Give your answer as a least residue.

   a) $6^2 + (5 \cdot 46) \bmod 35$

   b) $5^{256} \bmod 5$

   c) $25^2(31) \bmod 4$

   d) $70 + 36 + 48 + 35 + 20 + 18 \bmod 11$

3. Rewrite 5^{46} in terms of 5^4 and then find the least residue of 5^{46} modulo 12.

4. Rewrite 7^{151} in terms of 7^4 and then find the least residue of 7^{151} modulo 10.

5. Rewrite 5^{137} in terms of 5^2 and then find the least residue 5^{137} modulo 11.

6. Rewrite 3^{207} in terms of 3^4 and then find the least residue of 3^{207} modulo 7.

7. Find the remainder when 3^{152} is divided by 13.

8. Find the remainder when 2^{123} is divided by 7.

9. Find a if $a \equiv 32 \bmod 19$ and $52 \le a \le 70$.

10. Consider the congruence $ab \equiv 0 \bmod m$.

    a) Choose three different values for m, and then find values for a and b that make the congruence true. Some questions to think about when you are picking examples are: For every value of m, can you always make the congruence true without letting a or b be 0? Can you always find values for a and b that are smaller than m? Bigger than m?

    b) Write a conjecture about when you can find a and b such that $a \ne 0$, $b \ne 0$ and $ab \equiv 0 \bmod m$.

11. Find all solutions of the congruence: $15x \equiv 19 \bmod 16$

12. Find all solutions of the congruence: $15x \equiv 35 \bmod 12$

13. Prove the associative properties of congruences.

14. Prove the distributive property of congruences.

15. Prove the divisibility test for an integer to be divisible by 9.

16. Prove that the integer is divisible by 8 if the last three digits are divisible by 8.

Section 5.3   Solving Linear Congruences

In the last section, we compared axioms for working with equations to theorems for working with congruences. In this section, we will see how these theorems relate to solving linear congruences. In algebra, you learned that a linear equation (in one variable) is an equation of the form $ax + b = c$, where a, b, and c are constants and $a \ne 0$. Solving the equation means finding all values x_0 of x that make the equation true: $ax_0 + b = c$. We know that every linear equation has exactly one solution.

Definition 5.3 A *linear congruence* is a congruence of the form $ax \equiv b \bmod m$. As with equations, a number x_0 is a solution of the congruence if $ax_0 \equiv b \bmod m$.

So, solving a linear congruence means finding all values of x that satisfy the congruence. Some questions to think about are:

- Do all linear congruences have solutions?
- Can linear congruences have more than one solution?
- Can we find solutions in the same way as for equations?

Example 5.13 provides a few examples to start answering these questions.

Example 5.13. Solve the linear congruences. Give your final answer as a least residue

  a) $x + 4 \equiv 3 \bmod 7$

  b) $2x \equiv 3 \bmod 4$

  c) $2x \equiv 4 \bmod 6$

Solution:

  a) Subtract 4 from each sides of the congruence (Theorem 1).

$$x + 4 - 4 \equiv 3 - 4 \bmod 7$$
$$x \equiv -1 \bmod 7$$
$$x \equiv 6 \bmod 7$$

Notice that unlike linear equations, there is more than one integer that satisfies this congruence. In fact, we have already found two: -1 and 6. However, since $-1 \equiv 6 \bmod 7$, we call these *congruent solutions*, and we do not count them as distinct solutions to the congruence.

  b) We will use trial and error to solve the problem. We know that whatever value of x makes the congruence true, must be congruent to 0, 1, 2, or 3 modulo 4. Test all possible solutions to the congruence to see which (if any) works.

$$2(0) \equiv 0 \bmod 4 \text{ NO}$$
$$2(1) \equiv 2 \bmod 4 \text{ NO}$$
$$2(2) \equiv 0 \bmod 4 \text{ NO}$$
$$2(3) \equiv 2 \bmod 4 \text{ NO}$$

None of the possibilities work, so this congruence has no solutions! This is another difference from linear equations: All linear equations have a solution, but some linear congruences that do not have solutions.

c) Again, we can again check all possibilities for x to see if we get any solutions

$$2(0) \equiv 0 \bmod 6 \text{ NO}$$

$$2(1) \equiv 2 \bmod 6 \text{ NO}$$

$$2(2) \equiv 4 \bmod 6 \text{ Yes}$$

$$2(3) \equiv 0 \bmod 6 \text{ NO}$$

$$2(4) \equiv 2 \bmod 6 \text{ NO}$$

$$2(5) \equiv 4 \bmod 6 \text{ Yes}$$

The values $x = 2$ and $x = 5$ both satisfy the congruence $2x \equiv 4 \bmod 6$. These solutions are called *incongruent solutions*, since they are not congruent to each other modulo 6. When we talk about different solutions, we are counting the incongruent solutions, so this congruence has 2 different (or incongruent) solutions. Note that the incongruent solutions are least residues.

Let us consider the first question above: Does every linear congruence have a solution? If so, how many are there? It is useful to decide before trying to solve it. So far, we have used trial and error. But if we were trying to solve a congruence such as $57x \equiv 78 \bmod 121$, checking all the possibilities is not very appealing. In fact, we can discover how many solutions a congruence has before we solve it, and we can also find the solutions using something you already know. An example will demonstrate the process.

Example 5.14. Solve the linear congruence $9x \equiv 5y \bmod 35$.

Solution:

Using the definition of congruence, we can rewrite the congruence above as

$$35 \mid 9x - 5,$$

which is equivalent to

$$35y = 9x - 5, \text{ for some } y \in \mathbb{Z}.$$

By rewriting with the variables on one side of the equation, we arrive at the equation

$$5 = 9x - 35y$$

We know this is a Linear Diophantine equation from Chapter 3 and this equation has a solution, since gcd $(9, 35) = 1$, and $1 \mid 5$. First, use the Euclidean Algorithm backward to solve $1 = 9x - 35y$, and then multiply both sides by 5 to get back to our original equation.

$$35 = 3(9) + 8$$

$$9 = 1(8) + 1$$
$$8 = 8(1) + 0$$

Solving backward:

$$1 = 9 - 1(8)$$
$$= 9 - 1(35 - 3(9))$$
$$= 9(4) - 35(1)$$

Finally, multiplying by 5:

$$5 \cdot 1 = 9(4 \cdot 5) - 35(1 \cdot 5)$$
$$5 = 9(20) - 35(5)$$

Therefore, $x = 20$ is a solution to the congruence and any x such that $x \equiv 20 \bmod 35$ will also work.

Now, the general solution of linear equations, Theorems 3.5 and 3.6 from Chapter 3 can be stated for congruences.

Theorem 5.7 Let a, c, and $m > 0$ be integers, and let $d = \gcd(a, m)$. Consider the linear congruence $a \equiv c \bmod m$.

1. If $d \nmid c$, then the congruence $a \equiv c \bmod m$ has no solutions.

2. If $d \mid c$, then the congruence $a \equiv c \bmod m$ has exactly d incongruent solutions.

To find the solutions, first find one solution using the method above. Then, the rest of the solutions will be spaced a distance of $\dfrac{m}{d}$ from each other. Therefore, the general form for the incongruent solutions to $a \equiv c \bmod m$ given that x_0 is one solution is:

$$x = x_0 + k \cdot \frac{m}{d} \bmod m, \quad k = 0, 1, 2, \ldots, d - 1.$$

Example 5.15. Solve $12x \equiv 9 \bmod 15$.

Solution:

First, since $\gcd(12, 15) = 3$ and $3 \mid 9$, there will be 3 incongruent solutions to this congruence. To find the first solution, rewrite the congruence as an equation:

$$12x = 9 + 15y$$
$$12x - 15y = 9$$

To simplify, we can factor out the gcd, 3 in this case, and find the solution to $4x - 5y = 3$. Now, we can use the Euclidean Algorithm to solve $4x - 5y = 3$.

The solution is $x = -3$ and $y = -3$. Since we factored out a 3 from the original equation, we need to multiply these solutions by 3.

So, the first solution is $x_0 \equiv -3 \bmod 15$, or $x_0 \equiv 12 \bmod 15$. There is a total of 3 incongruent solutions, $\frac{15}{3} = 5$ units apart. So, the other solutions are:

$$x_0 \equiv 12 \bmod 15$$
$$x_1 \equiv 17 \bmod 15 \equiv 2 \bmod 15$$
$$x_2 \equiv 7 \bmod 15$$

Notice that if we add 5 again onto the last solution, we get 12 again, so the solutions start to repeat.

Exercise Set 5.3

1. Solve the following congruences. Give the least residue of the solution.
   a) $x + 12 \equiv 5 \bmod 8$
   b) $x - 5 \equiv 40 \bmod 11$
   c) $2x + 11 \equiv x + 4 \bmod 13$

2. Solve the congruence $51x \equiv 9 \bmod 54$.

3. For each linear congruence below, determine whether or not the congruence has any solutions, and if so, how many (incongruent) solutions it has.
   a) $4x \equiv 6 \bmod 13$
   b) $2x \equiv 5 \bmod 7$
   c) $3x \equiv 6 \bmod 9$
   d) $103x \equiv 444 \bmod 999$
   e) $15x \equiv 9 \bmod 25$
   f) $40x \equiv 3 \bmod 20$

4. Determine whether or not the congruences below have any solutions. If they do, find the incongruent solutions.
   a) $19x \equiv 30 \bmod 40$
   b) $6x \equiv 4 \bmod 8$
   c) $4x + 14 \equiv 6 \bmod 26$
   d) $2x - 8 \equiv 8 \bmod 5$

5. For which integers, $0 \leq c < 30$, does the congruence $12x \equiv c \bmod 30$ have solutions? When there are solutions, also determine how many incongruent solutions there are.

6. For each problem in exercise 3, solve any congruence that has solutions.

7. State the contrapositive of part 1 of **Theorem 5.7**.

8. Write an example of a linear congruence with exactly one solution.

9. Write an example of a linear congruence with exactly two solutions.

10. Write an example of a linear congruence with exactly five solutions.

11. If the congruence $ax \equiv b \bmod m$ has exactly one solution, what can you say about a, b and m? Explain.

12. Find the inverse of 3 mod 8. Does every integer have an inverse modulo 8? If not, which integers do?

13. Find the inverse of 3 mod 5. Does every integer have an inverse modulo 5? If not, which integers do?

14. Explain why 0 will not have an inverse modulo m if $m > 1$.

15. Find at least one solution of the congruence $2x = 3 \equiv 9 - 5x \bmod 13$.

16. Find all integers that leave a remainder of 3 when divided by 4.

17. Prove: The square of any integer never leaves a remainder of 2 when divided by 3.

18. Prove: If p is a prime other than 2 or 5, then p is congruent to 1, 3, 7, or 9 mod 10.

Section 5.4   An Application of Congruences—Identification Numbers and Check Digits

In 1997, a woman started receiving unexpected wire transfers into her bank account totaling about $700,000. She had not won a lottery as she guessed; instead, 13 different foreign governments tried to wire donations into the U.N. Environment Program's account. But they ended up in her account; the two account numbers differed by only one digit.

Since so much information is stored on and processed by computers, items from bank accounts to books to individuals are assigned identification numbers (ID numbers) to clearly identify them. Your school ID number ensures that that your bill or your grades are not sent to another student with the same name. Books have ID numbers (called International Standard Book Numbers, or ISBNs) to allow for cataloging, and to differentiate between different editions, or two different books that happen to have the same title. Products in the grocery store have ID numbers (called Universal Product Codes, represented by the UPC symbol (bar code) so that the cashier can quickly scan in the product, and your credit card number is an ID number that allows you (and hopefully no one else) to purchase things in stores or online.

When these numbers are hand copied, typed, or scanned into a computer, what happens if they are not transferred correctly? You can order the wrong book if you type in one digit of the ISBN incorrectly. You can be charged for lobster when you are trying to buy noodles if the grocery store scanner misreads the bar code on your purchase. Your credit card may be charged if someone else accidentally reverses two digits when entering his credit card number to amazon.com.

To avoid potential mix-ups like these, as well as make forgeries of things like money orders or airline tickets more difficult, most identification numbers are equipped with a digit called a *check digit* which is included somewhere in the ID number (often, but not always, at the end), and which is calculated using a formula called a *check digit scheme*. The formulas used to calculate check digits vary in difficulty, but many incorporate congruences. The check digit schemes are determined by the institution that formulates the ID numbers, so there are different schemes for different types of identification numbers. We will look at some examples below.

Definition 5.4 A *check digit* is a digit appended to a string of numbers for error detection.

Normally, the *check digit* is computed from the other digits in the string using modular arithmetic.

Section 5.4.1 Universal Product Codes

The Universal Product Code (UPC) is a 12-digit identification number that is used by stores to keep track of the items they sell. The digits of the ID number are encoded in the bar code symbol which is scanned by the cashier when you check out. Computerized cash registers are programmed with a check-digit scheme. If the number does not satisfy the scheme, then the cashier will have to rescan the item. The check digit scheme for UPC codes works as follows.

Check digit scheme for UPC symbols:

UPC numbers have 12 digits which we will represent as: $a_1a_2a_3a_4a_5a_6a_7a_8a_9a_{10}a_{11}a_{12}$.

The check digit, a_{12}, is chosen so that

$$3a_1 + a_2 + 3a_3 + a_4 + 3a_5 + a_6 + 3a_7 + a_8 + 3a_9 + a_{10} + 3a_{11} + a_{12} \equiv 0 \bmod 10$$

Example 5.16. The UPC on a square of Ghirardelli dark chocolate 747599700910 (Figure 5.2). Verify that this ID number satisfies the check-digit scheme for UPC symbols.

Source: Agnes Rash
Figure 5.2

Solution:

In this case, 0 is the check digit, chosen to make the sum on the left congruent to 0 modulo 10. Simplify the congruence using the rules from Section 5.2 which allow us to replace integers in a congruence with their least residue form. Substituting the given UPC into the left side of the check digit scheme, we obtain:

$$3 \cdot 7 + 4 + 3 \cdot 7 + 5 + 3 \cdot 9 + 9 + 3 \cdot 7 + 0 + 3 \cdot 0 + 3 \cdot 9 + 1 + 0$$
$$\equiv 21 + 4 + 21 + 5 + 27 + 9 + 27 + 0 + 0 + 9 + 3 + 0 \bmod 10$$
$$\equiv 1 + 4 + 1 + 5 + 7 + 9 + 1 + 9 + 3 \bmod 10$$
$$\equiv 40 \equiv 0 \bmod 10$$

The UPC ID number is correct.

Section 5.4.2   International Standard Book Numbers

The International Standard Book Number (ISBN) is an ID number assigned to each book to identify the book uniquely. Different editions of a book and different books of the same title will have different ISBNs.

In 2007, the book industry changed from 10-digit ISBNs to 13-digit ISBN. Books published prior to this change were issued a 13-digit ISBN in addition to their 10-digit ISBN. In each case, the last digit of the ID number is the check digit, but there is a separate check-digit scheme for each type of ISBN.

Check digit scheme for ISBNs with 10 digits: $a_1a_2a_3a_4a_5a_6a_7a_8a_9a_{10}$

The check digit a_{10} is chosen so that

$$10 \cdot a_1 + 9 \cdot a_2 + 8 \cdot a_3 + 7 \cdot a_4 + 6 \cdot a_5 + 5 \cdot a_6 + 4 \cdot a_7 + 3 \cdot a_8 + 2 \cdot a_9 + a_{10} \equiv 0 \bmod 11$$

Note that since this scheme is computed modulo 11, it is possible the check digit may be 10. Since it can only be one digit long, a 10 is replaced by an X in the ISBN.

a)   ISBNs with 13 digits: $a_1a_2a_3a_4a_5a_6a_7a_8a_9a_{10}a_{11}a_{12}a_{13}$

Check digit scheme for 13-digit ISBNs: The check digit a_{13} is chosen so that

$$a_1 + 3a_2 + a_3 + 3a_4 + a_5 + 3a_6 + a_7 + 3a_8 + a_9 + 3a_{10} + a_{11} + 3a_{12} + a_{13} \equiv 0 \bmod 10$$

Example 5.17. The ISBN for the paperback edition of the book *Zeitoun* by David Eggers is 9780307387943. Verify that it satisfies the appropriate check digit scheme.

Solution:

We will confirm that the check digit, 3, satisfies the scheme given for 13-digit ISBNs. Substituting into the left-hand side of the check digit scheme:

$$9 + 3 \cdot 7 + 8 + 3 \cdot 0 + 3 + 3 \cdot 0 + 7 + 3 \cdot 3 + 8 + 3 \cdot 7 + 9 + 3 \cdot 4 + 3$$
$$\equiv 9 + 21 + 8 + 3 + 7 + 9 + 8 + 21 + 9 + 12 + 3 \bmod 10$$
$$\equiv 9 + 1 + 8 + 3 + 7 + 9 + 8 + 1 + 9 + 2 + 3 \bmod 10$$
$$\equiv 10 + 11 + 16 + 9 + 11 + 3 \bmod 10$$
$$\equiv 1 + 6 + 9 + 1 + 3 \bmod 10$$
$$\equiv 7 + 10 + 3 \bmod 10$$
$$\equiv 0 \bmod 10$$

Check digit scheme for USPS money orders have serial numbers with 11 digits: $a_1a_2a_3a_4a_5a_6a_7a_8a_9a_{10}a_{11}$. The last digit is the check digit. The check digit a_{11} is chosen so that
$$a_{11} \equiv a_2 + a_3 + a_4 + a_5 + a_6 + a_7 + a_8 + a_9 + a_{10} \bmod 9$$

Section 5.4.3 Bank Checks

Bank checks have at least two numbers on the bottom of the check. One of these identifies the bank, called the *routing number.* Another number identifies the individual check number. Usually the routing number appears on the left side of the check. The first four numbers are the Federal Reserve routing system. The next four digits identify the financial institution, and the last digit is the check digit.

> *Check digit scheme for the nine-digit bank code is:* The check digit is chosen so that
>
> $$3(a_1 + a_4 + a_7) + 7(a_2 + a_5 + a_8) + (a_3 + a_6 + a_9) \equiv 0 \bmod 10$$

Example 5.17. The routing number for a particular bank is 231372691. Verify that this is a valid routing number.

Solution:

Using the check digit scheme, we have

$$3(2 + 3 + 6) + 7(3 + 7 + 9) + (1 + 2 + 1) = 33 + 133 + 4 \equiv 0 \bmod 10$$

So, the routing number is valid.

Exercise Set 5.4

1. If a customer wants to cash a check with routing number 75435899213, should the cashier give him the money, or call the police?

2. Find a product with a UPC code and test it to make sure that the check digit scheme works for the UPC code you find.

3. Apply the ISBN check digit scheme to the ISBN of your favorite book.

4. I can read all but one digit of the UPC code on my one-pound box of Domino Dark Brown Sugar. They are 0 4 9 2 0 0 0 5 x 0 0 4, where x represents the digit I cannot read. What is the missing digit?

5. In order to check the bank code, the more complicated check digit method is used. Use that method to determine if the number 310614836 is a correct bank code.

6. The bar code from a box of Kleenex tissues is 3600028300. Find the check digit that will make a correct UPC code.

7. The 10-digit ISBN for the children's book *The Math Curse* by Jon Scieszka and Lane Smith has the first 9 digits 0-670-86194-_ _ _.Show that the check digit is 4.

8. Check the ISBN number for this textbook and verify that it is a valid number.

9. A UPC for a product is 0 51000   02526 5

   Explain why the errors in the following misread versions of this UPC would not be detected as errors:

   0 51000   02625 5

   0 50000   05526 5

10. The ISBN 3-540-06395-6 is incorrect. Two adjacent digits have been transposed. The check digit is not part of the pair of reversed digits. What is the correct ISBN?

11. When Clark wrote down the ISBN code from the book *Mathematics and Common Sense* he thinks that he may have switched two digits in the code 7851688127009. Did Clark make this mistake? Explain your answer.

12. Consider the first 11-digits of a UPC code: 03300331439.

    a) Find the missing check digit.
    b) Write the solution using modulo form.

Section 5.5   The Chinese Remainder Theorem

Sun Zi – a third or fourth century military strategist. The first recorded proof of the Chinese Remainder Theorem appeared Sun Zi's book **Master Sun's Mathematical Manual** (Pommersheim, 278).

Very little is known about Sun Zi, except for his manual. He probably looked similar to the image to the left. This very old theorem has modern applications to systems of equations and congruences as well as to computer applications where the size of the "words" has a maximum limit. In this section we will consider two different methods for solving a system of linear congruences. We begin with a reminder.

Source: ©delcarmat/Shutterstock.com

Definition 5.5 A *reduced residue system modulo b* is the set of integers relatively prime to b in a complete residue system modulo b.

For example, from modulo 12, we have a complete least residue system $\{0, 1, 2, 3, 4, 5, 6, 7, 8, 9, 10, 11\}$ and reduced residue system $\{1, 5, 7, 11\}$.

Consider the expression $z = ax + by$ which is a function of two variables, x and y. Notice that

$$z = ax + by \equiv by \bmod a$$

and

$$z = ax + by \equiv ax \bmod b$$

This is the basis for finding a value, z, that satisfies two congruences, one with base a and one with base b. The simplest case consists of two easy congruences:

$$z \equiv x \bmod a \quad \text{and} \quad z \equiv y \bmod b$$

To use the method described in this section, a and b must be relatively prime. We begin with an example using the substitution method for solving a pair of linear equations from high school algebra.

Example 5.18. Use substitution to find a common solution to the congruences $z \equiv 4 \bmod 11$ and $z \equiv 3 \bmod 17$.

Solution:

Rewrite the first equation using the definition: $z - 4 = 11t$ for some integer t, or $z = 4 + 11t$.

Substitute this for z in the second equation: $4 + 11t \equiv 3 \bmod 17$

Now we have $11t \equiv -1 \bmod 17$ or $11t \equiv 16 \bmod 17$

By trying some values, we find that $t \equiv 3 \bmod 17$.

So, re-substituting we have $z = 4 + 11(3) = 37$. Since this value satisfies both equations, the value is a solution to two congruences with moduli that are relatively prime. Hence, the moduli can be rewritten as one modulus, mod $17 \cdot 11$.

Theorem 5.8 is the statement of the theorem when there are two congruences to solve simultaneously.

> **Theorem 5.8 The Chinese Remainder Theorem**
>
> Let a and b be integers with $\gcd(a, b) = 1$. Then the system of congruences $z \equiv k_1 \bmod a$ and $z \equiv k_2 \bmod b$ has exactly one solution with $0 \leq z < ab$. The solution is given by $ax \equiv 1 \bmod b$ and $by \equiv 1 \bmod a$.

Proof: The variables are color-coded to make the solution easier to see. Rewrite the first congruence $z \equiv k_1 \bmod a$ using the definition: $z - k_1 = ax$ or $z = ax + k_1$.

Substitute this value for z in the second congruence:

$$z \equiv k_2 \bmod b$$
$$ax \equiv -k_1 + k_2 \bmod b$$

Rewriting again, we have $ax + k_1 - k_2 = by$ for some integer y, so $ax - by = k_2 - k_1$.

The Linear Congruence Theorem says that there is exactly one solution to this equation mod ab.

∎

Example 5.19. (Example 5.1 revisited): Using this theorem, we can solve the system of congruences given in Example 5.1.

$$z \equiv 4 \bmod 11 \text{ and}$$
$$z \equiv 3 \bmod 17$$
$$a = 11, b = 17, k_1 = 4, k_2 = 3$$

Solution:

$$11x \equiv 1 \bmod 17$$
$$17y \equiv 1 \bmod 11$$
$$11x \equiv 154 \bmod 17$$
$$17y \equiv 6y \equiv 1 \bmod 11$$
$$x \equiv 14 \bmod 17 \text{ and } y \equiv 2 \bmod 11$$

So, the solution to the system is $z \equiv 11(14)(3) + 17(2)(4) \bmod 17 \cdot 11$.

Example 5.20. A professor feeds his pet cobra every four days and bathes it once a week. This week he fed it on Tuesday and bathed it on Wednesday. When, if ever, will he feed and wash the cobra on the same day?

Solution:

We will use the substitution method to solve this problem. Let us denote Tuesday as day 1. The cobra is fed on days 1, 5, 9, ... or when $x \equiv 1 \bmod 4$. (1) Also, since the cobra is bathed on Wednesday, day 2, and on days when $x \equiv 2 \bmod 7$. (2)

Solving (1) we have that $4 \mid (x-1)$, or $4y = x-1$ and hence $x = 4y+1$ (3)

Substituting this in (2) we have

$$4y + 1 \equiv 2 \bmod 7$$
$$4y \equiv 1 \bmod 7$$
$$y \equiv 2 \bmod 7$$

Substituting this into (3) we find x:

$$x = 4(2)+1 = 9$$

Checking this in both equations, we arrive at the final mod $4 \cdot y = 28$ and $x \equiv 9 \bmod 28$.

To generalize on the Chinese Remainder Theorem method to a collection of several moduli:

In the moduli called $m_1, m_2, \ldots, m_r$ let all positive integers be relatively prime in pairs. Then for the integers $a_1, a_2, \ldots, a_r$, the r congruences

$$x \equiv a_i \bmod m_i$$

have a common solution and any two solutions are congruent modulo $m_1 \cdot m_2 \cdot \ldots \cdot m_r$.

> **Theorem 5.9 General Chinese Remainder Theorem**
>
> Let $m_1, m_2, \ldots, m_n$ be positive integers such that $\gcd(m_i, m_j) = 1$ when m_i and m_j are two different integers from the list. Then the system of linear congruences
>
> $$z \equiv a_1 \bmod m_1$$
> $$z \equiv a_2 \bmod m_2$$
> $$\vdots$$
> $$z \equiv a_n \bmod m_n$$
>
> has a unique solution modulo $m_1 \cdot m_2 \cdot \ldots \cdot m_n$.

The solution is given by

$$z = a_1 m_2 m_3 x_1 + a_2 m_1 m_3 x_2 + a_3 m_1 m_2 x_3 \ldots + a_n m_1 m_3 x_3 \ldots m_n$$

Sketch of Proof.

The proof of the more general version follows the same pattern as the case for two congruences but is slightly more complicated and beyond this course, so we will not include it here.

However, we will construct the general solution for three congruences.

$$z \equiv a_1 \bmod m_1$$
$$z \equiv a_2 \bmod m_2$$
$$z \equiv a_n \bmod m_n$$

Starting with $z = a_1 + a_2 + a_3$, we need to cancel out two of the three terms in each congruence. For example, a_1 appears in the first congruence but not the second or third. Therefore, multiply a_1 by m_2 and m_3. Using similar reasoning for the other two terms, we obtain:

$$z = a_1 m_2 m_3 + a_2 m_1 m_3 + a_3 m_1 m_2$$

Now, the extra factors can be canceled out by computing inverses of $m_2 m_3$, $m_1 m_3$ and $m_1 m_2$. The congruences that need to be solved to find these inverses are:

$$m_2 m_3 x \equiv 1 \bmod m_1$$
$$m_1 m_3 x \equiv 1 \bmod m_2$$
$$m_1 m_2 x \equiv 1 \bmod m_3$$

Since one of the premises of the theorem is that none of the moduli have any common factors, in each case above the congruence will have a solution. Therefore, if the solutions are x_1, x_2, and x_3, we have the following congruences:

$$m_2 m_3 x_1 \equiv 1 \bmod m_1$$
$$m_1 m_3 x_2 \equiv 1 \bmod m_2$$
$$m_1 m_2 x_3 \equiv 1 \bmod m_3$$

Finally this allows us to find the general form for the solution when the system has three congruences:

$$z = a_1 m_2 m_3 x_1 + a_2 m_1 m_3 x_2 + a_3 m_1 m_2 x_3$$

∎

Example 5.21. Solve the system of congruences.

$$x \equiv 2 \bmod 3$$
$$x \equiv 5 \bmod 4$$
$$x \equiv -3 \bmod 7$$

Solution:

This is solvable since any two of the moduli are relatively prime, and the Chinese Remainder Theorem applies. From the general form for the solution of a system with three congruences,

$$z = 2 \cdot 4 \cdot 7 \cdot x_1 + 5 \cdot 3 \cdot 7 \cdot x_2 + (-3) \cdot 3 \cdot 4 \cdot x_3 \bmod 84$$

where

$$4 \cdot 7 \cdot x_1 \equiv 1 \bmod 3$$
$$3 \cdot 7 \cdot x_2 \equiv 1 \bmod 4$$
$$3 \cdot 4 \cdot x_3 \equiv 1 \bmod 7$$

Reducing the coefficients of x in each modulus, we can simplify each of these congruences into the following:

$$x_1 \equiv 1 \bmod 3$$
$$x_2 \equiv 1 \bmod 4$$
$$5x_3 \equiv -1 \bmod 7$$

In the last case, since $5 \cdot 3 \equiv 1 \bmod 7$, multiplying both sides by 3 yields:

$$x_3 \equiv 3 \bmod 7$$

Finally substituting these values into the formula for z, and simplifying, we obtain the solution to the original system of congruences.

$$z \equiv 2 \cdot 4 \cdot 7 \cdot 1 + 5 \cdot 3 \cdot 7 \cdot 1 + (-3) \cdot 3 \cdot 4 \cdot 3 \bmod 84$$
$$z \equiv 53 \bmod 84$$

Exercise Set 5.5

Exercises 1–5: Determine whether the given value of x is a solution of the system of congruences.

1. $x = 31$
    $x \equiv 4 \bmod 9$
    $x \equiv 9 \bmod 20$

2. $x = 28$
    $x \equiv 2 \bmod 3$
    $x \equiv 4 \bmod 8$

3. $x = 8$
    $4x \equiv 2 \bmod 5$
    $2x \equiv 1 \bmod 3$

4. $x = 34$

   $x \equiv 4 \bmod 10$

   $x \equiv 5 \bmod 7$

5. $x = 5$

   $3x \equiv 5 \bmod 10$

   $5x \equiv 1 \bmod 6$

Exercises 6–8: Find the least residue solution to each system of congruences below.

6. $x \equiv 3 \bmod 4$

   $x \equiv 2 \bmod 5$

7. $x \equiv 2 \bmod 3$

   $x \equiv 1 \bmod 8$

8. $x \equiv 1 \bmod 7$

   $x \equiv 4 \bmod 6$

9. Solve the system of congruences:

   $x \equiv 4 \bmod 7$

   $x \equiv 5 \bmod 8$

   Where $0 \le x \le 56$

10. Find the general form of the solution to a system of four linear congruences when their moduli do not have any common factors and show that it satisfies each congruence in the system. (Hint: Look for a pattern in the solution for two congruences and the solution for three congruences).

Exercises 11–16: Solve the system of linear congruences.

11. $z \equiv 3 \bmod 5$

    $z \equiv 3 \bmod 8, \; 0 \le z < 40$

12. $z \equiv 3 \bmod 5$

    $z \equiv 2 \bmod 8, \; 0 \le z < 40$

13. $z \equiv -5 \bmod 6$

    $z \equiv -5 \bmod 7, \; 0 \le z < 42$

14. $z \equiv 4 \bmod 5$

    $z \equiv 5 \bmod 7, \; 0 \le z < 35$

15. $z \equiv 4 \bmod 6$

    $z \equiv 5 \bmod 7, \; 0 \le z < 42$

16. $z \equiv 20 \bmod 9$

    $z \equiv -3 \bmod 10, \; 0 \le z < 90$

Exercises 17–19: Find a value of z that solves the system of congruences.

17. $z \equiv 1 \bmod 3$, $z \equiv 1 \bmod 5$, $z \equiv 1 \bmod 7$

18. $z \equiv 5 \bmod 7$, $z \equiv 2 \bmod 12$, $z \equiv 8 \bmod 13$

19. $z \equiv 2 \bmod 3$, $z \equiv 3 \bmod 5$, $z \equiv 2 \bmod 7$

20. Professor Costello buys a new car every three years; he bought his first car in 1981. He gets a sabbatical leave every seven years, starting in 1992. When does he first get both during the same year?

21. Verify that the general solution constructed in the proof of Theorem 5.9 satisfies the system of three linear congruence.

Section 5.6   Summary and Review Exercises

Vocabulary and Symbols

complete system of residues modulo m	modulus
congruence $a \equiv b \bmod m$	reducing an integer modulo m
congruent modulo m	set of least residues modulo m
congruent solutions	linear congruence
least residue of b modulo m	Bank Routing number
incongruent solutions	International Standard Book Number (ISBN)
inverse modulo m	system of linear congruences
check digit	Chinese Remainder Theorem
check digit scheme	Universal Product Code (UPC)

Suggested Readings

Gallian, J. S. "The Mathematics of Identification Numbers." *The College Mathematics Journal* 22 (1991): 194–202.

Khovanova, Tanya. "A Story of Storytelling Numbers." *Math Horizons* (September, 2009): 14–17. also at www.maa.org/mathhorizons

Plummer, Phil. "Divisibility Tests for Primes Greater Than 5." *Pi Mu Epsilon Journal* 10 (Spring, 1995): 96–98.

Snapp, Bart and Chris Snapp. "Automotive Number Theory." *Math Horizons* (September, 2009): 26–27. also at www.maa.org/mathhorizons

Review Exercises

1. How many solutions does the congruence $3x \equiv 6 \bmod 1810$ have?

2. The first 11 digits of a Universal Product Code (UPC) for a carton of frozen sweet potatoes are 31233100597. Find the 12th digit (the check digit).

3. How many distinct solutions does the congruence $9x \equiv 24 \bmod 18$ have? List them.

4. Prove that if a is an odd integer, then $a^2 \equiv 1 \bmod 8$.

5. Compute the value of $58^7 \bmod 7$.

6. The 13-digit ISBN for the fascinating novel Uncle Petros and Goldbach's Conjecture has the first 12 digits 978-158234128_. Show that the check digit is 6.

7. How many solutions does the congruence $3x \equiv 24 \bmod 18$ have? Find them.

8. Find all incongruent solutions, if any, to following congruence: $12x \equiv 18 \bmod 57$.

9. Solve if possible:

   a) $13x \equiv 25 \bmod 8$

   b) $9x \equiv 21 \bmod 25$

   c) $11x \equiv -15 \bmod 10$

10. Which integer(s) cannot occur at the unit's digit of a fifth power integer?

11. Which integer(s) can occur at the unit's digits of a third power of an integer?

12. Compute $27^{21} \bmod 38$.

13. Find the least solution to each of the following systems of the congruence below.

   $x \equiv 3 \bmod 4$

   $x \equiv 2 \bmod 5$

   $x \equiv 3 \bmod 7$

14. How many distinct solutions does the congruence $6x \equiv 24 \bmod 18$ have? Find them.

15. Compute the value of $37^3 \cdot 28^2 \bmod 31$

16. True or False. If false, explain why:

   a) $37 \equiv -3 \bmod 6$

   b) $37 \equiv 2 \bmod 5$

   c) If a is an odd integer, then $a^2 \equiv 1 \bmod 8$

   d) $327 \equiv 19 \bmod 11$

   e) 2 and 4 are congruent modulo 5

   f) 7 and 37 are congruent modulo 5

17. Solve the system of congruences below:

   $3x \equiv 1 \bmod 11$ and

   $3x \equiv 3 \bmod 17$

18. What is the remainder when 2015 is divided by 7?

19. The Chinese Remainder Theorem is applied to solve problems of which type?

20. Is $z \equiv 200 \bmod 255$ a solution to the system of congruences?

   $z \equiv 5 \bmod 15$

   $z \equiv 13 \bmod 17$

21. Explain why a congruence of the form $x + a \equiv b \bmod m$ will always have exactly one incongruent solution mod m.

22. Find the least residue of each of the following, in the given modulus

    a) $43 \equiv$ _____ mod 25

    b) $-157 \equiv$ _____ mod 11

    c) $9 \equiv$ _____ mod 4

    d) $442 \equiv$ _____ mod 26

    e) $-12 \equiv$ _____ mod 10

23. Find 10 integers that are congruent to 6 mod 12

24. Find 10 negative integers that are congruent to 4 mod 7

25. If $k \equiv 4$ mod 9, find the least residue of the expression $7k - 16$ (mod 9)

26. Determine whether each congruence is true or false

    a) $13 \equiv 1$ mod 2

    b) $22 \equiv 6$ mod 5

    c) $91 \equiv 0$ mod 13

    d) $-2 \equiv 2$ mod 3

    e) $-3 \equiv 0$ mod 11

    f) $1 \equiv 15$ mod 7

27. Find all values of a such that $0 \leq a \leq 25$ and $a \equiv 42$ mod 11.

28. Find 2 negative and 2 positive integers congruent to 7 mod 9.

29. Find 2 negative and 2 positive integers congruent to 4 mod 6.

30. Find all positive integers m such that $27 \equiv 5$ mod m.

31. What time does a clock read 29 hours after 11:00 am? Show how this problem is related to modular arithmetic.

32. Find the multiplicative inverse of each of the following, if possible:

    a) $a = 1, 2, \ldots$ 6 mod 7

    b) $a = 1, 2, \ldots$ 10 mod 11

    c) $a = 1, 2, \ldots$ 9 mod 10

    d) $a = 1, 2, \ldots$ 11 mod 12

33. Find the least positive value of x such that $54^7 \equiv x$ mod 7

34. A teacher brought apples to give her students. When she distributes the apples equally among the 13 students in the first class, there are four left. If she gives an equal number of apples to each of the 29 students in the second class, there are nine left. In the third class, she continues to distribute the apples equally to the 37 students and has 16 left over. What is the smallest number of apples she may have brought to class?

35. If books are removed from a table 2 at a time there is one left over. If they are removed 3 at a time, there are 2 left over. If removed 4 at a time, there are 3 left, and when removing 6 at a time, there are 5 left over. But if the books are removed 7 at a time there are no books left over. What is the least number of books that could have been on the table?

36. Wesley is on the student council, which meets every seven days. He also runs around the track every three days. If Wesley runs on March 2nd and has a student council meeting on March 5th, what are the next two dates that Wesley will have council meeting and also run around the track?

37. Ryann buys a new clothes washer every four years. She bought her first washer in 1975. She also buys a new clothes dryer every seven years, starting in 1981. When does she first purchase both items in the same year?

38. Dave brings cookies to math class. There are 17 people in Dave's class. If he gives each person an equal number of cookies, 3 were left. One student leaves class because he is sick. When Dave redistributes the cookies, 10 were left. Next, a student was called to the office, so Dave again redistributed the cookies and there were none left. How many cookies did Dave bring to math class?

39. Stephen is the CEO of a company that holds a board meeting every other week (14 days). Every three days, Stephen works with his personal trainer before work. If he works with the personal trainer on the July 1st and has a board meeting on July 13th when is the first time both will occur on the same day?

40. Solve each linear congruence below. Give the least residue of the solution.
    a) $x + 9 \equiv 6 \bmod 8$
    b) $x - 3 \equiv 5 \bmod 3$
    c) $2x + 11 \equiv x + 4 \bmod 13$

41. For each linear congruence below, determine whether or not the congruence has any solutions, and if so, how many (incongruent) solutions it has
    a) $4x \equiv 6 \bmod 13$
    b) $2x \equiv 5 \bmod 7$
    c) $3x \equiv 6 \bmod 9$
    d) $103x \equiv 444 \bmod 999$
    e) $15x \equiv 9 \bmod 25$

42. Solve the systems of congruences

    $x \equiv 4 \pmod 7$

    $x \equiv 5 \pmod 8$

    where, $0 \leq x < 56$

43. When Mike wrote down the UPC Code on my can of College Inn Light & Fat Free Chicken Broth, he thinks he may have switched the 3rd and 4th digits. The number he wrote down is 02040322009, where the last digit is the check digit. Did Mike make a mistake? Explain your answer.

44. Find all incongruent solutions of the congruences below. If there is no solution, explain why.
    a) $3x \equiv 6 \bmod 7$
    b) $4x \equiv 3 \bmod 8$
    c) $50x \equiv 60 \bmod 300$
    d) $3x \equiv 6 \bmod 1810$

45. Compute the value $17^{39} \bmod 21$. Express the result as a least residue.

46. Consider the following UPC 12-digit bar code: $3 - 12980 - x6115 - 8$.

    a) Show work that finds the value of the missing digit x.
    b) Write the solution in modular form.

47. Consider the following UPC 12-digit bar code: $0 - 8x411 - 49561 - 3$.

    a) Show work that finds the value of the missing digit x.
    b) Write the solution in modular form.

48. Find the least residue r of the congruence $7k \equiv r \bmod 5$ for $k = 1, 2, 3, 4, 5$.

49. For a parade, when a group of scouts are lined up in 4's, there is 1 person left out; when they try lining up in 5's, there are 2 left out; and when lining up in 7's there are 3 left out.

    a) Set up the system of three linear congruences for this situation.
    b) Use the method of the Chinese Remainder Theorem to determine the total number of scouts in the group.

50. Find a if $a \equiv 32 \bmod 19$ and $52 \le a \le 70$.

51. Without using numerical values, prove that for a any integer, $a \equiv a \bmod m$.

52. Consider the 10-digit textbook ISBN code as follows: $0198x38049$.

    a) Find the missing digit x.
    b) Write the solution using modulo form.

53. A band of 7 pirates stole an undetermined number of gold coins. When they divided the coins equally among themselves, 3 coins were left over. Then they fought over who should get the extra coins and one of the pirates was slain. When the remaining pirates divided the coins equally among themselves again, no coins were left over. What are the possibilities for the number of coins that they could have stolen? (Hint: Let x be the number of gold coins. Write the congruences that x must satisfy.)

54. What is the remainder when 65432^2 is divided by 9?

55. What is the remainder when 123456^3 is divided by 4?

56. Find all the solutions to the congruences

    a) $51x \equiv 0 \bmod 17$
    b) $165x \equiv 84 \bmod 221$
    c) $143x \equiv 169 \bmod 10$

Section 5.7   Activities

1. Research the proof of the divisibility test for 7.

2. Tables for modular arithmetic have many uses. They provide us with a way to visualize addition and multiplication of least residues mod m. We will use these arithmetic tables to illustrate a method of designing a quilt. The instructions below are for the addition table.

3. Modular Arithmetic Quilts Using Table 5.1 for addition modulo 5, replace each number with a symbol. For example, replace "0" with a polka dots, "1" with horizontal stripes, "2" with vertical stripes, "3" with diagonal lines upper left to lower right, and four with diagonal lines from upper right to lower left. You may find an interesting pattern.

4. More creative designs can be found. Create one for yourself. An example appears below.

Again, using 25 modulo 5 addition, each number was replaced by a figure taken from the Mount McKinley photo below. You can use any figure you would like, and choose completely different figures or choose one and rotate it into different positions. For this example, two squares were cut from the photograph below and then rotated to make 5 different figures.

The photo below is an original photo of Mount McKinley, taken by Agnes M. Rash.

The squares cut out of the photograph are part of the mountain and the sea gull, shown below.

To make the five different figures used to represent the five least residues modulo 5, the bird was rotated. Here is how the figures were matched up with the least residues. (There is no method for doing this; different assignments will just make different patterns.)

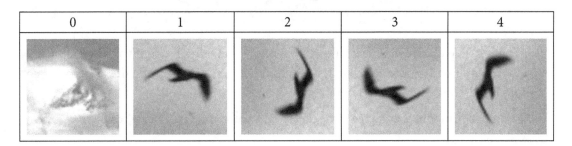

0	1	2	3	4

The pattern below comes from substituting the figures into the addition table modulo 5. Notice the different patterns in the table, forming a modulo 5 quilt.

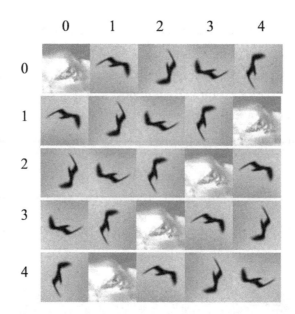

This next quilt was made by reflecting the pattern formed vertically and horizontally.

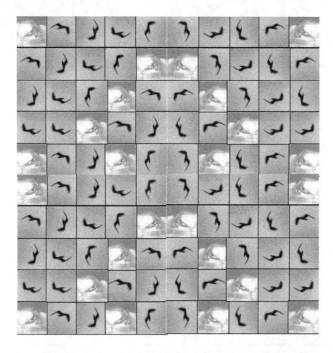

5. Form your own patterns and create a mod 5 picture table or quilt using your own design and either an addition or a multiplication table. (For example, try the six sides of a die as your patterns with a modulo 7 addition or multiplication table).

6. Use a composite modulus and create the table and a pattern for each least residue.

7. **Modular Sudoku**

   In Modular Sudoku, the integers in each row/column are congruent to the integers 1 through 9 mod 10. In this version of Sudoku, find the least residue mod 10 and then continue as for a regular Sudoku puzzle. Solve the Modular Sudoku puzzle. Then see if you can make up one of your own.

	15		27	49				44
	11	54	55	22	33	8		
	77	2	11	78	54	55	23	
								89
				25	29	57		12
22	19			67		66	18	33
14	12		23			49		65
	28	39		16	57			
		66			45			98

This game can be combined with Multi-Sudoku. For example, use large numbers and reduce those mod 100, resulting in two-digit numbers and then find the greatest common divisor and proceed as above.

+	0	1	2	3	4
0	0	1	2	3	4
1	1	2	3	4	0
2	2	3	4	0	1
3	3	4	0	1	2
4	4	0	1	2	3

×	0	1	2	3	4
0	0	0	0	0	0
1	0	1	2	3	4
2	0	2	4	1	3
3	0	3	1	4	2
4	0	4	3	2	1

Notice that multiplication by zero always results in zero, so this least residue is usually left out of the multiplication table.

Leonhard Euler

(1707–1783)

Leonhard Euler was born in Basel, Switzerland and is considered one of the most prolific mathematicians of all time. He published over 700 books and articles, averaging more than 800 pages per year until his untimely death! St. Petersburg Academy continued to publish his remaining work, which took 47 years!

Leonard Euler's father, Paul, was a ministry, but he also attended lectures given by Jakob Bernoulli, who belonged to a family of well-known mathematicians. He encouraged his son Leonhard to study mathematics. Euler had a photographic memory and could complete complicated mathematics in his head. Leonhard's primary school did not teach mathematics, so Paul hired a tutor to provide lessons in mathematics (Pommersheim, 596). Euler enrolled at the University of Basel at the young age of 13 and graduated at 15. There he studied mathematics under Johann Bernoulli, Jakob's brother. He published his first research paper at age 18.

Since Switzerland is land locked, travel to centers of mathematical activity was difficult for Euler. However, his friends Nicolaus and Daniel Bernoulli (Johann's sons) moved to Russia and were mathematics professors at the prestigious St. Petersburg Academy. They convinced the Academy to hire Euler in physiology. Euler studied the subject at the University of Basel before arriving in Russia. At St. Petersburg Academy, he studied the relationship between physiology and mathematics, became an adjunct faculty member in the Mathematics department and later, a professor of physics. At the age of 26 he became the head of mathematics at the Academy.

That year, he married Catherine Gsell, with whom he had 13 children. He was a devoted father, and could multi-task, doing mathematics in his head while he played with his children. Unfortunately, only five of his children survived to become adults.

His papers brought him to the attention of prominent people. In 1741, King Frederick the Great invited Euler to be the director of mathematics at the Berlin Academy. Reluctant to leave his ties with St. Petersburg Academy, Euler accepted the position yet continued his administrative duties at St. Petersburg. He remained in this dual role for 25 years. In 1755 the Paris Academy of Sciences named him a member in recognition of his winning the biennial prize 12 times (Katz, 594). After the president of the Berlin Academy died in 1759, Euler took over as president, reporting directly to King Frederick. This position did not suit Euler, and he preferred St. Petersburg Academy. In 1766, Catherine the Great offered him a position.

Special Congruences and Numerical Functions

"God created the integers; all the rest is the work of humanity."

—*Leopold Kronecker*

Section 6.1   Introduction

In Section 5.2, we saw that we can simplify arithmetic in any modulus by first reducing the integers involved to the least residues. In particular, we looked at the example of finding the least residue of $2^{50} \bmod 15$. In this case, we found that $2^4 \equiv 1 \bmod 15$, and we were able to use this fact to find the least residue of 4. However, we don't always have such convenient numbers. In this section, we will look at some special congruences.

In this chapter, we will look at functions whose domain is the natural numbers. We are interested in the topic of congruences and introduce useful special congruences that have great importance in cryptography. The first, Wilson's Theorem, was first stated by John Wilson, but the first published proof was by the mathematician Joseph Lagrange. Wilson's Theorem is about factorials in congruences. The second, Fermat's Little Theorem was stated by Pierre de Fermat, although the first published proof was by Leonhard Euler. The last, Euler's Theorem, was stated and proved by Euler himself. Fermat's Little Theorem and Euler's Theorem both address problems when powers of natural numbers have a least residue of 1 in a particular modulus. Both Fermat's Little Theorem and Wilson's Theorem require that the modulus is prime, but Euler was able to generalize Fermat's Little Theorem so that a prime modulus is not required.

Before introducing Euler's Theorem in Section 6.4, we consider how functions are used and defined in Number Theory, because one of these functions, called the Euler ϕ-function (read Euler "phi"-function) is part of the congruence Euler discovered. For example, functions in Number Theory can sometimes provide alternate methods to solve linear congruences. In Chapter 7, we will look at how Euler's Theorem is used to create a secret code that is very difficult to crack.

Section 6.2   Wilson's Theorem

Reminder: The *factorial* of an integer n, written $n!$, is the product of n and all natural numbers less than n. For example, $5! = 5 \cdot 4 \cdot 3 \cdot 2 \cdot 1$. Factorials are useful in reducing natural numbers to the least residues. Notice that if we choose a modulus, $m = 4$ for example, then $4!$, $5!$, and any larger factorial will all be congruent to

0 modulo 4, since each of these will contain a factor of 4. Thus, if we are interested in factorials modulo m, the largest one to consider is $(m-1)!$. Example 6.1 illustrates this idea.

Example 6.1. For each value of m, find the least residue of $(m-1)!$ modulo m.

a) $m = 3$ d) $m = 4$

b) $m = 5$ e) $m = 8$

c) $m = 11$ f) $m = 9$

Solution:

a) $m = 3$: $(3-1)! \equiv 2 \bmod 3$

b) $m = 5$: $(5-1)! \equiv 4! \equiv 24 \equiv 4 \bmod 5$

c) $m = 11$: $(11-1)! = 10! = 10 \cdot 9 \cdot 8 \cdot 7 \cdot 6 \cdot 5 \cdot 4 \cdot 3 \cdot 2 \cdot 1 \equiv 10 \bmod 11$

d) $m = 4$: $(4-1)! \equiv 3! \equiv 6 \equiv 2 \bmod 4$

e) $m = 8$: $(8-1)! \equiv 7! \equiv 0 \bmod 8$

f) $m = 9$: $(9-1)! \equiv 8! \equiv 0 \bmod 9$

In Example 6.1, the first three values chosen for m are prime, and the last three are composite. Notice the difference in the results. When the modulus m is composite, $(m-1)!$ has least residue 0, except in the case when $m = 4$. In fact, if m is a composite integer other than 4, $(m-1)!$ will always be congruent to 0 modulo m. (Can you see why?) The proof of this fact is left as Exercise 19. Let's look at another example.

Example 6.2. Let $p = 7$. Find the value of 6!

Solution:

Writing out the terms of 6!, we have that

$$6 \cdot 5 \cdot 4 \cdot 3 \cdot 2 \cdot 1 \equiv 6 \equiv -1 \bmod 7$$

$$\text{So, } 6! \equiv -1 \bmod 7.$$

Examining this example carefully, each of the values 6, 5, 4, 3, 2, and 1 has a multiplicative inverse modulo 7. Also, notice that 6 and 1 are each their own inverse since $1^2 \equiv 1 \bmod 7$ and $6^2 \equiv 36 \equiv 1 \bmod 7$. Therefore, since there are four terms left, we should be able to match them up as inverses of each other. We see that $5 \cdot 3 \equiv 1 \bmod 7$ and $2 \cdot 4 \equiv 1 \bmod 7$. Therefore, if we rearrange the terms of 6!, putting inverses next to each other,

$$6 \cdot (5 \cdot 3) \cdot (4 \cdot 2) \cdot 1 \equiv 6 \bmod 7$$

$$\equiv (6 - 7) \bmod 7$$

$$\equiv -1 \bmod 7$$

Notice the following facts used in this example:

1. By Theorem 4.3, when a and p are relatively prime, the linear congruence $ax \equiv 1 \bmod p$ always has a solution.

2. Consequently, a has a multiplicative inverse mod p.

3. Wilson's theorem is expressed in two different ways, illustrated in Example 6.2: When $p = 7$. $6! = (p-1)! \equiv p-1 \equiv -1 \bmod p$, since $p \equiv 0 \bmod p$.

4. Whenever the modulus is prime, the integer 1 and the integer $p-1$ are their own inverses modulo p. This fact is useful in the proof of Wilson's Theorem, so it is stated in Lemma 6.1.

Lemma 6.1   If p is prime, then $p-1$ is its own inverse modulo p. In other words, $(p-1)^2 \equiv 1 \bmod p$.

Proof: Let p be a prime number. Then to show that $p-1$ is its own inverse, we must show that the congruence $(p-1)^2 \equiv 1 \bmod p$ is true. Starting on the left side:

$$(p-1)^2 \equiv p^2 - 2p + 1 \bmod p$$
$$\equiv 0 - 0 + 1 \bmod p$$
$$\equiv 1 \bmod p$$

∎

Therefore, $(p-1)$ is its own inverse modulo p.

Lemma 6.2 is a generalization of Lemma 6.1.

Lemma 6.2   If $m > 0$, then $m-1$ is its own inverse modulo m, i.e., $(m-1)^2 \equiv 1 \bmod m$

Proof: Let m be a positive integer. Then to show that $m-1$ is its own inverse modulo m, show that the congruence $(m-1)^2 \equiv 1 \bmod m$ is true. Starting on the left side:

$$(m-1)^2 \equiv m^2 - 2m + 1 \bmod m$$
$$\equiv 0 - 0 + 1 \bmod m$$
$$\equiv 1 \bmod m$$

Therefore, $(m-1)$ is its own inverse modulo m.

∎

Another interesting fact is stated in Lemma 6.3.

Lemma 6.3: If p is prime, then b is its own inverse modulo p if and only if $b \equiv 1 \bmod p$ or $b \equiv p - 1 \bmod p$.

Proof: ($\Rightarrow$) Show that if p is prime and b is its own inverse modulo p then $b \equiv 1 \bmod p$ or $b \equiv p - 1 \bmod p$.

Let p be prime and suppose b is its own inverse modulo p. From the definition of inverse, this means that $b^2 \equiv 1 \bmod p$. Subtracting 1 from both sides of this congruence, $b^2 - 1 \equiv 0 \bmod p$. Factoring the left side of the congruence, $(b - 1)(b + 1) \equiv 0 \bmod p$. From the definition of congruence, $p | (b - 1)(b + 1)$. Now by Euclid's Lemma (Theorem 4.3) either $p | (b-1)$ or $p | (b + 1)$. If $p | (b - 1)$ then by the definition of congruence, $b \equiv 1 \bmod p$. If $p | (b + 1)$ then $b \equiv -1 \bmod p$, and since $p \equiv 0 \bmod p$ we have that $b \equiv p - 1 \bmod p$.

Therefore, in a prime modulus, if b is its own inverse then $b \equiv 1 \bmod p$ or $b \equiv p - 1 \bmod p$.

($\Leftarrow$) Show that if $b \equiv 1 \bmod p$ or $b \equiv p - 1 \bmod p$, then b is its own inverse modulo p.

If $b \equiv 1 \bmod p$, then $b^2 \equiv 1^2 \equiv 1 \bmod p$, and b is its own inverse.
If $b \equiv p - 1 \bmod p$, then by Lemma 6.1 b is its own inverse modulo p.

■

Conjecture 6.1: If p is prime, then $(p - 1)! \equiv p - 1 \bmod p$. This conjecture is true and is stated in Wilson's theorem.

> **Theorem 6.1 (Wilson's Theorem)** If p is prime, then $(p - 1)! \equiv -1 \bmod p$.

Proof of Wilson's Theorem: Let p be a prime integer.
Then, we want to prove that $(p - 1)! \equiv -1 \bmod p$. Writing out the terms in the factorial, we have that

$$(p - 1)! = (p - 1)(p - 2)\cdots 3 \cdot 2 \cdot 1.$$

Note that if $p = 2$, then $(p-1) = 1$ and is therefore its own inverse.

So, we will prove the theorem for $p > 2$. Since p is prime and $p > 2$ we know that $(p-1)$ is an even number. According to the remark above, each least residue has a multiplicative inverse modulo p. Now, by Lemma 6.1, $(p-1)$ is its own inverse, and 1 is also its own inverse. Therefore, each of the remaining factors can be paired with its inverse, so that their product is 1 modulo p. Therefore, all the paired factors result in a 1 in the product, except for $(p-1)$.. Then,

$$(p-1)! \equiv (p-1)(p-2)\cdots 3 \cdot 2 \cdot 1 \equiv (p-1) \equiv p-1 \bmod p.$$

$$\therefore (p-1)! \equiv -1 \bmod p.$$

■

Example 6.3. Find the least residue of each of the following expressions in the given modulus.

a) 12! mod 13

b) 6! mod 7

c) 8! mod 7

d) 9! mod 11

e) 3! mod 5

f) 13! mod 11

Solution:

a) According to Wilson's Theorem (with $p = 13$), $12! \equiv -1 \bmod 13$. To find the least residue of -1, add 13 to -1 to get $12! \equiv 12 \bmod 13$.

b) Applying Wilson's Theorem with $p = 7$ gives $6! \equiv -1 \bmod 7 \equiv 6 \bmod 7$.

c) Since $8! \equiv 8 \cdot 7 \cdot 6 \cdots 2 \cdot 1$ contains a factor of 7, $8! \equiv 0 \bmod 7$.

d) This looks similar to the form of congruence in Wilson's Theorem, and the modulus 11 is prime, but notice that $9 = 11 - 2$, not $11 - 1$. However, if we rewrite the problem in terms of Wilson's Theorem, then we can use the theorem to solve the problem:

Applying Wilson's Theorem with $p = 11$ yields $10! \equiv -1 \bmod 11$. Rewrite 10! as 10(9!).

$$10 \cdot 9! \equiv -1 \bmod 11$$

Multiply both sides of the congruence by the multiplicative inverse of 10, which is 10,

$$10 \cdot 10 \cdot 9! \equiv 10 \cdot (-1) \bmod 11$$
$$9! \equiv -10 \bmod 11$$
$$9! \equiv 1 \bmod 11.$$

e) $3! \bmod 5 \equiv 6 \bmod 5 \equiv 1 \bmod 5$

f) $13! \bmod 11 \equiv 13 \cdot 12 \cdot 11! \equiv 0 \bmod 11$

There are two more interesting properties of factorials given in the next two theorems.

Theorem 6.2 If p is prime, then $(p-2)! \equiv 1 \bmod p$.

The proof of Theorem 6.2 is left as Exercise 15.

Theorem 6.3 If $m > 1$, then $m - 1$ is its own inverse modulo m, i.e. $(m-1)^2 \equiv 1 \bmod m$.

Proof: $(m-1)^2 \equiv m^2 + 2m + 1 \equiv 1 \bmod m$.

∎

1. Determine if $n = 721$ is prime and evaluate $(n-1)!$.

2. Determine if $n = 40323$ is prime and evaluate $(n-1)!$.

3. Verify that Wilson's Theorem is true for $p = 5$.

4. Verify that Wilson's Theorem is true for $p = 13$.

5. Write an equation that relates $p!$ and $(p-1)!$.

6. Write an equation that relates $(p-1)!$ and $(p-3)!$.

7. Find the least residue of each expression in the given modulus without a calculator. Show your work.
   a) $11! \equiv$ _____ mod 13
   b) $7! \equiv$ _____ mod 8

8. Find the least residue of each expression in the given modulus without a calculator. Show your work.
   a) $17! \equiv$ _____ mod 18
   c) $6! \equiv$ _____ mod 5
   b) $11! \equiv$ _____ mod 14
   d) $30! \equiv$ _____ mod 31

9. What is the least residue when $22!$ is divided by 23?

10. What is the least residue when $42!$ is divided by 41?

11. What is the least residue when $15!$ is divided by 17?

12. What is the least residue when $21!$ is divided by 23?

13. What is the least residue when $26!$ is divided by 29?

14. Show that the following statement is false:
    If m is a positive integer and b is its own inverse modulo m, then $b \equiv 1 \bmod m$ or $b \equiv m - 1 \bmod m$.

15. Prove **Theorem 6.2**. $\left(\text{Hint} : (p-1)! = (p-1)(p-2)!\right)$.

16. Prove that if $p > 2$ is prime, then $2(p-2)! \equiv -1 \bmod p$.

17. a) Prove that if $m > 0$ then $(m-1) \equiv -1 \bmod m$.

    b) Use the result from part a) to find the least residue of 40^{82} modulo 41.

    c) Use the results from part a) to find the least residue of 42^{101} modulo 43.

18. Prove that if $m > 0$, then $(m-2) \equiv -2 \bmod m$.

19. Prove that if m is composite and $m > 4$ then $(m-1)! \equiv 0 \bmod m$.

20. State and prove the converse of **Wilson's Theorem**.

21. Using Theorems 6.1 and 6.2, evaluate $(p-3)! \bmod p$.

Section 6.3   Fermat's Little Theorem

In Section 5.2, we learned that arithmetic in any modulus can be simplified by first reducing integers to their least residues. In example 5.8, we found the least residue of $2^{50} \bmod 15$. Fortunately, $2^4 \equiv 1 \bmod 15$, and using the division algorithm we found that $2^{50} \equiv 4 \bmod 15$. However, integers are not always so convenient.

In some cases, it is more difficult to find an exponent that makes an expression reduce to 1, and in other cases there may not be an exponent that reduces the expression to 1.

For instance, looking at powers of 9 modulo 15, none results in a least residue of 1:

$$9 \equiv 9 \bmod 15$$

$$9^2 \equiv 6 \bmod 15$$

$$9^3 \equiv 9 \bmod 15, \text{ etc.}$$

(You can check that this pattern continues.) In other cases, it may just be difficult to find an exponent that makes an expression reduce to 1. Fermat's Little Theorem provides some help to obtain a residue of 1, with a prime modulus.

Theorem 6.4 (Fermat's Little Theorem) If p is a prime number, and a is an integer such that $p \nmid a$, then $a^{p-1} \equiv 1 \bmod p$.

Remark: Notice that there are two conditions required to apply this Theorem: (1) The modulus p must be prime, and (2) p does not divide a. Since p is prime, this means that a and p have no factors in common, so another way to think of this is that a and p must be relatively prime.

Proof of Fermat's Little Theorem:

Let p be prime and let $a \in \mathbb{Z}$ such that $p \nmid a$. Now, consider the list of integers $1 \cdot a, 2 \cdot a, 3 \cdot a, \ldots, (p-1) \cdot a$. None of these can be divisible by p because a prime number cannot share any factors with a smaller integer, and it was given that $p \nmid a$. Also, none of the numbers on this list are congruent to each other modulo p. To see why, suppose that $ka \equiv ma \bmod p$ for distinct integers k and m. Then, from the definition of congruence, $p \mid (ka - ma)$ which can be rewritten as $p \mid a(k-m)$. By Euclid's Lemma, since $p \nmid a$, it must be true that $p \mid (k-m)$. Applying the definition of congruence tells us that $k \equiv m \bmod p$, but this is impossible since k and m were chosen to be distinct integers less than p.

Now, we have a list of $(p-1)$ distinct integers modulo p. Therefore, in some order, their least residues must be $1, 2, 3, \ldots, (p-1)$. Therefore,

$$(1 \cdot a)(2 \cdot a)(3 \cdot a) \cdots ((p-1) \cdot a) = 1 \cdot 2 \cdot 3 \cdots (p-1)a^{p-1} \equiv (p-)!a^{p-1} \bmod p.$$

and by factoring out a from each parentheses

$$(p-1)!a^{p-1} \equiv (p-1)! \bmod p.$$

Applying Wilson's Theorem and simplifying, we obtain the following:

$$-1 \cdot a^{p-1} \equiv -1 \bmod p$$

$$a^{p-1} \equiv 1 \bmod p$$

This proves the congruence in Fermat's Little Theorem. ∎

Example 6.4. For each pair of integers a and p given below, determine whether or not Fermat's Little Theorem can be used. If so, verify that the congruence given in the Theorem is true. If not, explain why Fermat's Little Theorem does not apply.

a) $a = 5$, $p = 11$

b) $a = 14$, $p = 9$

c) $a = 22$, $p = 3$

Solution:

a)   Fermat's Little Theorem applies to this example: 11 is prime, and 5 is not divisible by 11. Therefore, according to the Theorem:

$$5^{(11-1)} \equiv 1 \bmod 11$$
$$5^{10} \equiv 1 \bmod 11$$

b)   Fermat's Little Theorem does not apply to this case because 9 is not prime.

c)   Fermat's Little Theorem applies to this case since 3 is prime, and $3 \nmid 22$. Then, according to Fermat's Little Theorem, $22^2 \equiv 1 \bmod 3$.

Example 6.5. Use Fermat's Little Theorem to find the least residue when 4^{185} is divided by 7.

Solution:

The exponent here is large so your calculator may put the result in scientific notation.

First, write the question as a congruence to relate it to Fermat's Little Theorem. Since 7 is prime and 7 does not divide 4, Fermat's Little Theorem tells us that $4^6 \equiv 1 \bmod 7$.

Now, by the Euclidean Algorithm,

$$\text{Since } 185 = 6 \cdot 30 + 5, \text{ we can write } 4^{185} = 4^{6 \cdot 30 + 5} = \left(4^{6 \cdot 30}\right)\left(4^5\right) = \left(4^6\right)^{30}(4^5).$$

Then, using Fermat's Little Theorem,

$$4^{185} \equiv \left(4^6\right)^{30}\left(4^5\right) \bmod 7$$
$$\equiv (1)^{30}\left(4^5\right) \bmod 7$$
$$\equiv 4^5 \bmod 7$$
$$\equiv 4^2 \cdot 4^3 \bmod 7$$
$$\equiv 16 \cdot 64 \bmod 7$$
$$\equiv 2 \cdot 1 \bmod 7$$
$$\equiv 2 \bmod 7$$

Therefore, 2 is the least residue when 4^{185} is divided by 7.

Fermat's Little Theorem can be used to solve linear congruences. In Chapter 5, we developed a method to solve linear congruences of the form $ax \equiv b \bmod m$, based on the linear equations of two variables we studied in Chapter 4. If the congruence satisfies the conditions of Fermat's Little Theorem—that the modulus m is prime and $a \not\equiv 0 \bmod m$, then we can use Fermat's Little Theorem to develop an alternate solution technique.

Example 6.6. Use Fermat's Little Theorem to find a solution for $2x \equiv 3 \bmod 5$.

Solution:

Since 5 is prime, and 5 does not divide 2, Fermat's Little Theorem applies: $2^4 \equiv 1 \bmod 5$. So $2^4 \cdot x \equiv 1 \cdot x \bmod 5$. Since we can multiply both sides of a congruence by the same value we get,

$$2^3 \cdot 2x \equiv 2^3 \cdot 3 \bmod 5$$
$$2^4 \cdot x \equiv 8 \cdot 3 \bmod 5$$
$$x \equiv 4 \bmod 5$$

Therefore, any integer congruent to 4 modulo 5 is a solution to the given congruence.

Example 6.7. For each congruence below, find the least residue if possible. If Fermat's Little Theorem cannot be used, explain why not.

a) $4x \equiv 5 \bmod 7$

b) $8x \equiv 9 \bmod 13$

c) $5x \equiv 2 \bmod 6$

Solution:

a) $4x \equiv 5 \bmod 7$

Since 7 is prime, and 7 does not divide 4, we can apply Fermat's Little Theorem to obtain the congruence $4^6 \equiv 1 \bmod 7$. Therefore, to get x by itself in the congruence, we can multiply both sides by 4^5.

$$4^5 \cdot 4x \equiv 4^5 \cdot 5 \bmod 7$$
$$4^6 \cdot x \equiv 4^5 \cdot 5 \bmod 7$$
$$x \equiv \left(4^2\right)^2 \cdot 4 \cdot 5 \bmod 7$$
$$x \equiv (16)^2 \cdot 20 \bmod 7$$
$$x \equiv 2^2 \cdot 6 \bmod 7$$
$$x \equiv 24 \bmod 7$$
$$x \equiv 3 \bmod 7$$

b) $8x \equiv 9 \bmod 13$

Again, since 13 is prime and 13 does not divide 8, Fermat's Little Theorem says $8^{12} \equiv 1 \bmod 13$. Therefore, to get x by itself multiply both sides of the congruence by 8^{11}.

$$8^{11} \cdot 8x \equiv 8^{11} \cdot 9 \bmod 13$$
$$8^{12}x \equiv 8^{11} \cdot 9 \bmod 13$$
$$x \equiv 8^{11} \cdot 9 \bmod 13$$

Least residue solutions are preferable so, reduce 8^{11} modulo 13.
First, $8^2 \equiv 12 \equiv -1 \bmod 13$. Therefore:

$$8^{11} \equiv \left(8^2\right)^5 \cdot 8 \bmod 13$$
$$\equiv \left(-1\right)^5 \cdot 8 \bmod 13$$
$$\equiv -8 \bmod 13$$
$$\equiv 5 \bmod 13$$

Substituting into the congruence for x,

$$x \equiv 8^{11} \cdot 9 \bmod 13$$
$$\equiv 5 \cdot 9 \bmod 13$$
$$x \equiv 6 \bmod 13$$

c) $5x \equiv 2 \bmod 6$

Fermat's Little Theorem does not apply since the modulus, 6, is not prime. However, you can check that if $x \equiv 4 \bmod 6$, then x is a solution to the congruence.

From Example 6.7, we see that while Fermat's Little Theorem is a quicker method of finding a solution to a congruence when the prime modulus is relatively small, the effort to find the least residue of the solution generally increases as the value of the modulus increases.

Exercise Set 6.3

1. For each pair of integers a and p given below, determine whether or not **Fermat's Little Theorem** can be used. If so, verify that the congruence given in the Theorem is true. If not, explain why not.

a) $a = 12$, $p = 5$
b) $a = 6$, $p = 7$
c) $a = 4$, $p = 15$
d) $a = 42$, $p = 3$

2. Apply **Fermat's Little Theorem** when appropriate to reduce the integer to one without an exponent. If it is not appropriate, state that the theorem does not apply.

a) $2^{10} \equiv ? \bmod 7$

b) $3^{12} \equiv ? \bmod 14$

c) $3^{17} \equiv ? \bmod 17$

3. For each pair of integers a and p given below, determine whether or not **Fermat's Little Theorem** can be used. If so, verify that the congruence given in the Theorem is true. If not, explain why not.

   a) $a = 8$, $p = 13$

   b) $a = 12$, $p = 33$

   c) $a = 21$, $p = 7$

   d) $a = 9$, $p = 5$.

4. Find the least residue of 2^{5000} modulo 13.

5. Find the least residue when 5^{204} is divided by 11

6. For each of the congruences below, first determine whether the congruence has a solution. If so, find the solution using Fermat's Little Theorem whenever possible. (If it is not possible, explain why not.)

   a) $3x \equiv 10 \bmod 11$

   b) $5x \equiv 2 \bmod 9$

   c) $4x \equiv 3 \bmod 7$

   d) $6x \equiv 8 \bmod 17$

Section 6.4   Euler's Function

Functions are very useful in Number Theory. The domain of these functions can be the integers or a subset of the integers. In fact, we are most interested in functions whose domains are natural numbers. These functions whose domains are positive integers are sometimes called *numerical functions*, *number theoretic functions*, or *arithmetic functions*.

Numerical functions are often used to count something. In this section, we consider the "Euler phi-function" and is denoted by $\phi(n)$, where ϕ is the lowercase Greek letter "phi".

> **Definition 6.1** *Euler phi-function,* $\phi(n)$: For an integer $n > 0$,
> $$\phi(n) = \text{the number of positive ingeters } x \leq n \text{ such that } \gcd(x, n) = 1$$

Example 6.8. Find the value of $\phi(n)$ in each example below.

a) $\phi(4)$

b) $\phi(7)$

c) $\phi(10)$

Solution:

a) The positive integers less than or equal to 4 are: 1, 2, 3, and 4. Since 2 and 4 both share a common factor with 4, only 1 and 3 are relatively prime to 4.
   Therefore, $\phi(4) = 2$.

b) The positive integers less than or equal to 7 are: 1, 2, 3, 4, 5, 6, 7. All of these are relatively prime to 7 except for 7 itself. Therefore, $\phi(7) = 6$.

c) The positive integers less than or equal to 10 that are also relatively prime to 10 are 1, 3, 7, and 9. Therefore, $\phi(10) = 4$.

Example 6.9. Find $\phi(40)$ and $\phi(41)$.

Solution:

To find $\phi(40)$, count the number of positive integers less than 40 that are relatively prime to 40. Since all even integers will share a divisor of 2 with 40, consider the odd integers less than 40. If an odd integer is not relatively prime to 40, they will share a common divisor of 5. So, the integers less than 40 and relatively prime to 40 are: 1, 3, 7, 9, 11, 13, 17, 19, 21, 23, 27, 29, 31, 33, 37, 39. Therefore, $\phi(40) = 16$.

To find $\phi(41)$, notice that 41 is prime, so its only divisors are 1 and 41. Therefore, each integer from 1 through 40 is relatively prime to 41 and $\phi(41) = 40$.

Although the definition of $\phi(n)$ is given in terms of counting, evaluating the function by listing and counting is difficult for large numbers such as 1000 or larger is very time-consuming. On the other hand, the case of $\phi(41)$ illustrates that the value of ϕ is easy to find for certain natural numbers. As another example, 733 is a relatively large number, but it is prime. Hence, its only divisors are 1 and 733, so all integers from 1 through 732 are relatively prime to 733. Therefore, $\phi(733) = 732$. This idea is generalized in Theorem 6.5.

> **Theorem 6.5** If p is prime, then $\phi(p) = p - 1$.

Proof: Let p be a prime number. Then the only divisors of p are 1 and p. Therefore, all positive integers less than p must be relatively prime to p. Therefore $\phi(p) = p - 1$.

The next example considers values of Euler's function when n is a power of a prime.

∎

Example 6.10. Find the value of $\phi(n)$ for each example below and look for a pattern for $\phi(n)$ when n is the power of a prime.

a) $\phi(2^3)$

b) $\phi(3^2)$

c) $\phi(5^2)$

d) $\phi(3^4)$

Solution:

a) To find $\phi(2^3)$, count the positive integers less than or equal to 8 and relatively prime to 8. The integers which share a common divisor with 8 are 2, 4, 6, and 8. Therefore, the number of integers relatively prime to 8 will be $8 - 4 = 4$, so $\phi(2^3) = 4$.

b) To find $\phi(3^2)$, count the positive integers less than or equal to 9, and relatively prime to 9. The integers which share a common divisor with 9 are 3, 6, and 9, so there are $9 - 3 = 6$ integers that are relatively prime. Therefore, $\phi(3^2) = 6$.

c) Again, count the positive integers less than or equal to 25 that are relatively prime to 25. Notice that as in the examples above, since 25 is a power of a prime, the only possible divisors are powers of that prime: in this case, 5 or 25. This makes it fairly easy to list the numbers less than or equal to 25 that will share a common factor other than 1. List the integers which have 5 as a factor: 5, 10, 15, 20, 25. Note that there are five such integers, and there are 25 integers from 1 to 25, so $\phi(5^2) = 25 - 5 = 20$.

d) In this example, let us see if we can inductively reason the value of $\phi(3^4) = \phi(81)$. We know that since three is prime, the integers that are not relatively prime to 81 must be multiples of 3. The question is, how many multiples of 3 are there between 1 and 81. We can start counting them: $1 \cdot 3$, $2 \cdot 3$, $3 \cdot 3$,..., and we will stop when we get to $81 = 3^4 = 27 \cdot 3 = 3^3 \cdot 3$. So, there are 3^3 multiplies of 3 from 1 to 81 which means that the rest of the integers are relatively prime to 81. Therefore, $\phi(3^4) = 3^4 - 3^3 = 81 - 27 = 54$.

Each of the examples above fits the same pattern which is generalized in Theorem 6.6.

Theorem 6.6 If p is prime and a is a positive integer, then $\phi(p^a) = p^a - p^{a-1}$.

The proof of Theorem 6.6 is left as Exercise 14.

Example 6.11. Evaluate $\phi(64)$ and $\phi(2401)$.

Solution:

$64 = 2^6$. Apply Theorem 6.5: $\phi(64) = 2^6 - 2^5 = 64 - 32 = 32$

$2401 = 7^4$. Hence $\phi(2401) = \phi(7^4) = 7^4 - 7^3 = 2401 - 343 = 2058$.

To evaluate $\phi(n)$ for values of n that are not prime, look for another pattern in values of $\phi(n)$, when n is composite. The next step is to consider Euler phi-function if the number is the product of two distinct primes, $\phi(p \cdot q)$. Example 6.12 provides several examples to discover a pattern.

Example 6.12. Find the value of $\phi(n)$ for each example below and look for a pattern for $\phi(n)$ at the product of two distinct primes.

    a) $\phi(6)$

    b) $\phi(10)$

    c) $\phi(15)$

    d) $\phi(21)$

Solution:

a) The integers less than 6 and relatively prime to 6 are 1 and 5. Therefore, $\phi(6)=2$. Also, notice that $6=2\cdot3$, and $\phi(2)=1$, and $\phi(3)=2$.

b) From Example 6.8 (c), we know that $\phi(10)=4$. Also, notice that $10=2\cdot5$, and $\phi(2)=1$, and $\phi(5)=4$. So, $\phi(10)=\phi(2)\phi(5)$.

c) The integers less than 15 and relatively prime to 15 are 1, 2, 3, 4, 7, 8, 11, 13, 14. Therefore, $\phi(15)=8$. Now, $15=3\cdot5$, and in this list, the numbers left out are those with a factor of 5 or a factor of 3. Also, $\phi(3)=2$, and $\phi(5)=4$. So, $\phi(15)=\phi(3)\phi(5)$.

d) Using the examples above, if the natural number is the product of primes, it appears that we can find the value of $\phi(21)$ by factoring the number into the product of two primes: $21=3\cdot7$, so integers that are divisible by 3 or divisible by 7 will share a factor with 21. There are seven multiples of 3 less than or equal to 21: $1\cdot3,2\cdot3,\ldots,7\cdot3$. Also, there are three multiples of 7 less than or equal to 21: $1\cdot7,2\cdot7$, and $3\cdot7$. In each case, the last multiple is 21, so subtract the seven multiples of 3 less than or equal to 21 and the two multiples of 7 that are less than 21 to get $\phi(21)=21-7-(3-1)=12$. Again, notice that $\phi(3)=2$ and $\phi(7)=6$. The pattern continues to work: $\phi(21)=\phi(3)\phi(7)$.

The pattern illustrated in Example 6.12 always holds and is stated in Theorem 6.7.

Theorem 6.7 If p and q are distinct primes, then $\phi(p\cdot q)=\phi(p)\cdot\phi(q)=(p-1)(q-1)$.

Proof: Let p and q be distinct primes. To calculate the value of $\phi(p\cdot q)$, systematically count the number of integers less than or equal to $p\cdot q$ that are relatively prime to $p\cdot q$. In order to do this, we will first look at the number of integers that do share a common factor, and then subtract this number from $p\cdot q$, the total number of integers from 1 to $p\cdot q$. Table 6.1 shows the multiples of q that are relatively prime to p, and the multiples of p that are relatively prime to q.

$1\cdot q$	$2\cdot q$	$3\cdot q$	$\ldots$	$(p-1)\cdot q$
$1\cdot p$	$2\cdot p$	$1\cdot p$	$\ldots$	$(q-1)\cdot p$

Table 6.1

There are $p-1$ multiples of q less than pq. Similarly, there are $q-1$ multiples of p less than pq. Therefore, the total number of integers less than $p \cdot q$ is

$$\phi(p \cdot q) = = (p-1)(q-1)$$
$$= \phi(p) \cdot \phi(q)$$

∎

In fact, Theorem 6.7 can be generalized beyond two distinct primes. For example, what if we want to find $\phi(20)$. Since $20 = 2 \cdot 10$, is it true that $\phi(20) = \phi(2) \cdot \phi(10) = 1 \cdot 4 = 4$? Unfortunately, the answer is NO. If we count up the integers less than 20 and relatively prime to 20, we get $\phi(20) = 8$. There is a general formula for $\phi(n)$, though, based on the prime power factorization of n.

Theorem 6.8 If $n = p_1^{n_1} \cdot p_2^{n_2} \cdots p_k^{n_k}$ is the prime power factorization of n, then

$$\phi(n) = (p_1 - 1)\left(p_1^{n_1-1}\right)(p_2 - 1)\left(p_2^{n_2-1}\right) \ldots (p_k - 1)(p_1^{n_k-1})$$

The proof of this theorem is beyond the scope of this textbook, but we will apply it without proof.

Example 6.13. Find $\phi(100)$ and $\phi(315)$.

Solution:

To use Theorem 6.8, first find the prime factorizations of 100 and 315.
$100 = 2^2 \cdot 5^2$ and $315 = 3^2 \cdot 5 \cdot 7$ Now, applying the theorem we get

$$\phi(100) = (2-1)\left(2^1\right)(5-1)\left(5^1\right) = 2 \cdot 4 \cdot 5 = 40$$

and

$$\phi(315) = (3-1)(3^1)(5-1)5^0(7-1)(7^0) = (2)(3(4)(6) = 144.$$

In the next section, we will explore Euler's Theorem which generalizes Fermat's Little Theorem.

Exercise Set 6.4

1. Find all values of n for which $\phi(n) = 1$.

2. Find $\phi(n)$ for $1 \le n \le 12$. Describe any patterns you see in the values of ϕ.

3. Evaluate $\phi(96)$.

4. Evaluate $\phi(100)$.

5. Find the value of $235^3 \bmod 124$

6. Compute the least residue of each integer.

   a) $29^{198} \pmod{21}$

   b) $29^{198} \pmod{20}$

   c) $29^{198} \pmod{35}$

7. Find the last three digits of the integer 3^{246}.

8. Find the last two digits of the integer 11^{244}.

9. Find the last four digits of the integer 9^{404}.

10. Find the least residue when 6^{341} is divided by 5.

11. Find a counterexample to show that the following statement is false: If $n < m$ then $\phi(n) < \phi(m)$.

12. Prove that if n is a power of 2, then $\phi(n)$ is an even integer.

13. What must be true about n for $\phi(n)$ to be divisible by 4?

14. Prove **Theorem 6.6.**

15. Show that if $\gcd(a, m) = 1$, then the inverse of a modulo m is $a^{\phi(m)-1}$.

16. Prove that if p is prime and $p \nmid a$ then $a^{p-1} \equiv 1 \bmod p$.

Section 6.5   Euler's Theorem

Euler's Theorem is more general than Fermat's Little Theorem. The congruence in this theorem provides a method of counting the number of natural numbers relatively prime to m when the number has a least residue of 1. The modulus does not have to be prime. We will prove the theorem using a sequence of lemmas. Theorem 6.9 is the statement that we prove in this section.

> **Theorem 6.9 Euler's Theorem** If m is a positive integer and a is an integer with $\gcd(a, m) = 1$, then
> $$a^{\phi(m)} \equiv 1 \bmod m.$$

In order to prove Euler's Theorem, the following Lemmas are useful.

> **Lemma 6.4:** If $\gcd(c, m) = 1$ and $ac \equiv bc \bmod m$ then $a \equiv b \bmod m$.

Proof: Let $\gcd(c, m) = 1$ and suppose $ac \equiv bc \bmod m$. By the definition of congruence, $m \mid (ac - bc)$. Therefore, by the definition of divides, $ac - bc = mk$ for an integer k. Factoring the left-hand side, $c(a - b) = mk$. Now, since $\gcd(c, m) = 1$, m must divide $(a - b)$. (The proof of this fact is Exercise 8 in Section 4.3). Since $m \mid (a - b)$, $a \equiv b \bmod m$ by the definition of congruence. ∎

> **Lemma 6.5:** If $\gcd(a, m) = 1$ and $\gcd(b, m) = 1$ then $\gcd(ab, m) = 1$.

Proof: Suppose $\gcd(a, m) = 1$ and $\gcd(b, m) = 1$. Then there must be integers r and s such that $ra + sm = 1$, and integers k and l such that $kb + lm = 1$. Then, $(ra + sm)kb + lm = 1$. Simplifying the left side, we obtain:

$$rakb + smkb = lm = 1$$
$$rk(ab) + (skb + l)m = 1.$$

This shows that a linear combination of ab and m is equal to 1. Now, call $\gcd(ab, m) = d$. Since $d \mid ab$ and $d \mid m$, it is also true that $d \mid (rk(ab) + (skb + l)m)$. Therefore, $d \mid 1$. Since d must be a positive integer, this tells us that $d = 1$. Therefore, $\gcd(ab, m) = 1$.

$\blacksquare$

Lemma 6.5 can be generalized to more than two pairs of integers. The general statement is given below in Lemma 6.6. The proof is similar to that of Lemma 6.5 but is beyond the scope of this course.

Lemma 6.6: If $\gcd(b_1, m) = \gcd(b_2, m) = \cdots = \gcd(b_n, m) = 1$, then $\gcd(b_1 \cdot b_2 \cdots b_n, m) = 1$.

Now we will proceed with the proof of Theorem 6.9 (Euler's Theorem).

Proof of Euler's Theorem:

Let $m > 0$ and let a be an integer such that $\gcd(a, m) = 1$. Since $\phi(m)$ counts the number of integers less than m that are relatively prime to m, listing these integers will produce $\phi(m)$ numbers.

Let $1, b_1, b_2, \ldots, b_{\phi(m)}$ be the integers less than m and relatively prime to m.

Multiply each element of this list by a. This produces a second list of integers:

$$a, ab_1, ab_2, \ldots, ab_{\phi(m)}.$$

By Lemma 6.5, since $\gcd(a, m) = 1$ and $\gcd(b_i, m) = 1$ it is also true that $\gcd(ab_i, m) = 1$ for $i = 1, 2, \ldots, \phi(m)$. Therefore, the least residues of each of the ab_i terms must be on the first list since it includes all the least residues of integers relatively prime to m. The question is, are any of the ab_i congruent to each modulo m, or are they matched one for one with the terms on the original list? To find out, suppose that $ab_i \equiv ab_j \bmod m$. Applying the definition of congruence, we obtain the following:

$$ab_i \equiv ab_j \bmod m$$
$$m \mid (ab_i - ab_j)$$
$$m \mid a(b_i - b_j)$$

Since $\gcd(m, a) = 1$, $m \mid (b_i - b_j)$ by Exercise 19 of Section 4.3.

Again, applying the definition of congruence, this means that $b_i \equiv b_j \bmod m$. But this is a contradiction since the list of the b_n's were the distinct integers less than m and relatively prime to n. Therefore, the least residues of the integers ab_i in some order are $1, b_1, b_2, \ldots, b_{\phi(m)}$. This means that:

$$a \cdot ab_1 \cdot ab_2 \cdots \cdots ab_{\phi(m)} \equiv 1 \cdot b_1 \cdot b_2 \cdots \cdots b_{\phi(m)} \bmod m.$$

Factoring the a out of the terms on the left,

$$a^{\phi(m)}(b_1 \cdot b_2 \cdots \cdots b_{\phi(m)}) \equiv b_1 \cdot b_2 \cdots \cdots b_{\phi(m)} \bmod m.$$

By Lemma 6.5, $\gcd\left(b_1 \cdot b_2 \cdots \cdots b_{\phi(m)}, m\right) = 1$. Therefore, by Lemma 6.3,

$$a^{\phi(m)} \equiv 1 \bmod m.$$

This proves Euler's Theorem.

■

Example 6.14. Find the value of the least residue of $22165^{\emptyset(441)}$ (mod 441).

Solution:

The prime power factorization of 441 is $3^2 7^2$, and 22165 is relatively prime to 441.
$\emptyset(441) = \emptyset(3^2 7^2) = 2(3)(6)(7) = 252$ by Theorem 6.8.

$$\therefore 22165^{\emptyset(441)} \ (\bmod \ 441) \equiv 22165^{221} \bmod 441 \equiv 1 \bmod 441.$$

In the next section, we will look at two more examples of numerical functions: the "number of positive divisors function", and the "sum of positive divisors function."

Exercise Set 6.5

1. Use Euler's theorem to evaluate $9^{13} \bmod 11$

2. Evaluate $10^{13} \bmod 11$ by any method.

3. Find values for a, b and m so that Lemma 6.5 applies.

4. Find values for a, b and m so that Lemma 6.5 does not apply.

5. Find values for a, b and m so that Lemma 6.6 applies.

6. Find values for a, b and m so that Lemma 6.6 does not apply.

7. If p is an odd prime, explain why $\phi(p^3)$ is even.

8. Determine whether $\phi(p^4)$ is even or odd for $p > 2$.

9. Prove or disprove: $\phi(pq)$ is always divisible by 4 when p and q are primes.

10. Prove or disprove: $\phi(pqr)$ is always divisible by 8 when p, q, and r are all primes.

Section 6.6   More Numerical Functions

Another numerical function is the "number of positive divisors function," $d(n)$. The letter d is used to represent the function, as a reminder that this function counts divisors. Although its name isn't catchy, it does describe what this function does. Again, $d(n)$ is defined on the positive integers, and $d(n)$ counts the number of positive divisors of n.

> **Definition 6.2** For an integer $n > 0$, $d(n) =$ *the number of positive divisors of n.*

Example 6.15. Find the value of $d(n)$ in each example below.

   a) $d(4)$

   b) $d(7)$

   c) $d(10)$

Solution:

   a)   The positive divisors of 4 are 1, 2, and 4, so $d(4) = 3$.

   b)   Since 7 is prime, 1 and 7 are the only positive divisors of 7, so $d(7) = 2$.

   c)   The positive divisors of 10 are 1, 2, 5, and 10, so $d(10) = 4$.

The following theorem specifies how to find the number of divisors of any natural number.

> **Theorem 6.10** If $n = p_1^{a_1} \cdot p_2^{a_2} \cdot p_3^{a_3} \cdots\cdots p_k^{a_k}$, then $d(n) = (a_1 + 1)(a_2 + 1)\cdots\cdots(a_k + 1)$

Example 6.16. Find the value of $d(n)$ in each example below.

   a) $d\left(2^4 3^2 7^{12}\right)$

   b) $d\left(2^6 5^4 11^{10}\right)$

   c) $d\left(5^5 41^{41}\right)$

Solution:

   a) $d\left(2^4 3^2 7^{12}\right) = (4+1)(2+1)(7+1) = (5)(3)(8) = 120$

   b) $d\left(2^6 5^4 11^{10}\right) = (6+1)(4+1)(10+1) = (7)(5)(11) = 385$

   c) $d\left(5^5 41^{41}\right) = (5+1)(41+1) = (6)(42) = 294$

The last numerical function we will look at in this section is called the "sum of positive divisors function," and is written as $\sigma(n)$, using the lowercase Greek letter "sigma," σ, to represent "sum."

Definition 6.3 The *sum of the divisors function*: For an integer $n > 0$,
$$\sigma(n) = \textit{the sum of the positive divisors of } n.$$

Example 6.17. The value of $\sigma(n)$ in each example below.

  a) $\sigma(4)$
  b) $\sigma(7)$
  c) $\sigma(10)$

Solution:

  a) Since the positive divisors of 4 are 1, 2, and 4, $\sigma(4) = 1 + 2 + 4 = 7$.

  b) Since the positive divisors of 7 are 1 and 7, $\sigma(7) = 1 + 7 = 8$.

  c) Since the positive divisors of 10 are 1, 2, 5 and 10, $\sigma(10) = 1 + 2 + 5 + 10 = 18$.

Again, there is a formula for the sum of the divisors of a number, given is Theorem 6.11.

Theorem 6.11 If $n = p_1^{a_1} \cdot p_2^{a_2} \cdot p_3^{a_3} \cdots p_k^{a_k}$, then $\sigma(n) = \dfrac{p_1^{a_1+1} - 1}{p_1 - 1} \cdot \dfrac{p_2^{a_2+1} - 1}{p_2 - 1} \cdots \dfrac{p_k^{a_k+1} - 1}{p_k - 1}$.

The proof of Theorem 6.10 and 6.11 are beyond the scope of this textbook; however, we will use these theorems without proof.

Example 6.18. Find the value of $\sigma(n)$ in each example below.

  a) $\sigma(2^4 7^2)$
  b) $\sigma(3^3 11^2)$
  c) $\sigma(2^5 5^3 13^2)$

Solution:

  a) $\sigma\left(2^4 7^2\right) = \dfrac{2^5 - 1}{1} \cdot \dfrac{7^3 - 1}{6} = 1{,}767$.

  b) $\sigma\left(3^3 11^2\right) = \dfrac{3^4 - 1}{2} \cdot \dfrac{11^3 - 1}{10} = 5{,}320$.

  c) $\sigma\left(2^5 5^3 13^2\right) = \dfrac{2^6 - 1}{1} \cdot \dfrac{5^4 - 1}{4} \cdot \dfrac{13^3 - 1}{12} = 884{,}988$.

Definition 6.4 An integer n is a **perfect number** if and only if n is equal to the sum of all of its divisors except for itself.

Example 6.19. Make a conjecture about $\sigma(n)$ when n is a perfect number.

Solution:

In order to make a conjecture, we will test some examples. The two smallest perfect numbers are 6 and 28 ($6=1+2+3$ and $28=1+2+4+7+14$). Start by comparing σ for these two perfect numbers, as well as two numbers which are not perfect. For variety, we'll pick an even, 12, and a prime, 17.

$$\sigma(6)=1+2+3+6=12$$
$$\sigma(28)=1+2+4+7+14+28=56$$
$$\sigma(12)=1+2+3+4+6+12=28$$
$$\sigma(7)=1+7=8$$

Notice that $\sigma(6)=2\cdot6=12$ and $\sigma(28)=2\cdot28=56$. That is not the case in the last two examples: $\sigma(12)$ is greater than $2\cdot12=24$ and $\sigma(7)$ is less than $2\cdot7=14$. At this point, one possible conjecture is the following:

Conjecture 6.2: If n is a perfect number, then $\sigma(n)=\sigma(2n)$.

This conjecture is true. The proof is left as Exercise 18.

The function $\sigma(n)$ has another formula that can be used to calculate it. Although the formula is less esthetically appealing, it is useful in Chapter 7 for producing codes.

Theorem 6.12 If $n=p_1^{n_1}\cdot p_2^{n_2}\cdots\cdots p_k^{n_k}$ is the prime power factorization of n, then

$$\phi(n)=n\left(1-\frac{1}{p_1}\right)\left(1-\frac{1}{p_2}\right)\left(1-\frac{1}{p_3}\right)\cdots\left(1-\frac{1}{p_k}\right)$$

Note that if p_i represents one of the prime factors in the prime factorization of n, then since p_i is a divisor of n, this expression will always produce an integer, even though it contains fractions.

Example 6.20. Find $\phi(315)$ using theorem 6.8.

Solution:

$$\phi(315)=315\left(1-\frac{1}{3}\right)\left(1-\frac{1}{5}\right)\left(1-\frac{1}{7}\right)=315\left(\frac{2}{3}\right)\left(\frac{4}{5}\right)\left(\frac{6}{7}\right)=3(48)=144.$$

Exercise Set 6.6

1. What is the smallest possible value for $d(n)$? What are the possible choices for n that result in this value?

2. Can $d(n)$ be negative? Explain.

3. Find all values of n for which $d(n) = 1$.

4. Find all values of n for which $d(n) = 2$.

5. Find all values of n for which $d(n) = 3$.

6. Find all values of n for which $\sigma(n) = 1$.

7. Find all values of n for which $\sigma(n) = 2$.

8. Prove that if p is prime and $a > 0$ then $d(p^a) = a + 1$.

9. Find $\phi(n)$ for $1 \leq n \leq 12$. Describe any patterns you see in the values of ϕ.

10. Evaluate $\phi(98)$.

11. Evaluate $\phi(105)$.

12. What is the smallest possible value for $d(n)$ if $n > 1$?

13. Find all the values of n where $\phi(n) = 1$.

14. Prove Conjecture 6.2.

Section 6.7   Summary and Review Exercises

Vocabulary and Symbols

arithmetic functions

Wilson's Theorem

Euler's Theorem

Euler phi-function, $\phi(n)$

$d(n)$ the sum of positive divisors of n

Fermat's Little Theorem

numerical functions

number theoretic functions

$\phi(n)$ the number of positive divisors of n

$\sigma(n)$ the sum of the divisors of n

Suggested Readings

Robinson, Raphael M. "Mersenne and Fermat Numbers." *Proceedings of the American Mathematical Society* 5 (1954): 842–846.

Burckhardt, J. J. "Leonhard Euler, 1707–1783." *Mathematics Magazine* 56 (1983): 262–273.

Colquitt, W. M. and L. Welsh Jr. "A New Mersenne Prime." *Mathematical Computation* 56 (1991): 867–870.

Crandall, R., J. Doenias, C. Norrie, and J. Young. "The Twenty-Second Fermat Number Is Composite." *Mathematical Computation* 64 (1995): 863–868.

Chapter 6 Review Exercises

1. Find a counterexample to the following statement and explain the example: If a and b are positive integers, then $\phi(ab) = \phi(a)\phi(b)$.

2. Find the least residue of 2^{32} mod 47.

3. Find the least residue of 16! mod 17.

4. Find the least residue of 15! mod 16.

5. List the possible least residues of modulo 17.

6. Which integer(s) cannot occur at the unit's digit of the sixth power of an integer?

7. Which integer(s) can occur at the unit's digits of the fourth power of an integer?

8. Find the least residue when $36 \cdot 15 \cdot 22 \cdot 18 \cdot 39$ is divided by 7.

9. Compute 35^{21} mod 11.

10. Compute 58^{49} mod 38.

11. Compute the value of $37^{31} \cdot 29^2$ mod 31.

12. Compute the value of $33^{31} \cdot 26^2$ mod 31.

13. Calculate $d(n)$, $\sigma(n)$, $\phi(n)$ for $n = 3^3 \cdot 5^2 \cdot 23$.

14. Explain why $2^{3711} - 1$ is divisible by $2^{1237} - 1$.

15. Find the least residue of 3^{95} mod 19.

16. Find the least residue of 7^{288} mod 360.

Exercises 17–20: Use Euler's Theorem to compute the least residue of the expression.

17. 29^{118} mod 20

18. 79^{79} mod 8

19. 3^{1000} mod 14

20. 9^{13} mod 11

Exercises 21–23: Apply Fermat's Little Theorem when appropriate to find the least residue of the expression in the given modulus. If Fermat's Little Theorem does not apply, explain why.

21. 2^{10} mod 15

22. 3^{112} mod 20

23. 3^{120} mod 101

24. How many integers less than 500 have exactly three divisors.

25. Use Euler's theorem or Fermat's Little Theorem to evaluate 10^{13} mod 11.

26. Find a negative solution to $235^3 \equiv$ mod 124.

27. Prove or disprove: If m is composite, then $(m-1)! \equiv 0$ mod m.

Section 6.8   Activities

1. Factorials are very important in many fields of mathematics. You may have discussed this concept in high school algebra, in a statistics course, or a probability course. Research the history of factorials and when the notation was invented.

2. As mentioned in this chapter, and also in Chapter 3, some theorems are named after the proposer who is also the person who proved the theorem, and in other instances, after a person who made the conjecture, but this person did not provide the proof. Research the other people who proved (or disproved) the results, or partially proved the results to determine their interest and contribution to Number Theory. Examples include Wiles, Germain, and Lagrange.

3. Determine what is the largest power of 2 that your calculator can find before having to resort to scientific notation.

4. Use the alternate formula (Theorem 6.12) for the sum of divisors to solve the problems in Example 6.17.

5. Find out more about the famous Bernoulli family of mathematicians. Were there any women mathematicians in the family?

Alan Turing

(1912–1954)

Turing was an English mathematician, computer scientist, logician, cryptanalyst, philosopher, and theoretical biologist. Born in London and returned to Great Britain after receiving his Ph.D. from Princeton in 1938.

Alan Turing is often called the *father of modern computing*. A brilliant mathematician and logician, he developed the ideas of the modern computer and artificial intelligence. During World War II, he worked for the government breaking the "enigma" codes used by Germany and its allies. The Enigma was a type of enciphering machine used by the German armed forces to send messages securely. According to Winston Churchill, Turing's work shortened the war by two years.

Turing, with code-breaker Gordon Welchman created a machine known as the "Bombe." This was a decoding machine. Turing considered the process of computation and looked for the essential components. He showed that it is possible to create a theoretical machine [now called a Turing machine (Katz, 913) that can calculate any function of any specialized machine.

In 1952, Alan Turing was arrested for homosexuality—which was against the law in Britain. He was found guilty of 'gross indecency' but avoided a prison sentence by accepting chemical castration. In 1954, he committed suicide by eating an apple laced with cyanide poisoning (ibid.) His conviction was overturned in 2013.

Turing's influence on computer science is generally acknowledged. The annual 'Turing Award' has been the highest prize in that industry since 1966. But the work done at Bletchley Park—and Turing's role there in cracking the Enigma code—was kept secret until the 1970s. The full story was not known until the 1990s. What is certain is that they saved countless lives and helped to determine the course and outcome of the conflict.

For a more information see https://www.pbs.org/newshour/science/8-things-didnt-know-alan-turing

Cryptography

There is nothing we like to communicate to others as much as the
seal of secrecy together with what is under it.

– Friedrich Nietzsche

Section 7.1   Introduction

For as long as there have been civilizations, people have tried to keep secrets—where the food is stored, where the treasure is hidden, who has the money, and so on. Now that so much information is transmitted over the internet, this information must be kept secure. Civilizations have developed methods to keep information private and as time goes on, secure methods of sending and receiving information becomes more difficult. Security concerns are widespread because so much personal information is stored on computers or on a cloud; internet accounts are protected by passwords, and many monetary transactions take place online. Eavesdroppers try to intercept online transactions, hoping to steal your credit card information or even your identity. Over the years, governments have relayed vital information to allies while attempting to keep enemies from obtaining it. Entire agencies, such as the National Security Agency, employ hundreds of mathematicians, and exist solely to keep their government's information a secret while trying to intercept and decode information belonging to other governments or groups.

In this chapter, there are two interesting questions that we will answer:

1. How can you give information to some individuals while keeping it a secret from others?
2. In the age of high-speed computers, how can you safely transfer information across the internet without that information being obtained by the wrong person?

The field of *cryptology* encompasses all aspects of secret codes. The subfield of *cryptography* is concerned with developing and implementing codes and the subfield of *cryptanalysis* focuses on how to break these codes. There are several terms associated with this process that we will use. These are listed below.

Definition 7.1 *Plaintext* is the original message that is to be securely transmitted.

Once the message has been determined, it is then converted to a coded form.

Definition 7.2 The coded form is called the *ciphertext*.

Definition 7.3 The process of turning the plaintext into ciphertext is called the *cipher* or *encryption method*.

Definition 7.4 The process used by the intended receiver to convert the ciphertext back into plaintext is called the *decryption method*.

Definition 7.5 The *key* is the mechanism used to encrypt or decrypt messages.

Definition 7.6 A *cryptosystem* consists of the encryption and decryption methods as well as the key needed to use them.

There are two types of keys, described in the next definitions.

Definition 7.7 In a *private key code*, either the same key is used for encryption and decryption or knowing one key will allow you to find the other.

These private key code systems are called *private key* because anyone who obtains either key will be able to decrypt messages, whether they are the intended recipient or not. Only the sender and the intended recipient can have access to the key.

Definition 7.8 In a *public key code*, anyone can have access to the encryption key, but the decryption key is still private.

While any person can know the encryption key, they are not able to figure out the decryption key without very sophisticated computer algorithms. Public key codes were first invented in the 1970s and one of the most famous examples are discussed in Section 7.4. Although early and modern methods of cryptography vary greatly, almost every cryptosystem follows the same basic process, outlined below.

Step 1: The sender and intended receiver agree on an encryption method, and exchange keys if necessary.

Step 2: The message is encrypted using the chosen encryption method and key. This converts the plaintext to ciphertext.

Step 3: The ciphertext is transmitted to the intended receiver.

Step 4: The receiver decrypts the ciphertext by using the key and obtains the plaintext.

Section 7.2   Private Key Cryptography

7.2.1 Substitution Cipher

The simplest form of encrypting a message is a ***substitution cipher***. In a substitution cipher, the ciphertext is produced by replacing each letter of the plaintext by another letter (or possibly number or symbol) according to the agreed-upon key. Many newspapers include a puzzle consisting of a famous quote encrypted with a substitution cipher. These types of puzzles are called ***cryptograms***. The organization American Cryptogram Association has cryptograms available for fun on their web page: www.cryptogram.org.

Although the hobby of deciphering coded messages for fun goes back to the Middle Ages and was also popularized by Edgar Allen Poe in the 1800s, the ciphers now commonly used in cryptograms and other puzzles were not originally developed for entertainment. Originally, ciphers of this type were used for encrypting military or personal secrets. However, especially with the availability of computers, these encryption techniques are no longer secure. Using a combination of frequency analysis (for example "e" is the most common letter in English) and pattern recognition (for example, a one-letter word will be "I" or "a"), these codes can be broken easily.

Example 7.1. Use the substitution cipher given below to encrypt the message BRAVO.

Plaintext	A	B	C	D	E	F	G	H	I	J	K	L	M	N	O	P	Q	R	S	T	U	V	W	X	Y	Z
Ciphertext	F	G	H	I	J	K	L	M	N	O	P	Q	R	S	T	U	V	W	X	Y	Z	A	B	C	D	E

Solution:

To encrypt the message, find each letter of the message **BRAVO** in the plaintext row of the key and replace it with the corresponding ciphertext. This leads to the following encryption:

$$B \rightarrow G$$
$$R \rightarrow W$$
$$A \rightarrow F$$
$$V \rightarrow A$$
$$O \rightarrow T$$

Therefore, the ciphertext is: GWFAT.

7.2.2 Caesar Cipher

Julius Caesar (100 – 44 BC) was a prominent military leader who used a substitution cipher method to send sensitive military information to his legions. He used a simple shift method of replacing each letter with the letter three spaces away. Table 7.1 shows the encryption key for Caesar's cipher.

Plaintext $\mathcal{P}$	A	B	C	D	E	F	G	H	I	J	K	L	M	N	O	P	Q	R	S	T	U	V	W	X	Y	Z
Ciphertext $\mathcal{C}$	D	E	F	G	H	I	J	K	L	M	N	O	P	Q	R	S	T	U	V	W	X	Y	Z	A	B	C

Table 7.1 Caesar Cipher Encryption Key

Example 7.2. Use the Caesar Cipher in Table 7.1 to encrypt the message: **BE READY**.

Solution:

Using the encryption key provided in Table 7.1, we obtain the following ciphertext.

EH UHDGB

Notice that a blank space is still represented by a blank space.

Example 7.3. Decrypt the following message that was encrypted using the Caesar Cipher.

QHYHU JLYH XS

Solution:

In order to decrypt this message, we could simply use the encryption key in Table 7.1, finding the letters in the encrypted message in the ciphertext row rather than the plaintext row. For example, Q in ciphertext corresponds to N in plaintext. For a long message, and especially for more complicated keys, it is easier and quicker to rewrite the key with the ciphertext in alphabetical order to find the letters in the encrypted message. The Caesar cipher decryption key is shown below in Table 7.2.

Ciphertext $\mathcal{C}$	A	B	C	D	E	F	G	H	I	J	K	L	M	N	O	P	Q	R	S	T	U	V	W	X	Y	Z
Plaintext $\mathcal{P}$	X	Y	Z	A	B	C	D	E	F	G	H	I	J	K	L	M	N	O	P	Q	R	S	T	U	V	W

Table 7.2 Caesar Cipher Decryption Key

Using the decryption key to decode the message, we obtain:

NEVER GIVE UP

While this encryption method may have been secure in Caesar's time (partly because many people were illiterate), today it is obsolete except perhaps as a game for children.

Notice that many different shift ciphers similar to the one used by Caesar are possible. An encryption key can be generated by shifting letters by one, two, three or more letters, all the way to 25 spaces, before A would match up again with A.

By replacing each letter of the alphabet with a numerical equivalent, we can represent encryption techniques of this type using modular arithmetic and congruences, a modern technique. There is no specific way to match the letters of the alphabet up with integers. For simplicity, in this section, we will use the numerical equivalents given in Table 7.3.

A	B	C	D	E	F	G	H	I	J	K	L	M	N	O	P	Q	R	S	T	U	V	W	X	Y	Z
0	1	2	3	4	5	6	7	8	9	10	11	12	13	14	15	16	17	18	19	20	21	22	23	24	25

Table 7.3 Numerical equivalents

Example 7.4. Represent the Caesar Cipher encryption method using modular arithmetic. Then, encrypt the message: **CIPHER.**

Solution:

To represent the Encryption Key for the Caesar cipher using modular arithmetic, suppose that N is the numerical equivalent for one of the letters appearing in the plaintext mod 26. So, for the plaintext letter E, $N = 4$. Now, shifting to the right three letters in the alphabet is equivalent to adding 3 to the value of N. Therefore, if C represents the ciphertext, $C = N + 3$ is the rule for converting letters to numerical values. The letter **E** has the numerical value $C = N + 3 = 4 + 3 = 7$. The encoding table, or ciphertext is given in Table 7.4

A	B	C	D	E	F	G	H	I	J	K	L	M
3	4	5	6	7	8	9	10	11	12	13	14	15
N	O	P	Q	R	S	T	U	V	W	X	Y	Z
16	17	18	19	20	21	22	23	24	25	26	27	28

Table 7.4 Encoding Table

Caesar would write this encoded message as

FLSKHU

Using a numerical code, given in Table 7.4 the encoded message is **5 11 18 10 7 20**. We can check this by decoding the message using Table 7.4, we will retrieve the plaintext: **CIPHER.**

The formula mod 26 works, except for the plaintext letters $X = 23$, $Y = 24$, and $Z = 25$. For example, if we are encrypting an X, $\mathcal{P} = 23$, so $C = 23 + 3 = 26$ which is not matched up with a letter. From the Caesar cipher encryption key in Table 7.1, we see that X should be encrypted as A, whose numerical equivalent is 0. In order to make the numerical equivalents restart at 26, we will calculate the ciphertext modulo 26. Therefore, the numerical encrypted form of plaintext $\mathcal{P}$ is $C = \mathcal{P} + 3 \bmod 26$, where C is the least residue of $\mathcal{P} + 3$ modulo 26. Note that this means C will be between 0 and 25. In Example 7.3, we did not use the last few letters of the alphabet, so we did not have a problem.

Caesar Cipher Encryption Process

1. Match each letter in the plaintext P with its numerical equivalent C.
2. For each number representing a letter of plaintext, use the formula $C \equiv P + 3 \bmod 26$, where P is a number from the plaintext and C is the coded ciphertext.

$$C \equiv P + 3 \bmod 26$$

This produces the list of numerical equivalents for the ciphertext.

3. Send the numerical ciphertext or convert to the original letter equivalents to form the ciphertext.

Congruences can also be used to decrypt messages that were encrypted with the Caesar Cipher. Solving the formula $C \equiv P + 3 \bmod 26$ for the plaintext P by subtracting 3 from both sides of the congruence reveals the decryption key $P \equiv C - 3 \bmod 26$.

Example 7.5. Use the decryption key $P \equiv C - 3 \bmod 26$ to decrypt the following message encrypted with the Caesar cipher.

$$\textbf{V Q R R S B}$$

Solution:

Decryption process:

1. Rewrite the ciphertext using the numerical equivalents from Table 7.3 for each letter:

$$21\ 16\ 17\ 17\ 18\ 1$$

2. Apply the formula $P \equiv C - 3 \bmod 26$ to each number C in the ciphertext.

$$P \equiv 21 - 3 \equiv 18 \bmod 26$$
$$P \equiv 16 - 3 \equiv 13 \bmod 26$$
$$P \equiv 17 - 3 \equiv 14 \bmod 26$$
$$P \equiv 17 - 3 \equiv 14 \bmod 26$$
$$P \equiv 18 - 3 \equiv 15 \bmod 26$$
$$P \equiv 1 - 3 \equiv -2 \bmod 26 \equiv 24 \bmod 26$$

Therefore, the numerical equivalent of the plaintext is:

$$18\ \ 13\ \ 14\ \ 14\ \ 15\ \ 24$$

3. Convert each number to its alphabetical equivalent to reveal the plaintext.

$$\text{SNOOPY}$$

Example 7.6. Use the Caesar cipher method of Example 7.4 to encrypt the message **THEOREM.**

Solution:

1. Begin with the word THEOREM.
2. Convert each letter in the word to its numerical equivalent: 19 7 4 14 17 4 15.
3. To encrypt the message, use the formula $C \equiv P + 3 \bmod 26$, where P is a number from the plaintext and C is the numerical ciphertext.

$$C \equiv 19 + 3 \bmod 26 \equiv 22$$
$$C \equiv 7 + 3 \bmod 26 \equiv 10$$
$$C \equiv 4 + 3 \bmod 26 \equiv 7$$
$$C \equiv 14 + 3 \bmod 26 \equiv 17$$
$$C \equiv 17 + 3 \bmod 26 \equiv 20$$
$$C \equiv 15 + 3 \bmod 26 \equiv 18 \bmod 26$$

Therefore, the numerical ciphertext is: 22 10 7 17 20 1018

4. Converting each number back to alphabetical form, we obtain the encrypted message.

WKHRUKP

Example 7.7. Show that decrypting the ciphertext **WKHRUKP** from Example 7.6 results in the original plaintext, **THEOREM.**

Solution:

Follow the decryption process on the ciphertext WKHRUKP.

1. Convert the ciphertext to numerical form: WKHRUKP → 22 10 7 17 20 10 18.
2. Apply the formula $P \equiv C - 3 \bmod 26$ to each number C in the ciphertext.

$$P \equiv 22 - 3 \bmod 26 \equiv 19$$
$$P \equiv 10 - 3 \bmod 26 \equiv 7$$
$$P \equiv 7 - 3 \bmod 26 \equiv 4$$
$$P \equiv 17 - 3 \bmod 26 \equiv 14$$
$$P \equiv 18 - 3 \bmod 26 \equiv 15 \bmod 26$$

Therefore, the numerical form of the plaintext is

19 7 4 14 17 4 15

3. Converting back to letters using Table 7.3 shows that the original message THEOREM is recovered.

7.2.3 Vigenère Cipher

The Vigenère Cipher is named after the French cryptographer Blaise de Vigenère (1523–1596). This is also a private key code, with a more complicated encryption process than the Caesar cipher. To use the Vigenère Cipher the "key" used is called a *keyword*. To encrypt the plaintext, the *keyword* is used to vary the way the letter is encrypted each time it occurs. The steps in using Vigenère coding are given next, and they will be clarified in the examples that follow. The longer the keyword, the more difficult it is to guess.

Vigenère Cipher Encoding Process

1. Select a **keyword** of any length $n > 2$, represented by the letters, $k_1, k_2, \ldots, k_n$, that the sender and receiver both know.
2. Use Table 7.3 to assign numerical values mod 26 to the plaintext in the message.
3. Assign numerical values to the letters in the keyword.
4. Arrange the numerical plaintext in blocks of length n.
5. For a block of plaintext with numerical equivalents $p_1 p_2 p_3 \ldots p_n$, and keyword with numerical equivalents $k_1 k_2 k_3 \ldots k_n$, use the formulas with addition mod 26 to produce the encrypted message or ciphertext

$$c_i \equiv p_i + k_i \bmod 26 \text{ where } i = 1, 2, \ldots, n$$

6. Step 6: Repeat Step 5 for each block of numerical plaintext. The result is the desired Vigenère cipher.

The process is illustrated in Examples 7.8 with a four-letter keyword, denoted $k_1 \, k_2 \, k_3 \, k_4$. Example 7.9 illustrates decoding with a five-letter keyword, denoted $k_1 \, k_2 \, k_3 \, k_4 \, k_5$.

Example 7.8. Encrypt the message **BE STILL** using Vigenère Cipher with the keyword **SNOW**.

Solution:

Encryption process:

1. The sender and receiver have agreed on the keyword SNOW.
2. Rewrite the plaintext message BESTILL using the numerical equivalent of each letter from Table 7. 3.

1 4 18 19 8 11 11

3. Match the letters of the keyword with their numerical equivalents from Table 7.3.

$$S = 18, \ N = 13, O \ O = 14, \ W = 22$$

So, in this example, $k_1 = 18$, $k_2 = 13$, $k_3 = 14$, and $k_4 = 22$.

4. Arrange the numbers in the numerical plaintext in groups of the same length as the keyword, in this case four letters. You may have a block shorter than 4 for the last group.

$$1 \quad 4 \quad 18 \quad 19 \qquad 8 \quad 11 \quad 11$$

5. For a block of plaintext with numerical equivalents $p_1\, p_2\, p_3\, p_4$, and keyword with numerical equivalents $k_1 k_2 k_3 k_4$, use the formulas with addition mod 26 to produce the encrypted message or ciphertext:

$$c_1 \equiv p_1 + k_1 \bmod 26$$
$$c_2 \equiv p_2 + k_2 \bmod 26$$
$$c_3 \equiv p_3 + k_3 \bmod 26$$
$$c_4 \equiv p_4 + k_4 \bmod 26$$

6. Repeat this process for each block and notice that the encrypted form of the same letter is not always the same. This process is shown for each numerical block of the plaintext in Table 7.5.

7.

Plaintext	Plaintext (numerical)	Encryption Formula	Ciphertext (numerical)	Ciphertext
B	1	$c_1 \equiv 1 + 18 \bmod 26$	19	T
E	4	$c_2 \equiv 4 + 13 \bmod 26$	17	R
S	18	$c_3 \equiv 18 + 14 \bmod 26$	6	G
T	19	$c_4 \equiv 19 + 22 \bmod 26$	5	F
I	8	$c_1 \equiv 8 + 18 \bmod 26$	11	I
L	11	$c_2 \equiv 18 + 13 \bmod 26$	5	F
L	11	$c_3 \equiv 11 + 14 \bmod 26$	25	Z

Table 7.5 Vigenère Cipher

Numerical plaintext: 1 4 18 19   8 11 11
Numerical ciphertext: **19 17 6 5   11 5 25**
Alphabetic ciphertext: TRGF IFZ

Comparing the ciphertext to the plaintext shows that the same letter (L in this case) can be encrypted differently, because of the use of the keyword.

Plaintext	B	E	S	T	I	L	L
Ciphertext	T	R	G	F	I	F	Z

Vigenère Cipher Decoding Process

1. Rewrite the keyword with its numerical plaintext from Table 7.3.
2. Rewrite the ciphertext using the same table.
3. Create the block of numerical ciphertext according to the number of letters in the keyword.
4. $p_i \equiv c_i - k_{1i} \bmod 26$ to obtain the numerical plaintext.
5. Use Table 7.3 to retrieve the original message.

Example 7.9. The ciphertext **ZZDASXLJK** was obtained using a Vigenère cipher (mod 26) and keyword **GIFTS**. Decrypt the message to find the original plaintext.

Solution:

Decryption Process for the Vigenère cipher:

1. Rewrite the keyword in terms of its numerical equivalents from Table 7. 3.

$$G = 6, I = 8, F = 5, T = 19, S = 18$$

2. Rewrite the ciphertext using the numerical equivalent of each letter from Table 7. 3. Notice that since the keyword in this example has five letters, the blocks (except for the last one) have length five.

$$25\ 25\ 3\ 018 \quad 9\ 9\ 12\ 22$$

3. For keyword numerical equivalents $k_1k_2k_3k_4k_5$ and ciphertext block $c_1c_2c_3c_4c_5$, solve each encryption formula in Example 7.8 for plaintext p_i to obtain:

$$p_1 \equiv c_1 - k_1 \bmod 26$$
$$p_2 \equiv c_2 - k_2 \bmod 26$$
$$p_3 \equiv c_3 - k_3 \bmod 26$$
$$p_4 \equiv c_4 - k_4 \bmod 26$$
$$p_5 \equiv c_5 - k_5 \bmod 26$$

In this example, the numerical equivalents for the keyword are the values found in Step 1: $k_1=6$, $k_2 = 8$, $k_3 = 5$, $k_4 = 19$, $k_5 = 18$.

Repeat the process for each block of the ciphertext to recover the plaintext numerical equivalents.

This process is shown for each numerical block of the ciphertext in Table 7.6.

Ciphertext	Ciphertext (numerical)	Decryption Formula	Plaintext (numerical)	Plaintext
Z	25	$c_1 \equiv 25 - 6 \bmod 26$	19	T
Z	25	$c_2 \equiv 25 - 8 \bmod 26$	17	R
D	3	$c_3 \equiv 3 - 5 \bmod 26$	24	Y
A	0	$c_4 \equiv 0 - 19 \bmod 26$	7	H
S	18	$c_5 \equiv 18 - 18 \bmod 26$	0	A
X	23	$c_1 \equiv 23 - 6 \bmod 26$	17	R
L	8	$c_2 \equiv 11 - 8 \bmod 26$	3	D
J	9	$c_3 \equiv 9 - 5 \bmod 26$	4	E
K	10	$c_4 \equiv 10 - 19 \bmod 26$	17	R

Table 7.6

Ciphertext, grouped in blocks: ZZDAS XLJK
Ciphertext in numerical form 25 25 3 0 18   23 8 9 10
Plaintext in numerical form: 19 17 24 7 0 17 3 4 17
The message, Plaintext: TRY HARDER

Vigenère's method was employed for at least two centuries and was thought to be unbreakable. However, British mathematician Charles Babbage (1791–1871) discovered a test to determine the keyword length in 1854. His result was not published immediately because the British national security organization used the method to decode secret messages and did not want their enemies to know about it.

The primary fault of Vigenère's approach is the frequency of a repeated letter. In 1920 a process was developed by US Army cryptographer William Friedman (1891–1960) to determine if the correct key length can be found. Once the key length is known, frequency analysis can be used to break this code.

One difficulty with any private key code is that the key must be *private*. At some point this key must be transferred to the receiver of the secret messages, and the key may be intercepted. Section 7.4 presents an example of a *public* key code that does not have this issue – the encryption key can be known by anyone because it does not lead to the decryption key.

Exercise Set 7.2

When numerical equivalents are needed in this exercise section, use the values from Table 7.3.

1. The encryption key used to encrypt the message below is given here. Decrypt the message to find the plaintext.

Plaintext	A	B	C	D	E	F	G	H	I	J	K	L	M	N	O	P	Q	R	S	T	U	V	W	X	Y	Z
Ciphertext	Q	R	S	N	O	P	K	L	M	H	I	J	W	F	G	C	D	E	A	B	T	X	Y	Z	U	V

FOXOE MFHTEO Q PEMOFN OXOF MF HOAB

--WQESTA SMSOEG

2. Use the Caesar cipher to encrypt the plaintext: SAVE THE DATE.

3. Use the Caesar cipher to decrypt the ciphertext: VDQLWB LV QRW LQ QXPEHUV.

4. Use a Vigenère Cipher, with keyword GLEE, to encrypt the message: THE FINAL IS NEXT WEEK.

5. Decrypt the following message, encrypted using a Vigenère Cipher with keyword WHISPER: SOILXWK DLUSIVZ T.

6. A slightly more complicated code than the Caesar cipher can be created by using a formula of the following type: $C \equiv aP + b \mod 26$. (In the Caesar cipher, $a = 1$ and $b = 3$). The following ciphertext was encrypted using the formula $C \equiv 21P + 5 \mod 26$: YLCLF TLOWL WNJSQ T.

a) What is the decryption key?

b) Using the key from part a), decrypt the coded message.

Section 7.3   Encryption by Exponentiation

The problem with using modular addition is that when one letter is correctly discovered, the rest can be easily determined by counting forward and backward from this letter. The method does not mix up the numbers very well. This section provides an example of a more complex and more secure method of encryption. A method of encryption, introduced in 1978 by Stephen Pohlig and Martin Hellman, is another example of a private key code, but breaking the code without having the key is considerably more difficult than the methods discussed in Section 7.2. To make the encryption process more difficult to decrypt, the method uses exponentiation with a prime modulus to encrypt the plaintext.

Encryption Process for Exponentiation Cipher

1. Convert the plaintext to numerical equivalents, using Table 7.3.

2. Choose a prime $q > 25$, since 25 is the largest number in our mod 26 numbering system. In practice, q is very large. To make our calculations easier, we will keep p relatively small.

3. Choose a number e such that $\gcd(e, q-1) = 1$. The value e will become the exponent in the encryption formula.

4. To find the ciphertext, C, raise each plaintext numerical equivalent P to the power e, and then reduce modulo p.

$$C \equiv P^e \mod q$$

Example 7.10. Use the exponentiation method to encrypt the message **"NO MORE SNOW."**

Solution:

Encryption Method:

1. Convert each letter of the plaintext to its numerical equivalent.

13 14 12 14 17 4 18 13 14 22.

2. Choose a prime $q > 25$: Let $q = 29$.

3. Choose an integer e such that $\gcd(e, q-1) = 1$. Let $e = 3$. Since $\gcd(3, 28) = 1$, this is an acceptable pair.

4. Create the ciphertext by raising each of the letters in plaintext to the exponent $e = 3$ and then find the least residue modulo 29.

Message	Plaintext $\mathcal{P}$	$\mathcal{P}^3$	Ciphertext $\mathcal{C} \equiv \mathcal{P}^3 \bmod 29$
N	13	2197	22
O	14	2744	18
M	13	1728	17
O	14	2744	18
R	17	4913	12
E	4	125	9
S	18	5832	3
N	13	2197	22
O	14	2744	18
W	22	10648	5

Therefore, the ciphertext for NO MORE SNOW is:

$$22 \ 18 \ 17 \ 18 \ 12 \ 9 \ 3 \ 22 \ 18 \ 5$$

To decrypt a message encrypted with this exponentiation technique, reverse the encryption process. The decryption technique is explained below, followed by an example.

Decryption Process for the Exponentiation Cipher

Suppose that the ciphertext was encrypted with prime q and exponent e using the congruence $\mathcal{C} \equiv \mathcal{P}^e \bmod p$, where $\mathcal{P}$ is the plaintext.

1. Choose an integer d such that $de \equiv 1 \bmod (q-1)$. (Since $\gcd(e, q-1) = 1$, this will always be possible by Theorem 5.7).

2. Then, for each numerical ciphertext $\mathcal{C}$:

$$\mathcal{P} \equiv \mathcal{C}^d \bmod q$$

where $\mathcal{P}$ is the numerical equivalent of the plaintext.

Theorem 7.1 Let q be prime and let e be an integer such that $\gcd(e, q-1) = 1$. If $\mathcal{C}$ and $\mathcal{P}$ are integers such that $\mathcal{C} \equiv \mathcal{P}^e \bmod q$, then there is an integer d such that $\mathcal{P} \equiv \mathcal{C}^d \bmod q$. d is the solution to the congruence $de \equiv 1 \bmod (q-1)$.

Proof:

Premises: $d \in N$, q is prime and $de \equiv 1 \bmod (q-1)$.

Rewrite this congruence using Theorem 5.1:

$$de = 1 + k(q-1) \text{ where } k \text{ is an integer.}$$

Then,

$$\begin{aligned}
C^d &\equiv \left(P^e\right)^d \bmod q \\
&\equiv P^{de} \bmod q \\
&\equiv P^{1+k(q-1)} \bmod q \\
&\equiv P \cdot P^{(p-1)k} \bmod q.
\end{aligned}$$

Now, since $P \leq 25$ and $q > 25$ is prime, $\gcd(P, q) = 1$:

$$P^{p-1} \equiv 1 \bmod q, \text{ by Fermat's Little Theorem (Theorem 6.3),}$$

$$\Rightarrow C^d \equiv P\left(P^{q-1}\right)^k \bmod q \equiv P \bmod q, \text{ by substitution,}$$

Since P represents the numerical equivalent of the plaintext, the message has been decrypted.

Example 7.11. Use the exponentiation cipher with $p = 29$ and $e = 3$ to encrypt the message **MUSE**. Then, use the decryption process to show that correct plaintext is recovered.

Solution:

The encryption process:

1. Replace each letter of the message MUSE with its numerical equivalent from Table 7.3.

$$12 \ 20 \ 18 \ 4$$

2. Since $q = 29$ and $e = 3$, use the formula $C \equiv P^3 \bmod 29$ to obtain the numerical ciphertext C from each number P in the plaintext. After the numerical equivalents of the ciphertext are found, convert them to alphabetical form. The results of this process are shown in Table 7.7.

Message	Plaintext (P) (numerical)	P^3	Ciphertext (numerical) $C \equiv P^3 \bmod 29$	Ciphertext
M	12	1728	17	R
U	20	8000	25	Z
S	18	5832	3	D
E	4	64	6	G

Table 7.7

Thus, the ciphertext is RZDG.

The decryption process:
1. Begin with the ciphertext RZDG.
2. Convert each letter of the ciphertext to its numerical equivalent.

$$17 \ 25 \ 3 \ 19 \ 8$$

3. Find an integer d such that $3d \equiv 1 \bmod (29-1)$, or $3d \equiv 1 \bmod 28$. Notice that this congruence is asking for the inverse of 3 modulo 28, which does exist since $\gcd(3, 28) = 1$. Using the method of solving linear congruences from Section 5.3, or by trial and error, we find that $d = 19 \bmod 28$.
4. To recover the plaintext $\mathcal{P}$, for each ciphertext numerical equivalent $\mathcal{C}$, $\mathcal{C}^{19} \equiv \mathcal{P} \bmod 29$.
5. Table 7.8 shows the calculations along with the conversion from numerical plaintext to alphabetical plaintext.

Numerical Ciphertext	$\mathcal{C}^{19}$	Numerical Plaintext $\mathcal{P} \equiv \mathcal{C}^{19} \bmod 29$	Alphabetical Plaintext
17	2390724356685151324847153	12	M
25	363797880709171295166015625	20	U
3	1162261467	18	S
6	60935900496	4	E

Table 7.8

Exercise Set 7.3

Exercises 1–4: Find a value for the encryption exponent in the exponentiation cipher for the given value of p.

1. $p = 17$
2. $p = 43$
3. $p = 29$
4. $p = 53$

Exercises 5–8: Find the value of the decryption exponent in the exponentiation cipher for the given values of p and e.

5. $p = 13, e = 5$
6. p 47, $e - 15$
7. $p = 41, e = 9$
8. $p = 71, e = 13$

9. a) Encrypt the message "SMILE" using the exponentiation cipher. Choose $e = 5$ and modulus $p = 19$ to find the ciphertext. (Since the largest numerical equivalent for this message is 18, a prime modulus of 19 is large enough).

   b) Find d the decryption exponent and decrypt the ciphertext in Exercise 1 to show the original plaintext is recovered.

10. a) Encrypt the message "LEMON" using the exponentiation cipher. Choose $e = 7$ and modulus $p = 17$ to find the ciphertext. (Since the largest numerical equivalent in this message is $O = 14$, the prime 17 is large enough for the modulus).

b) Find d the decryption exponent and decrypt the ciphertext in Exercise 3 to show the original plaintext is recovered.

11. a) Encrypt the message "STUDY" using the exponentiation cipher. Choose $e = 5$ and modulus $p = 29$ to find the ciphertext.

b) Find d the decryption exponent and decrypt the ciphertext in Exercise 5 to show the original plaintext is recovered.

12. The ciphertext **13 0 25 3 17 19 6** was created using an exponentiation cipher with $e = 7$ and $p = 31$. Verify that $d = 13$ is a valid decryption exponent and use it to decrypt the message. Use Table 7.3 to replace the numerical plaintext with the letters.

Section 7.4   Public Key Cryptography—The RSA Cryptosystem

All of the examples we have seen so far have been private key ciphers, wherein the encrypting key and the decrypting key are either the same, or one can be used to find the other. Therefore, the keys can only be shared with the sender and the intended recipient of the message. This creates the problem of securely transmitting the key, so that only the intended recipient will be able to decrypt the messages.

In a **public key cryptosystem**, however, the encryption process can be publicly shared, without jeopardizing the security of the codes produced using the encryption process. Public key cryptosystems were first invented in the 1970s. The most famous public key system, called **RSA**, is named after its inventors Ronald Rivest (1948–), Adi Shamir (1952–), and Leonard Adleman (1945–). Public key ciphers are vital to maintaining security, particularly in sending and receiving information over the internet. For example, when you open a web page that asks you for a credit card number, the page's address begins with "https." The "s" indicates that you are using a secure server that encrypts your personal information. This encryption is done using the RSA encryption method. This modern application has its roots in the number theory that was developed long before computers.

In public key cryptosystems there is both a public key and a private key. The public key is the encryption key, which contains all of the information necessary to encrypt information to be sent. The public key is available to the public because it can only be used to encrypt information for the owner of the key. Even if one knows the entire RSA process for creating keys and encrypting and decrypting information, the knowledge of someone's public key does not lead to finding their private key.

The private key is the decryption key, which is secret and contains all the information necessary to decrypt the message encrypted using the public key. The information in the private key is secret. An example of this use is a bank account. You can allow someone (e.g. your employer or your parents) to deposit money into your account, but not withdraw money.

The security of the RSA encryption method is due to the surprising property that knowledge of the public (encryption) key does not lead to discovering the private (decryption key), and is based on the following fact:

It is easy to find the product of two large whole numbers, but it is generally difficult to find the factors of a large number, particularly if it is the product of two large primes.

For example, if you are asked to find the product of 34141 and 28249 (two primes), with the help of a calculator you can quickly compute that the answer is 970594489, but now suppose you are asked the reverse question: Can you factor the number 1321306601? Even with a calculator, it is not so simple. Even if you are told that the number is the product of two primes, it doesn't make the task much easier. We could use the Primality Test from Chapter 3 to reduce the number of factors that must be checked. Recall that only primes less than or equal to the square root of the number must be tested; however, in this case, $\sqrt{1321306601} \approx 36349.8$. This would be manageable on a computer, but if we start with primes that are hundreds of digits long, even a powerful computer will not be able to test the possibilities fast enough to find the factors, even if we waited one hundred years.

In the RSA cryptosystem, the person intended to receive encrypted messages chooses very large primes p and q which he or she keeps secret. (These are used to compute the private key). After multiplying them together, the product $m = pq$ is part of the *public key* used to encrypt information. In order to decrypt the message, the individual values of p and q are necessary, but they cannot be found easily, even knowing m.

> **Definition 7.9** The RSA public key includes two pieces of information: *the encryption exponent* is a natural number e, and the modulus m is the product of two large primes. two numbers are frequently written as a pair (e, m) called the ***public key***.

Now we explain the details of choosing the public and private keys for the RSA system, as well as the encryption and decryption formulas and a discussion of why the formulas work.

7.4.1 RSA Encryption

RSA encryption uses modular arithmetic and the fact that products of large primes are difficult to factor. The RSA public key includes two pieces of information: a number e, called the ***encryption exponent***, which is chosen by the person who knows the private key, and the modulus, m, which is the product of two very large primes, also chosen by the owner of the private key. These two numbers are often written as a pair, (e, m). In the RSA system, the person who wishes to receive encrypted information makes public the two numbers, e and m, so that anyone who wants to send encrypted information has access to them. This pair of values is called the ***public key***. The process of creating an RSA public key is explained next.

Creating an RSA Public (Encryption) Key

1. Choose two different large primes, p and q.
2. Let $m = p \cdot q$. (In an actual RSA key, m would have several hundred digits.)
3. Compute the value of the Euler phi-function, $\phi(m)$. By Theorem 6.6,

$$\phi(m) = \phi(p \cdot q) = (p-1)(q-1).$$

4. Choose a positive integer e such that $\gcd(e, \phi(m)) = 1$.

Public Encryption Key: the pair of numbers (e, m) is the ***public encryption key***.

Remarks: In RSA encryption, p and q would be primes with 150 or more digits. The values of p, q, and $\phi(m)$ are secret; they are not necessary to encrypt information. These values allow you to compute the private key used to decrypt coded information.) Example 7.12 illustrates the process of forming an RSA public key. To make computations possible, we are working with small primes in these examples.

Example 7.12. Create an RSA public key for the primes $p = 3$ and $q = 11$.

Solution:

Using the steps above:

1. We are given *primes* p $= 3$ *and* q $= 11$
2. $33 = 3 \cdot 11$, so $m = 33$ in this example.
3. By Theorem 6.6 $\phi(33) = \phi(3 \cdot 11) = 2 \cdot 10 = 20$.
4. Chose e so that $\gcd(e, 20) = 1$. One choice is $e = 3$. In this case, the public key would be (3, 33).

Note that there are many possibilities, each of which will result in a different public key. A public key is used by a person to encrypt a message using the following procedure. When creating the numerical values for each plaintext letter, the letters are represented by the same number of digits. We will use two digits to represent each letter, shown in Table 7.5.

The RSA Encryption Method

1. Choose the public key (e, m) for the intended receiver of the message.
2. Convert the message into numerical equivalents. In the RSA method, each letter must be represented by the same number of digits, so each letter will be represented by two digits using the system shown below in Table 7. 4.
3. Group the numerical plaintext into blocks of the same length so that the integer represented by each block is less than m. If the last block is not the same length as the rest, add some "dummy digits" onto the end to make all the blocks have the same length. Often, numerical equivalents of less common letters such as Z or X are added to the last block if it needs to be longer.
4. Each block of plaintext, $\mathcal{B}$, is encrypted separately using the following congruence:

$$C \equiv \mathcal{B}^e \bmod m,$$

where C is reduced modulo m and is the ciphertext representing $\mathcal{B}$.

Note that while the plaintext blocks all have the same length, the ciphertext blocks may not all be of the same length.

A	B	C	D	E	F	G	H	I	J	K	L	M
01	02	03	04	05	06	07	08	09	10	11	12	13
N	O	P	Q	R	S	T	U	V	W	X	Y	Z
14	15	16	17	18	19	20	21	22	23	24	25	26

Table 7.8 Numerical Equivalents for RSA Cryptosystem

Example 7.13. Use the RSA cryptosystem with public key (3, 33) to encrypt the message **EMUS**.

Solution:

1. Convert the message into numerical equivalents.
2. Since $m = 33$ in this example, each block of plaintext must be less than 33. Therefore, each block will consist of the numerical equivalent of one letter and will have length two.
3. Encrypt each block B using the formula

$$C \equiv B^e \bmod 33,$$

since $m = 33$ and $e = 3$. This will produce the numerical ciphertext. The steps of the process are shown in the Table 7.9.

Plaintext	Plaintext (B) (numerical)	B^3	Ciphertext $C \equiv B^3 \bmod 33$
E	06	216	18
M	13	2197	19
U	21	9261	21
S	19	6859	28

Table 7.9

Therefore, the ciphertext blocks are: 18 19 21 28.

To recover the original message, find the private or decryption key. If the public key is (e, m), here is the method for forming the private key.

7.4.2 RSA Decryption

Creating an RSA private (decryption) key for public key (e, m)

1. Start with $m = p \cdot q$. (Note that m is public but p and q are not.)
2. Calculate $\phi(m) = \phi(p \cdot q) = (p-1)(q-1)$.
3. Find a positive integer d such that $d < \phi(m)$ and d is the inverse of e modulo $\phi(m)$. To do this solve the congruence $d \cdot e \equiv 1 \bmod \phi(m)$ for d. Notice that this will always be possible since e was chosen so that $\gcd(e, \phi(m)) = 1$.

Private (decryption) key: the pair of integers (d, m).

The private key is used to decrypt any messages sent to you that were encrypted using your public key.

Example 7.14. Create the private key for the public key (3, 33).

Solution:

We must find the least residue d so that $d \cdot e \equiv 1 \bmod \phi(33)$. Substituting $e = 3$ and $\phi(33) = 20$ results in the congruence $3d \equiv 1 \bmod 20$. Since the modulus 20 is small, we can check values for d to find that $d = 7$. Therefore, the private key is (7, 33).

The general decryption process for RSA:

RSA Decryption Method

To decrypt a message encrypted with public key (e, m) using the private key (d, m).

1. Begin with the numerical ciphertext to be decrypted.

2. Decrypt each block C of ciphertext separately using the following formula, where B represents a numerical block of plaintext.

$$B \equiv C^d \bmod m$$

3. Once all blocks have been decrypted into numerical plaintext, replace each pair of numbers with the corresponding letter.

Example 7.15. Decrypt the ciphertext from Example 7.14, using the private key (7, 33).

Solution:

The ciphertext is 13 5 21 28. The decryption formula is

$$B \equiv C^7 \bmod 33$$

Where C is a block of ciphertext and B is a block of plaintext? The calculations are shown in the table below, using the numerical equivalents in Table 7.4 to find the plaintext.

Ciphertext (C)	C^7	Plaintext (numerical) $B \equiv C^7 \bmod 33$	Plaintext
13	62748517	07	G
5	78125	14	N
21	1801088541	21	U
28	13492928512	19	S

Before going on to some more complicated examples, we will examine why the RSA encryption method works.

7.4.3 Why RSA Encryption Works

In this section we will examine why the decryption technique will always correctly return the original message. So far, we know the following:

The RSA encryption process begins by choosing two (large) primes, p and q and creating the public key (e, m). Then each block, $\mathcal{B}$, of plaintext is encrypted into ciphertext $\mathcal{C}$ using the relationship

$$C \equiv \mathcal{B}^e \bmod m.$$

To find the decryption key, the congruence below must be solved for d:

$$ed \equiv 1 \bmod \phi(m)$$

Since $\phi(m) = \phi(pq)$, applying the definition of congruence produces the following equation:

$$\phi(pq) \mid (ed - 1).$$

Therefore,

$$(ed - 1) = k\phi(pq).$$

Solving for ed,

$$ed = k\phi(pq) + 1$$

Euler's Theorem is used to verify that the decryption technique does actually reproduce the original plaintext. Recall the statement of Euler's Theorem (Theorem 6.10):

$$\text{If } m > 0 \text{ and } \gcd(m, a) = 1, \text{ then } a^{\phi(m)} \equiv 1 \bmod m.$$

Applying Euler's Theorem with $m = pq$ and $a = \mathcal{B}$,

$$C^d \equiv \left(\mathcal{B}^e\right)^d \equiv \mathcal{B}^{k\phi(pq)+1} \equiv \mathcal{B}^{k\phi(pq)} \cdot \mathcal{B} \equiv (\mathcal{B}^{\phi(pq)})^k \cdot \mathcal{B} \equiv 1 \cdot \mathcal{B} \equiv \mathcal{B} \bmod m.$$

This shows that when the decrypting exponent, d, is applied to the ciphertext we do in fact get back the plaintext $\mathcal{B}$.

This proves Theorem 7.2, stated below.

Theorem 7.2 Let p and q be different primes. Let $m = pq$, and let e be an integer such that $\gcd(e, \phi(m)) = 1$. If $\mathcal{B}$ and $\mathcal{C}$ are integers such that $\mathcal{C} \equiv \mathcal{B}^e \bmod m$, then there exists an integer d such that $\mathcal{B} \equiv \mathcal{C}^d \bmod m$. In face, d is the positive integer less than $\phi(m)$ such that $de \equiv 1 \bmod \phi(m)$.

Euler's Theorem applies when the modulus is composite. This is central to the RSA method. What happens when we have an extremely large modulus, made up of the product of two huge primes, is that it is almost impossible to find these two prime factors when we are only given the product. In fact, it is estimated that a modern computer would take longer than all of recorded history to find the two primes! Thus, we can only decrypt the message if we already know what these two primes are.

It is interesting at this point to note the importance of very large primes to modern cryptosystems. Because of their necessity, these large prime numbers are quite the commercial commodities. In fact, in 1994, computer programmer Roger Schlafly obtained U.S. Patent 5,373,560 on two prime numbers that he discovered!

The next two examples use a slightly larger pair of primes to illustrate how quickly the process gets complicated.

Example 7.16. Use the public key (77, 527) to encrypt the message: W.

Solution:

1. Convert the plaintext **W** into a numerical equivalent. Using Table 7.4, **W** = 23, which is less than the modulus of 527.
2. The next task is to encrypt **W** using the encryption exponent $e = 77$. The ciphertext is

$$C \equiv 23^{77} \bmod 527$$

3. Using the techniques for reducing large exponents from Chapter 5, we find that the ciphertext to be transmitted is $C = 401$.

The whole numbers in Example 7.16 can be simplified using the techniques of Chapter 5, but for a longer message or even larger primes, this will become quite labor-intensive. An online computational engine such as WolframAlpha (www.WolframAlpha.com) is very useful for longer problems of this type.

Example 7.17. Use the public key (77, 527) to encrypt the message: **W.**

Solution:

1. Convert the plaintext **W** into a numerical equivalent. Using Table 7.4, **W**=23, which is less than the modulus of 527.
2. The next task is to encrypt **W** using the encryption exponent $e = 77$. The ciphertext is

$$C \equiv 23^{77} \bmod 527$$

3. Using the techniques for reducing large exponents from Chapter 5, we find that the ciphertext to be transmitted is $C = 401$.

Example 7.18. The ciphertext 55 281 240 281 was created using the public key (77, 527) from Example 7.17. Decrypt the message to retrieve the original plaintext.

Solution:

For the private key (d, m), the plaintext, $\mathcal{B}$, represented by a block of ciphertext, $\mathcal{C}$, can be found using the congruence

$$\mathcal{B} \equiv \mathcal{C}^d \bmod m.$$

So, find d. To do this, solve the congruence $77d \equiv 1 \bmod \phi(527)$. Here, we run into trouble finding the value of $\phi(527)$. To compute it, find the prime factors of 527. According to the Primality Test from Chapter 3, just test primes less than or equal to $\sqrt{527} \approx 22.96$. Because the primes we are using are so small compared to those used in an actual RSA system, it is not a huge problem to check these values and find that $527 = 17 \cdot 31$. Therefore, $\phi(527) = 16 \cdot 30 = 480$, and to find d we must solve

$$77d \equiv 1 \bmod 480.$$

This congruence has a solution since $\gcd(77, 480) = 1$, and we can find it using the method described in Section 5.3. Alternatively, after rewriting the congruence as a linear equation in two variables, a computational system such as WolframAlpha can be used to find the solution. After solving the congruence, we find that $d = 293$. Note that the decryption exponent, d, is large in comparison with the original prime factors of 527.

Now, the plaintext $\mathcal{B}$ for each block of ciphertext is found using the following congruence:

$$\mathcal{B} \equiv \mathcal{C}^{293} \bmod 527.$$

Therefore, calculating the least residue modulo 527 of each block of the ciphertext, we obtain:

$$55^{293} \equiv 21 \bmod 527$$
$$281^{293} \equiv 8 \bmod 527$$
$$240^{293} \equiv 15 \bmod 527$$
$$281^{293} \equiv 8 \bmod 527$$

(The calculations above were done using WolframAlpha.)

Therefore, the numerical plaintext is: 21 08 15 08. Using Table 7. 4, this corresponds to the message UH OH.

Example 7.19. Given the primes 41 and 67 for an RSA encryption scheme

a) Find m and $\phi(m)$.
b) Which of the following are valid encryption exponents: 7, 9, 15, 35, 49, 91?

Solution:

a) $m = 41 \cdot 67 = 2747$, and $\phi(m) = \phi(41 \cdot 67) = 40 \cdot 66 = 2640$ by Theorem 6.6.

b) The encryption exponent e is chosen so that $\gcd(e, 2640) = 1$. To find out which of the given numbers are relatively prime to 2640, first write out the prime factorization of $2640 = 2^4 \cdot 3 \cdot 5 \cdot 11$. Therefore, the valid exponents are the numbers 7, 49, and 91. All the others share a factor with 2640 and therefore are not relatively prime to 2640.

Example 7.20. Create two possible RSA public keys using the primes $p = 29$ and $q = 41$.

Solution:

First, the value of m is $m = 29 \cdot 41 = 1189$. Now, the value of e is selected so that $\gcd(e, \phi(m)) = 1$. Since $\phi(m) = \phi(29 \cdot 41) = 28 \cdot 40 = 1120$, the value of e can be any integer relatively prime to 1120. The prime factorization of 1120 is $1120 = 2^5 \cdot 5 \cdot 7$, so e can be any positive integer that does not share any of these prime factors. Two possible choices for e are $e = 9$ or $e = 13$. These will produce the public keys $(9, 1189)$ or $(13, 1189)$.

Example 7.21. After her first week of college, Penny is out of money. Her parents have provided her with their RSA public key for just this type of situation, so that there is no sibling rivalry. Help Penny by using the RSA method with public key $(3, 2173)$ to encrypt the message **SEND MONEY**.

Solution:

We start by using Table 7.4 to pair each letter of the message with its numerical equivalent:

$$19 \ \ 05 \ \ 14 \ \ 04 \ \ 13 \ \ 15 \ \ 14 \ \ 05 \ \ 25$$

Since $m = 2173$ in this example, blocks of length three will ensure that no block has a value larger than m. Therefore, the blocks of plaintext we will encrypt are listed below.

$$190 \ \ 514 \ \ 041 \ \ 315 \ \ 140 \ \ 525$$

Now, apply the formula $C \equiv B^e \bmod m$ to each block to obtain the ciphertext.

$$190^3 \equiv 1012 \bmod 2173$$
$$514^3 \equiv 1628 \bmod 2173$$

$$41^3 \equiv 1558 \bmod 2173$$

$$315^3 \equiv 1616 \bmod 2173$$

$$140^3 \equiv 1674 \bmod 2173$$

$$525^3 \equiv 882 \bmod 2173$$

(These calculations were done using WolframAlpha.)

Therefore, the encrypted message to be sent out to Penny's parents is:

$$1012 \quad 1628 \quad 1558 \quad 1616 \quad 1674 \quad 882$$

Example 7.22. Penny's parents (of Example 7.20) have just received the encrypted message from Penny given in Example 7.20. Of course, they were not present when it was encrypted so they pull out their RSA private key (1387, 2173). Decrypt the message for them so they know what Penny needs.

Solution:

Each block of the ciphertext sent by Penny can be decrypted using the congruence $\mathcal{B} \equiv C^d \bmod m$, where $d = 1387$ is the decryption exponent included in the private key. Applying this to each block of Penny's ciphertext, we obtain the following results (using WolframAlpha).

$$1012^{2173} \equiv 190 \bmod 1387$$

$$1628^{2173} \equiv 514 \bmod 1387$$

$$1558^{2173} \equiv 41 \bmod 1387$$

$$1616^{2173} \equiv 315 \bmod 1387$$

$$1674^{2173} \equiv 140 \bmod 1387$$

$$882^{2173} \equiv 525 \bmod 1387$$

Therefore, the numerical blocks of plaintext are:

$$190 \quad 514 \quad 041 \quad 315 \quad 140 \quad 525$$

Notice that the value 41 has a zero added in front since the blocks of plaintext all started with the same length.

Now, the numerical equivalents are two digits long, so group the digits in pairs to convert back to the original plaintext message, using Table 7.4.

19	05	14	04	13	15	14	05	25
S	E	N	D	M	O	N	E	Y

This reveals Penny's message to her parents: SEND MONEY.

Exercise Set 7.4

1. Does the encryption exponent e from the public key have to be prime? Explain why or why not.

2. Can the encryption exponent e from the public key be even? Explain why or why not.

Exercises 3–6: If the primes used for an RSA encryption scheme are $p = 31$ and $q = 97$, find the private key for each choice of the encryption exponent e given below.

3. $e = 7$

4. $e = 11$

5. $e = 13$

6. $e = 77$

Exercises 7–10: Find a public key and the corresponding private key for the primes p and q.

7. $p = 5, q = 11$

8. $p = 13, q = 43$

9. $p = 19, q = 31$

10. $p = 17, q = 23$

11. If an RSA public key is created using the primes $p = 13$ and $q = 17$, which of the following values are possible choices for the encryption exponent, e: 8, 9, 11, 25, 35, 36?

12. Find the numerical plaintext, using the numerical equivalents from Table 7.4, for the message: STUDY HARD.

13. Find the numerical plaintext, using the numerical equivalents from Table 7.4, for the message: HARD WORK PAYS OFF.

14. Using RSA encryption with primes 43 and 73, and encryption exponent $e = 5$, encrypt the following message: HAPPY.

15. Using the public key $(77, 527)$ from Example 7.16, encrypt the message YES.

16. After decrypting a message, the following blocks of numerical plaintext were obtained. Use them to retrieve the original message. (Hint: Remember that the plaintext blocks all started out with the same length. They should be the same length before using the table of numerical equivalents.)

    Plaintext: 161   518   32   116   91   405

17. You received the encrypted message **413 240**. Decrypt the message if your private key is (53, 527).

18. A person with RSA private key (103, 287) received the encrypted message **199 62 100 276**. Decrypt the message to find the original plaintext.

19. A person with RSA private key (7, 33) received the encrypted message **13 9 13 24 26 26 5**. Decrypt the message using their private key.

20. Find the decryption exponent given the value $e = 7$ and $\phi(pq) = 1200$.

21. In an RSA coding, the public key is 221 and $e = 3$.

a) Find the private key.

b) What equation must be solved to find the decryption exponent, d?

22. Watch the following special from the History Channel. What do you find most interesting about the history of cryptography? https://www.youtube.com/watch?v=H9Cu36Qj3dQ

Section 7.5   Summary and Review Exercises

Vocabulary

cipher	decrypt
plaintext	decode
ciphertext	decryption method
cryptography	encode
cryptology	decode
cryptanalysis	keyword
cryptogram	private key
Caesar ciphers	public key
Vigenère ciphers	private key cryptography
encrypt	public key cryptography
encode	substitution cipher
encryption method	RSA encryption method
encryption by exponentiation	

Suggested Readings

Diffie, Whitfield, and Susan Landau. "September 11th Did Not Change Cryptography Policy." *Notices of the American Mathematical Society* 49 (April, 2002): 448–464.

Fried, John J. "Can You Keep a SECRET?" *The Philadelphia Inquirer*, tech. life section, pp. F1–F2.

Kirsch, Rachel. "Cryptography: How to Keep a Secret." *MAA Focus*, February/March 2011. www.maa.org/pubs/focus.html

McGrayne, Sharon Bertsch. "The Secrets of a Master Number Cruncher." *The Philadelphia Inquirer*, October 23, 2012. www.philly.com

Poe, Edgar Allan. "The Gold Bug." In *Edgar Allan Poe: Complete Tales and Poems*, 75–99. Edison, NJ: Castle Books, November, 2009.

Chapter 7 Review Exercises

1. Use the Caesar cipher to encrypt the plaintext: ATTACK AT DAWN.

2. Use the Caesar cipher to decrypt the ciphertext: LFDPH LVDZL FRQTX HUHG.

3. Decrypt the following message, encrypted using a Vigenère Cipher with keyword SECRET: MMNVRV WMUXSD VIP.

4. Use the Caesar cipher to decrypt the ciphertext: LFDPH LVDZL FRQTX HUHG.

5. Decode $C_1 = 2179$ with $m = 2911$ and $e = 13$.

6. In an RSA coding the public key is 221 and $e = 3$.
   a) Find the private key.
   b) What equation must be solved to find the decryption exponent, d?
   c) Find the decryption exponent given the value $e = 7$ for the encryption exponent and $\phi(pq) = 1200$.

Exercises 7–10: Create RSA public and private keys using the primes p and q.

7. $p = 5, q = 11$

8. $p = 11, q = 23$

9. $p = 3, q = 41$

10. $p = 5, q = 37$

11. Decrypt the cipher text: **10 1 16 16 2 1 9 49 24** which was encrypted using the RSA method, if the private key is (23, 55).

Exercises 12–17: Suppose $p = 59$ and $q = 71$ are used to for an RSA encryption system. Is the number listed a valid encryption exponent, e, for the RSA public key?

12. 7

13. 9

14. 15

15. 35

16. 49

17. 91

18. Decrypt the following message, encrypted using a Vigenère Cipher with keyword SECRET: WBRCS LAZGJ MGKMF V.

19. The cipher test is **845 1065** was encrypted in two-letter blocks using the RSA method. Use the private key (11, 3127) to decrypt the message.

20. a) Find the numerical plaintext for the message FERMAT using the numerical equivalents in Table 7.4.

    b) Encrypt this message using the pair (11, 29).

    c) Decrypt the message by first finding the value of x such that $dx \equiv 1 \bmod 28$. Find the decrypted message.

21. Suppose that in an RSA cryptosystem, the author uses the primes $p = 71$ and $q = 41$. Then $m = pq = (71)(41) = 2911$. Furthermore, suppose the author uses $e = 13$ so that the public key is $(e, m) = (13, 2911)$.

    a) Calculate $\phi(m)$ and $\gcd(e, \phi(m).)$

    b) If the first part of the original message to be sent is $P_1 = 15$, then what is the equivalent coded message C_1 needed to send using the RSA cryptosystem?

22. Let your message be W = 1234, and the two public key numbers be 3 and 55. Find the coded message, C.

23. When forming an RSA coding scheme, you are given two numbers, *m* and *e*. One is the mod, and the other is the encoding power to use on your word, W. If you are given the numbers 4947 and 7, which one is the power used to code W and which one is the mod?

24. In RSA encryption, if the public key is 1261, what primes make up the private key?

25. Choose an appropriate value for e, the other part of the public key encryption, if the public key is 233411,

    a) What primes make up the private key?
    b) Choose an appropriate value for *e*, the other part of the public key.

26. Using the plaintext values given and the Caesar cipher method with "5" as the encoding key. Encode the word FINAL.

27. The following ciphertext was produced using a Vigenère Cipher with keyword JUNE, modulo 26, and Table 7.3. Decrypt the message **KYFGJLG** to find the original plaintext.

28. Using the plaintext values given, encode WORK using the Caesar cipher method with "5" as the encoding key.

29. In RSA encryption, if the public key is 1313,

    a) What primes make up the private key?
    b) Choose an appropriate value for *e*, the other part of the public key.
    c) Find the decoding exponent given the value that you chose for *e* for the encryption exponent.

30. Suppose $p = 59$, $q = 71$ for an RSA encryption system.

    a) Find *m*.
    b) Find $\phi(m)$.
    c) Which of the following are valid encryption exponents: 7, 9, 15, 35, 49, 91? Justify your response.

31. Given the primes 41 and 67 for an RSA encryption scheme

    a) Find *m*.
    b) Find $\phi(m)$.
    c) Find valid encryption exponent *e*.

32. The cipher text 845 1065 was encrypted in two-letter blocks using RSA with modulus $n = 3127 = 53 \times 59$ and encryption exponent $e = 1371$.

    a) Find the decryption exponent *d*.
    b) Decrypt the message.

Section 7.6   Activities

1. In Section 7.2.1 we mentioned that a single letter in a cryptogram has to be an I or an A and this is a clue to decrypting the phrase. Similarly, there are only a few two-letter words in the English language.

2. Determine how many two-letter pairs of letters are possible if one of the letters must be a vowel.

3. Of these, list the pairs that are actually words in the English language.

4. Using spaces between the words in Caesar ciphers helps the receiver decrypt the message. Instead, discuss what would happen if you used mod 27 and let a blank be represented by zero?

5. Using mod 27 as suggested in Activity 2, encode a message to pass to your friend in class and see if they can decrypt the message. For example, encode the message: THANK YOU

6. Discuss this question: Are blank spaces really necessary when you send encrypt a message? For instance, can you read this message: THEEXAMWILLBE DIFFICULT.

7. Coding theory has gotten very sophisticated. Secret codes can include "noise." Find out what this means and how it is used.

8. Watch the Enigma film and create a synopsis.

9. Watch the film *The Imitation Game* (2014) and create a synopsis.

10. Do research to discover how Rivest, Shamir, and Adleman worked together to create the RSA cryptosystem.

11. In *The Philadelphia Inquirer*, Brain Busters section on August 29, 2019, p. 37 there is a puzzle entitled Simon Shuker's **Code-Cracker** that is a combination of a crossword and code breaking. Solve the puzzle.

Epilogue

You and I are on this journey together. We began at the base of this mountain, in Babylonian times when the only known numbers were the natural numbers. To prepare for our journey, we had to do many exercises (cerebral exercises) to strengthen our mental abilities to deal with the long path ahead. We became adept at logic and rational thinking before continuing along our way. We also stopped at an overlook to peer into Pythagorean triples and noted how Pythagoras struggled to comprehend irrational numbers.

Source: ©iko/Shutterstock.com

Sometime mathematical advances are made by just enjoying the challenge of studying something new. Other times, advances take place because of a need to prove scientific theories or to advance new theories. Then again, several mathematical concepts developed for military reasons. We took a brief look at how important it was over many centuries to keep military information secret and keep strategies from being intercepted by an enemy.

Once back on the main trail, we focused on our goal: To understand the mathematics of protecting our privacy and our assets by exploring internet security methods. There were many aspects of mathematics along the way, all contributing to this goal: The Euclidean algorithm (third century BC), the study of primes with Fermat in the seventeenth century, the great creation of congruences with Gauss in the eighteenth century, and the advances made by Turing, the father of computer science in the twentieth century.

Technological advances in the twentieth century developed at a rapid pace, going from calculators to computers to supercomputers in the span of less than one century. Hopefully, we ended our journey with an understanding of how mathematical knowledge advances. For example, Andrew Wiles connected a twentieth century branch of mathematics to prove a conjecture made by Fermat. Rivest, Adleman, and Shamir used their knowledge of computer science and mathematics to create the RSA code that we explored together at the end of our journey.

Now, I am raising my arms to show you this beautiful scene, from where our trek started in Babylonia to a high place where we can appreciate the trail we have taken and well as the magnificence of what lies ahead. I hope you notice that we are not at the top of the hill. Mathematics keeps expanding its boundaries, finding new ideas, and new ways to connect old ideas. At this time, computers have advanced so far that even a complex RSA code is insufficient for internet security. More sophisticated algorithms are being created every year.

Thank you for taking this journey with me. The author wishes you the joy of discovery, in whatever field you pursue.

Mathematics never gets old –
it just gets more mature.
Agnes M. Rash

Bibliography

Bell, Eric Temple. Men of Mathematics. New York: Simon and Schuster. 1986.

Burckhardt, J. J. *Leonhard Euler, 1707 – 1783*, **Mathematics Magazine, v.** 56, 262-273, 1983.

Colquitt, W. M. and L. Welsh Jr. *A new Mersenne Prime*, **Mathematical Computation, v. 56** 867-870, 1991.

Cox, David A. *Introduction to Fermat's Last Theorem.* **The American Mathematical Monthly.** 101, (Jan., 1994) 3-14.

Crandall, R., J. Doenias, C. Norrie, and J. Young, *The Twenty-Second Fermat Number is Composite,* **Mathematical Computation, v. 64** 863-868, 1995.

Dalezman, Michael. *From 30 to 60 is Not Twice as Hard.* **Mathematics Magazine.** 73 (Feb., 2000); 151-53.

Devlin, Keith. *World's Largest Prime.* **Focus** (The newsletter of the Mathematical Association of America) 17, (December, 1997) 1.

Diffie, Whitfield and Susan Landau. *September 11th Did Not Change Cryptography Policy.* **Notices of the American Mathematical Society.** Vol. 49 (April, 2002); 448-464.

Dodge, Clayton W. *What is a Proof?* **Pi Mu Epsilon Journal** 10, (Fall, 1998) 725-727.

Forman, Sylvia and Agnes M. Rash. **The Whole Truth about Whole Numbers.** New York: Springer, 2015.

Gallian, J. S. *The Mathematics of Identification Numbers.* **The College Mathematics Journal.** 22, (1991) 194-202.

Granville, Andrew. *Prime Number Patterns.* **The American Mathematical Monthly.** 115 (April, 2008) 279-296.

Guy, Richard K. *Nothing's New in Number Theory?* **The American Mathematical Monthly.** 105 (Dec., 1998) 951-954

Fried, John J. *Can you keep a SECRET?* **The Philadelphia Inquirer**, tech. life section, F1-F2.

Kahn, D. **The Code Breakers**, NY: Macmillan. 1967.

Katz, Victor J. **A History of Mathematics,** An Introduction. 3rd edition. .Boston: Addison-Wesley, 2009

Khovanova, Tanya *A Story of Storytelling Numbers.* **Math Horizons.** (Sept. 2009): 14-17. also at www.maa. org/mathhorizons

Kirsch, Rachel. *Cryptography: How to keep a secret.* **MAA Focus**, February/March 2011. www.maa.org/ pubs/focus.html

Krantz, Steven G. **An Episodic History of Mathematics, DC: MAA, 2006.**

Lamport, Leslie. *How to Write a Proof.* **The American Mathematical Monthly.** 102, (Aug.- Sept., 1995) 600-608.

Marchall, David C., Edward Odell, Michael Starbird. **Number Theory Through Inquiry.** NewYork: McGraw Hill. 2007.

Newman, James R. **The World of Mathematics.** New York:Simon and Schuster, 1956.

Osen, Lynn M. **Women in Mathematics**. Cambridge: MIT Press, 1975.

Plummer, Phil. *Divisibility tests for primes greater than 5.* **Pi Mu Epsilon Journal.** 10 (Spring, 1995) 96-98.

Polya, George. **How to Solve It.** New York: New York: Pearson, 2009.

Pomerance, Carl, *The Search for Primes* in **Scientific American**, December 1982, 136 – 147.

Pommersheim, James e. Tim K. Marks, Erica L. Flapan. **Number Theory, A Lively Introduction with Proofs, Applications and Stories.** N.Y.: John Wiley & Sons, Inc. 2010.

Prime number *Student Finds Largest Known Prime Number* **CNN.com** Dec. 11, 2003 http://www.cnn.com/2003/TECH/science/12/11/prime.number.ap/index.html

Ribenboim, P. **The Little Book of Primes.** NY: Springer-Verlag. 1991.

Robinson, Raphael M. *Mersenne and Fermat Numbers,* **Proceedings of the American Mathematical Society,** 1954, 842-846

Ross, David, editor. Lewis Carroll biography get details.

Schwartz, Richard Evan. *You Can Count on Monsters.* Natick: A. K. Peters, Ltd. 2010.

Silverman, Joseph H. *A Friendly Introduction to Number Theory. 4th ed.* New York: Pearson. 2013.

Snapp, Bart and Chris Snapp. *Automotive Number Theory.* **Math Horizons.** (Sept. 2009): 26-27. also at www.maa.org/mathhorizons

Tanton, James. *A Dozen Questions About the Powers of Two.* **math horizons.** 9 (Sept. 2001), 5-10.

The Philadelphia Inquirer, "Brain Buster" section, August 29, 2019. Philadelphia, PA.

Wolfram Research, Wolfram Alpha, Toronto: Wolfram Alpha LLC, a subsidiary of Wolfram Research. Toronto.

Vanden Eynden, Charles. **Introduction to Number Theory.** New York: McGraw Hill, 2006.

Zagier, D. in "The first 50 million prime numbers," ***The Mathematical Intelligencer.*** 0 (1977) 8.

Index

CPSIA information can be obtained
at www.ICGtesting.com
Printed in the USA
LVHW060413310120
645401LV00001B/1